S0-CQS-873

A CHECK LIST
OF NORTH AMERICAN
AMPHIBIANS AND REPTILES

A CHECK LIST
OF NORTH AMERICAN
AMPHIBIANS AND REPTILES

By Karl P. Schmidt

SIXTH EDITION

QL
651
S34
1953

AMERICAN SOCIETY OF
ICHTHYOLOGISTS AND HERPETOLOGISTS
1953

89576

Composed and printed by The University of Chicago Press
Chicago · Illinois · U.S.A.

PREFACE

ASIDE from childhood interest, my own work in herpetology began in 1915 with collecting and observation in Natchitoches Parish, Louisiana, as I have elsewhere written. I was thus extremely conscious of the importance of the standardization of nomenclature provided by the first Stejneger and Barbour *Check List* in 1917, and could not fail to observe the stimulation to more critical systematic studies afforded by the successive later editions. With the death of Leonhard Stejneger, as the fifth edition was about to appear, the time became ripe, I thought, for the American Society of Ichthyologists and Herpetologists to take over further editions as a proper societal function. As then president, I appointed a committee to take charge of check list operations. It was extremely disappointing to find that the committee machinery, through some years of nominal existence, failed to function. It was this experience that led me to recommend that a new edition of the *Check List* be placed in the hands of a single individual. This course of necessity carries with it the continued involvement of a personal equation, which was in some respects sufficiently evident in the successive editions under the editorship of Stejneger and Barbour. Finally, in the full realization that an individual editor would be exposed to bitter criticism alike for what he did and did not do, I was moved to undertake this labor, which, however vulnerable, has not been without love.

K. P. S.

v

CONTENTS

* See also "Introduced Forms."

INTRODUCTION

THE introductory remarks in the first five editions of the *Check List of North American Amphibians and Reptiles* were brief prefaces only. A more extended introduction seems to be appropriate to the new edition to allow for explanation of the divergences of form and content and from taxonomic theory of the earlier editions. Much of this introductory matter might have been placed in footnotes, but these, I feel, would have been unduly extended.

By far the most important sources for the new list (after the earlier editions of the *Check List*) are the several handbooks now available for the North American amphibians and reptiles. A list of these works is appended, together with the list of books or papers that have been especially useful as sources. But for certain residual matters, the illustrated handbooks would make a formal check list superfluous. Such works represent the normal evolution for which the earlier check lists were a necessary preliminary stage. The mapping of ranges, essential at the handbook level, is so much more meaningful than any verbal statement of distribution that I have abandoned the effort to improve on earlier check lists in this respect. For this reason, the only supplementary references supplied are to papers including maps. Reference to the several handbooks and faunal works is assumed. The availability of the several check lists of the amphibians and reptiles of Mexico makes it possible to limit the present edition to North America north of Mexico. The inclusion of Lower California (the Mexican state of Baja California) in the earlier editions was in conformity with the check lists of North American birds, and was not without justification, for the Lower Californian fauna is of the greatest importance to an understanding of the fauna of the Sonoran region in general. The northern tier of Mexican states, mentioned repeatedly in statements of range in the present list, are, in west-east order, Baja California, Sonora, Chihuahua, Coahuila, Nuevo León and Tamaulipas; acquaintance with the names of the provinces of Canada is assumed. Mills' Canadian check list is available for the limits of the fauna to the north of the United States–Canadian border. Several recent state lists have been especially useful in defining ranges whose limits fall within

1

their borders, but I have made no attempt to list them beyond the four cited below.

As a special segment of bibliographic matter not covered by the handbooks, at the suggestion of various colleagues, the new check list brings together the synonyms as far as I have found them. This is of necessity limited strictly to a list of the synonymic names, with no effort to provide the index to the literature sometimes referred to as "synonymy," and with no attempt to pursue the partitions, combinations, and permutations of the synonymic names. The names recognized necessarily apply to form and not concept; the fact that *Natrix erythrogaster erythrogaster* Burt is only in part equal to *Natrix erythrogaster erythrogaster* Conant is beyond the scope of a check list. Such an analysis lies in the province of monographic revisions. I have attempted to add to the usefulness of the synonymy given by stating the type localities, and when these are vague, I have restricted them. I have not included mere variant spellings, and have followed Stejneger's practice (and precept, *in litt.*) of dropping hyphens, diaereses, and the duplicated *i* or *y* in family names. The list of synonyms may be gravely incomplete, for I have discovered omissions quite by accident in the last stages of preparation of the manuscript. It is hoped that the users of the *Check List* will accumulate additions in their personal copies for the use of an editor or committee in charge of a future edition. I have not attempted a comprehensive generic synonymy.

The extension of trinomials to geographically representative forms, against which Stejneger so bitterly inveighs in the introduction to the fifth edition of the *Check List,* is perhaps the most radical change from the earlier lists. I have followed the precedents established in ornithology in this matter. I interpret Ernst Mayr's thoughtful *Systematics and the Origin of Species* (1943) as supporting vicariation *per se* as the principal criterion for trinomial classification within groups of species. I have long ago expressed my own opinion on this point (1944). The juxtaposition of closely related and geographically representative forms by means of the trinomials makes the list more meaningful as an evolutionary conspectus of a generic group, and carries with it an obvious mnemonic usefulness to the student. The revision of such classifications is the obvious province of further zoological studies.

The continuing subdivision of genera leads logically to the point at which there is one monotypic genus for each species, and at this point the generic classification has lost its usefulness. The generic category should be synthetic, based on similarities instead of on differences; it is essentially *not* analytic; and it has in any case a different conceptual basis from that of the species. Thus I deplore the fragmentation of the genus *Uta* in the fifth edition of the *Check List;* and I have not accepted the partition of *Hyla* (e.g., *Smilisca*) or of *Crotaphytus* (e.g., *Gambelia*). It would now be entirely logical to unite *Uma* and *Callisaurus,* on account of the transitional species *Uma exul* in Coahuila described by Charles M. Bogert and myself; in this case I have followed current practice. As to taxonomic theory, I should define genera as groups of species and establish them after the species have been defined. I should not attempt to set up a special category of characters of "generic value." Monotypic genera, if maintained, assume the existence of extinct related species.

A further divergence from the earlier editions is related to this more extended use of trinomial series. It is desired to emphasize the *species* category as inclusive of all the subspecies; and it is urged that the binomial species name be more widely used in both technical and popular writing when the distinction of the subspecies is not at issue. This also has much recent precedent, e.g., in the works of Stebbins and of Hobart M. Smith. The species *includes* its several subspecies; the subspecies duplicating the species name (the "trivial" name of recent usage) is typical of the species only in a nomenclatural sense. The fact that this nomenclaturally typical subspecies has the type locality of the species as a whole further obscures its relations of equivalence among the remaining subspecies.

It was originally hoped that the ranges of the species might be stated in terms of natural regions or provinces; in testing this matter, I have found no uniformity in degree of correspondence of individual range with either biotic or physiographic provinces. Anything like a definitive delimitation of range remains to be made for most species and subspecies. The expanding species are likely to overflow the limits of any particular province, and those that are in process of decline may inhabit only a small fraction of a province. Nevertheless, as a first approximation in any study of the factors that affect or limit geographic range it is evidently the *physiographic provinces* that are to be considered. These reflect something of geological history, and often present sharply defined barriers. Next come the *phytogeographic provinces,* which may reflect further adjustment to more recently established climatic conditions, some of which are of course likewise conditioned by physiography. *The Atlas of American Agriculture* is especially to be recommended for its various maps of climatic features and of vegetation. Since the limiting factors may be radically different on the different sides of a given range, and limit effectively only for such time as a particular combination of factors continues, the geographic range of a species must be understood in something other than static terms, as I have elsewhere attempted to show (1950). The reader is referred to the maps of Atwood (1940) and Fenneman (1931 and 1938), to Dice (1943), and especially to Goode (1943). The grave criticisms to which the life zone theory has been subjected apply rather to the theory than to the distribution pattern on which it was based. The studies of various states in the framework of "life zones" by the United States Biological Survey (especially in *North American Fauna*), and by many authors concerned with distribution in mountains, have by no means lost all significance because the theory of temperature summation proves to be a gross over-simplification as an explanation of the discernible pattern. A colored life zone map of the continent is most readily accessible in Goode's *School Atlas* (1943).

Among more trivial matters of form, I have preferred "Linnaeus" to "von Linné," following what seems to be the preponderant practice, e.g., in the British Museum's *Catalogue of the Works of Linnaeus* (1933).

In the matter of enclosing the names of the authors of specific (trivial) names in parentheses when these names have been transferred from one generic combination to another I have followed the thoughtfully defended suggestion of the late Wilfred H. Osgood (1939) that such parentheses be dropped altogether as an "outworn nomenclatural practice." The rule was quite erroneously applied to *every* change of combination in previous editions of the *Check List*. One of the most cogent arguments against the practice is the fact that there were numerous errors in every edition even in the application of this modified rule.

Too few zoologists appear to recognize that the International Rules of Zoological Nomenclature were drawn up in a humorless and legalistic atmosphere, in which the presence of the "l" in *Amblystoma* or its absence in *Ambystoma* were treated as matters worthy of expenditure of time by zoologists. One of the necessary steps toward the rehabilitation of systematic botany and zoology in the eyes of non-systematists is to give more than lip service to the most fundamental of nomenclatural rules, that the rules are made for all biologists and not as the basis for a glorified game to be played by scholars in ivory towers.

As to the modifications of the rules of nomenclature adopted at the International Zoological Congress at Paris in 1948, in view of some widespread objections, I have in general avoided changes that would be involved by adherence to them. The dropping of the second *i* when this is duplicated and a slightly greater freedom in emendation seem to be desirable. The point has now been made that the Congress of 1948 was not properly international, and the whole subject of the rules seems to be up for active discussion at Copenhagen in 1953. A flagrant example of eagerness to change well-known names is afforded by the rush to apply the 1948 rules to the names of boas and pythons. The substitution of the earlier name *Siredon* for *Ambystoma,* which American authors have long consciously avoided as a too flagrant disregard of usage, has been proposed and adopted by Aloys Stäuble (1942, Rev. Suisse Zool., **49**: 457 ff.). The change of a name of such wide currency in branches of biology other than systematics is so clearly undesirable that such action should of course be reviewed by the International Commission of Zoological Nomenclature, which has been petitioned to invalidate *Siredon* and place *Ambystoma* on the list of Nomina Conservanda. It now seems clear that the function of the International Commission should be to rule on proposed changes prior to their adoption in the literature, rather than to leave changes of familiar names to individual authors, who follow a pattern of action long established but clearly bad. Certainly no harm to zoology can accrue from the use of a familiar name pending such ruling.

Much of the uncritical, over-hurried, and needlessly inadequate descriptive work in the early history of systematics was motivated by vanity and the spirit of competition rather than by the desire to advance science and to co-operate with fellow scientists. We are now engaged in an exhaustive revision of this work. The merit of our new system will have very little relation to nomenclatural problems. Its worth will be in direct ratio to the amount of understanding of the whole field of biology we bring to it. The preparation of a conspectus of the animal and plant kingdoms, and of the segments of that conspectus, I regard as a noble program, worthy of lifetimes of devoted study. The usefulness of such syntheses is not confined within the limited field of systematic studies; they form a foundation for all of the biological sciences, and are of interest to all literate mankind.

REFERENCES

HANDBOOKS

BISHOP, S. C.
1943. Handbook of salamanders. The salamanders of the United States, of Canada, and of Lower California. Comstock Publ. Co., Ithaca: xiv, 555 pp., 144 figs., 56 maps.

CARR, A. F., JR.
1952. Handbook of turtles. The turtles of the United States, Canada, and Baja California. Cornell Univ. Press, Ithaca: xv, 542 pp., 82 pls., 37 text figs., 23 maps.

SCHMIDT, K. P., and D. DWIGHT DAVIS
1941. Field book of snakes of the United States and Canada. Putnams Sons, New York: xiii, 365 pp., 34 pls., 103 text figs.

SMITH, H. M.
1946. Handbook of lizards of the United States and Canada. Comstock Publ. Co., Ithaca: xxi, 557 pp., 135 pls., 136 text figs.

WRIGHT, A. H., and ANNA ALLEN WRIGHT
1949. Handbook of frogs and toads of the United States and Canada. Comstock Publ. Co., Ithaca: xii, 640 pp., 126 pls., 37 maps.

CHECK LISTS

BROWN, BRYCE C.
1950. An annotated check list of the reptiles and amphibians of Texas. Baylor Univ. Press, Waco: xii, 257, 2 pp.

MILLS, R. COLIN
1948. A check list of the reptiles and amphibians of Canada. Herpetologica, 4, Suppl. 2, pp. 1–15.

SMITH, H. M., and E. H. TAYLOR
1945. An annotated checklist and key to the snakes of Mexico. Bull. U. S. Nat. Mus., 187: 239 pp.
1948. An annotated checklist and key to the Amphibia of Mexico. Bull. U. S. Nat. Mus., 194: iv, 118 pp.
1950. An annotated checklist and key to the reptiles of Mexico exclusive of the snakes. Bull. U. S. Nat. Mus., 199: v, 253 pp.

6

STEJNEGER, LEONHARD, and THOMAS BARBOUR
  1917. A check list of North American amphibians and reptiles. Harvard Univ. Press, Cambridge: 125 pp.
  1923. Idem, 2nd Edition, x, 171 pp.
  1933. Idem, 3rd Edition, xiv, 185 pp.
  1939. Idem, 4th Edition, xvi, 207 pp.
  1943. Idem, 5th Edition, Bull. Mus. Comp. Zool., **93**: xix, 260 pp.

GEOGRAPHIC WORKS

ATWOOD, WALLACE W.
  1940. The physiographic provinces of North America. Ginn and Co., New York: xvi, 536 pp., 5 pls., 281 text figs., 1 map.

DICE, LEE R.
  1943. The biotic provinces of North America. Univ. of Michigan Press, Ann Arbor: viii, 78 pp., 1 map.

FENNEMAN, NEVIN M.
  1931. Physiography of western United States. McGraw-Hill, New York: xiii, 534 pp., 1 pl. (map), 173 text figs.
  1938. Physiography of eastern United States. McGraw-Hill, New York: xiii, 714 pp., 7 pls., 197 text figs.

GOODE, J. PAUL
  1943. Goode's school atlas, 2nd Edition, xvi, 286 pp.

SCHANTZ, H. L., and RAPHAEL ZON
  1924. Grassland and desert shrub [and] forests, *in* Atlas of American Agriculture, Government Printing Office, Washington: 29 pp., 1 map, 60 text figs. [folio].

MISCELLANEOUS

CONANT, ROGER
  1951. The reptiles of Ohio, 2nd Edition. Univ. Notre Dame Press, Notre Dame: pp. 1–172, 201–284, 27 pls., 77 maps.

LINSDALE, JEAN M.
  1940. Amphibians and reptiles in Nevada. Proc. Amer. Acad. Arts Sci., **73**: 197–257, 29 figs.

MAYR, ERNST
  1943. Systematics and the origin of species. Columbia Univ. Press, New York: xiv, 334 pp., 29 figs.

OSGOOD, WILFRED H.

1939. An outworn nomenclatural practice. Science, **89**: 9–11.

SCHMIDT, K. P.

1944. The lower systematic categories in vertebrate zoology. Ecology, **25**: 254–255.

1950. The concept of geographic range, with illustrations from amphibians and reptiles. Texas Jour. Sci., **1950**: 326–334.

SMITH, HOBART M.

1950. Handbook of amphibians and reptiles of Kansas. Univ. Kansas Mus. Nat. Hist. Misc. Publ., **2**: 336, 232 figs.

STEBBINS, ROBERT C.

1951. Amphibians of western North America. Univ. Calif. Press, Berkeley: xviii, 539, 64 pls., 35 text figs.

ACKNOWLEDGMENTS

GRATEFUL acknowledgment is made to the great number of my colleagues without whose alternate encouragement and prodding the manuscript would not have been finished. The section on the salamanders passed through the hands of Emmett Reid Dunn, and was read also by the late Sherman C. Bishop, and by Clifford H. Pope, to its great advantage. For the lizard section I have profited from the critical comments of Hobart M. Smith and of several of his students. In the first stages of preparation of the manuscript I had the faithful aid of Robert F. Inger; but with Mr. Inger's transfer to ichthyological studies and duties in 1949 it seemed best for him to withdraw from the project. My first draft of the manuscript was prepared at the Senckenberg Museum, while serving as exchange professor for the University of Chicago. There I had the frequent and valued advice of Robert Mertens, one of the authors of the European check list.

The typing and retyping of the manuscript was the work of Margaret J. Bauer and Pearl Sonoda, who have aided me greatly with the checking and rechecking of the trivia of form that assume so much importance in so purely formal a list. Lillian A. Ross, Associate Editor of Publications in Chicago Natural History Museum, has aided with advice and given generously of her time in the final preparation of the manuscript for the press.

Roger Conant and M. Graham Netting have gone over the entire list of common names, which forms one of the innovations of the present edition, and I have largely followed their advice. For the western fauna I have consulted C. B. Perkins and Charles E. Shaw for the reptiles, and have mainly followed Robert C. Stebbins for the amphibians. I have had the advantage that English names have been used in the several newer handbooks.

It was originally intended to expand the section for introduced species into a more comprehensive account of such introductions and transplantations. This I have reluctantly given up, for lack of the necessary time.

Much manuscript material has been made available to me in the course of preparation of the check list. I have to thank especially Duart Vinson Brown, of Stanford University, who sent me his unpublished maps prepared as a study of the relations between the ranges of western amphibians and reptiles and accepted biotic provinces; Harold Dundee, of the University of Kansas, who let me have his manuscript maps of distributions in Oklahoma; and Herndon G. Dowling, of Haverford College, whose studies of *Elaphe* are in active progress, and whose conclusions I have followed.

Class AMPHIBIA

Order CAUDATA

CRYPTOBRANCHIDAE

Cryptobranchus Leuckart

Cryptobranchus Leuckart, 1821, Isis, **1821**, Liter. Anz., p. 260.—Type: *gigantea* = *alleganiensis*.

Abranchus Harlan, 1825, Ann. Lyc. Nat. Hist. New York, **1**: 233.—Type: *alleghaniensis* = *alleganiensis;* not of Van Hasselt, 1824.

Menopoma Harlan, 1825, Ann. Lyc. Nat. Hist. New York, **1**: 270.—Substitute name for *Abranchus.*

Salamandrops Wagler, 1830, Syst. Amph., p. 209.—Type: *gigantea.*

Cryptobranchus alleganiensis Daudin

Salamandra alleganiensis Daudin, 1802, Hist. Nat. Rept., **8**: 231.—Allegheny Mountains in Virginia.[1]

Cryptobranchus alleghaniensis Van der Hoeven, 1837, Tijdschr. Nat. Geschied. Physiol., **4**: 384.

Range.—Eastern North America.

Common name.—Hellbender.

Cryptobranchus alleganiensis alleganiensis Daudin
[New comb.]

Salamandra horrida Barton, 1808, Some acount of the *Siren lacertina* and other species of the same genus. Philadelphia, privately publ., p. 8.—Waters of the Ohio and Susquehanna rivers and other parts of the United States; restr. to the Muskingum River, Ohio.

Salamandra gigantea Barton, 1808, Some account of the Siren . . . , p. 8.—Substitute name for *horrida.*

Salamandra maxima Barton, 1808, Some account of the Siren . . . , p. 8.—Substitute name for *gigantea.*

Cryptobranchus salamandroides Leuckart, 1821, Isis, **1821**, Liter. Anz., p. 260, pl. 9.—Substitute name for *gigantea.*

Cryptobranchus terrassodactylus Wellborn, 1936, Zool. Anz., **114**: 63.—North America; restr. to Allegheny Mountains in Virginia.

Range.—Ohio and Wabash River systems; Susquehanna River; upper courses of the Tar River, North Carolina, the Savannah River,

[1] See Harper, 1940, Amer. Midl. Nat., **23**: 720.

11

Georgia, and the Tennessee River; lower Missouri River; southeastern Iowa; southeastern Kansas.

Common name.—Hellbender.

Cryptobranchus alleganiensis bishopi Grobman
[New comb.]

> *Cryptobranchus bishopi* Grobman, 1942, Occ. Papers Mus. Zool. Univ. Mich., **470**: 6.—Current River at Big Spring Park, Carter County, Missouri.

Range.—Greer Springs, Current and Eleven Point rivers, Missouri (White River system); Spring Creek in Missouri and Spring River in Arkansas (Black River system).

Common name.—Ozark hellbender.

PROTEIDAE

Necturus Rafinesque

> *Necturus* Rafinesque, 1819, Blainville's Jour. Phys., **88**: 417.—Type: *maculatus* Rafinesque = *maculosus* Rafinesque.
> *Menobranchus* Harlan, 1825, Ann. Lyc. Nat. Hist. New York, **1**: 233.—Type: *lateralis* = *maculosus*.
> *Phanerobranchus* Leuckart, 1821, Isis, **1821**, Liter. Anz., p. 260.—Type: *tetradactylus* = *cepedii* (Fitzinger, 1826, Neue Classif. Rept., p. 66).

Necturus maculosus Rafinesque

> *Siren maculosa* Rafinesque, 1818, Amer. Monthly Mag. Crit. Rev., **4**: 41.—Ohio River.
> *Necturus maculosus* Rafinesque, 1820, Ann. Nat., Lexington, no. 1, p. 4.

Range.—Eastern North America, in the Atlantic and Gulf drainages.

Common name.—Mudpuppy, waterdog.

Necturus maculosus maculosus Rafinesque

> *Necturus* [*maculosus*] *maculosus* Brimley, 1924, Jour. Elisha Mitchell Sci. Soc., **11**: 167.
> *Necturus maculatus* Rafinesque, 1819, Blainville's Jour. Phys., **88**: 417.—Substitute name for *maculosus*.
> *Phanerobranchus tetradactylus* Leuckart, 1821, Isis, **1821**, Liter. Anz., p. 260.—North America.
> *Triton lateralis* Say, 1823, *in* Long's Exped. Rocky Mts., **1**: 5.—Vicinity of Pittsburgh.
> *Phanerobranchus cepedii* Fitzinger, 1826, Neue Classif. Rept. . . . , p. 66.—North America.
> *Menobranchus lacepedii* Gray, 1831, *in* Griffith's Anim. Kingd., **9**: 108.—Substitute name for *cepedii*.

Siredon hyemalis Kneeland, 1856, Proc. Boston Soc. Nat. Hist., **6**: 152.–
Lake Superior.

Menobranchus lateralis var. *latastei* Garnier, 1888, Proc. Canadian Inst., (3),
5: 218–219.–Maitland River, Ontario.

Range.–The Mississippi River system from northern Alabama and the Arkansas River northward in eastern Oklahoma and Kansas to southeastern Manitoba; the Great Lakes and St. Lawrence River system, with its tributaries in Manitoba, Ontario, and Quebec.

Common name.–Mudpuppy, waterdog.

Necturus maculosus stictus Bishop

Necturus maculosus stictus Bishop, 1941, Occ. Papers Mus. Zool. Univ. Mich.,
451: 9.–Lake Winnebago, Wisconsin.

Range.–Lake Winnebago drainage in Wisconsin.

Common name.–Lake Winnebago mudpuppy.

Necturus maculosus beyeri Viosca

Necturus beyeri Viosca, 1937, Copeia, **1937**: 123.–Upper Calcasieu River,
near Oakdale, Allen Parish, Louisiana.

Necturus alabamensis Viosca, 1937, Copeia, **1937**: 121.–Black Warrior
River, Tuscaloosa, Alabama.[2]

Range.–Gulf Coast streams from eastern Texas to western Georgia and Florida, north in the Appalachian streams at lower altitudes through eastern Tennessee and western North and South Carolina to Virginia.

Common name.–Gulf Coast waterdog, Beyer's waterdog.

Necturus maculosus louisianensis Viosca

Necturus louisianensis Viosca, 1938, Proc. Biol. Soc. Wash., **51**: 143.–Big
Creek, a few miles from Pollock, Grant Parish, Louisiana.

Range.–Red River drainage in Louisiana (known only from Grant and Rapides parishes).

Common name.–Red River waterdog.

Necturus maculosus lewisi Brimley

Necturus maculosus lewisi Brimley, 1924, Jour. Elisha Mitchell Sci. Soc.,
11: 167.–Neuse River, near Raleigh, Wake County, North Carolina.

Range.–Neuse and Tar River systems in North Carolina.

Common name.–Neuse River waterdog.

[2] Allocation following S. C. Bishop (*in litt.*).

Necturus lödingi Viosca

Necturus lödingi Viosca, 1937, Copeia, **1937**: 126.—Enslava Creek, near Mobile, Mobile County, Alabama.

Range.—Vicinity of Mobile, Alabama.

Common name.—Mobile waterdog.

Necturus punctatus Gibbes

Menobranchus punctatus Gibbes, 1850, Proc. Amer. Assoc. Adv. Sci., Charleston, **1850**: 159.—Dr. Schoolbred's plantation on the South Santee River, a few miles from its mouth, South Carolina.

Necturus punctatus Cope, 1889, Bull. U. S. Nat. Mus., **34**: 27.

Range.—Streams of Atlantic coastal plain in North Carolina, South Carolina, and Georgia.

Common name.—Dwarf waterdog.

SIRENIDAE

Siren Linnaeus

Siren Linnaeus, 1766, Syst. Nat., ed. 12, **1**, pt. 2, sign. Rrrr 5, Addenda [not paged].—Type: *lacertina*.

Siren lacertina Linnaeus

Siren lacertina Linnaeus, 1766, Syst. Nat., ed. 12, **1**, pt. 2, sign. Rrrr 5, Addenda [not paged].—In swampy Carolina; restr. to vicinity of Charleston.

Phanerobranchus dipus Leuckart, 1821, Isis, **1821**, Liter. Anz., p. 260.—Substitute name for *lacertina*.

Range.—Maryland and Virginia on the west side of Chesapeake Bay, coastal North and South Carolina, southern Georgia and Alabama, and throughout Florida.

Common name.—Great siren.

Siren intermedia Le Conte

Siren intermedia Le Conte, 1827, Jour. Acad. Nat. Sci. Phila., (1), **5**: 322.—Southern states; restr. to Liberty County, Georgia.

Range.—Southeastern United States, from South Carolina to Texas, northward to Illinois and Indiana.

Common name.—Dwarf siren.

Siren intermedia intermedia Le Conte

Siren intermedia intermedia Goin, 1942, Ann. Carnegie Mus., **29**: 211.

Range.—Coastal South Carolina through southern Georgia and northern Florida to extreme eastern Louisiana.

Common name.—Eastern dwarf siren.

Siren intermedia nettingi Goin

> *Siren intermedia nettingi* Goin, 1942, Ann. Carnegie Mus., **29**: 211.—Imboden, Lawrence County, Arkansas.

Range.—Gulf Coast of Texas and Louisiana and northward through Arkansas and southeastern Missouri, western Mississippi, Tennessee, and Kentucky; Illinois and Indiana to the Kankakee drainage.

Common name.—Netting's dwarf siren.

Pseudobranchus Gray

> *Pseudobranchus* Gray, 1825, Ann. Phil., (n.s.), **10**: 216.—Type: *striatus.*

Pseudobranchus striatus Le Conte

> *Siren striata* Le Conte, 1824, Ann. Lyc. Nat. Hist. New York, **1**: 53, pl. 4.—Riceborough, Liberty County, Georgia.
> *Pseudobranchus striatus* Gray, 1825, Ann. Phil., (n.s.), **10**: 216.

Range.—South Carolina to Florida.

Common name.—Mud siren.

Pseudobranchus striatus striatus Le Conte

> *Pseudobranchus striatus striatus* Netting and Goin, 1942, Ann. Carnegie Mus., **29**: 183, pl. 1, figs. 3, 4.

Range.—Southern South Carolina through lowland Georgia.

Common name.—Broad-striped mud siren.

Pseudobranchus striatus axanthus Netting and Goin

> *Pseudobranchus striatus axanthus* Netting and Goin, 1942, Ann. Carnegie Mus., **29**: 183, pl. 1, figs. 1, 2.—East edge of Paynes Prairie, at junction of Prairie Creek and River Styx, about 5 miles southeast of Gainesville, Alachua County, Florida.

Range.—Peninsular Florida.

Common name.—Narrow-striped mud siren.

Pseudobranchus striatus lustricolus Neill

> *Pseudobranchus striatus lustricolus* Neill, 1951, Publ. Res. Div. Allen's Rept. Inst., **1**: 39, figs. 1, 2.—7.8 miles southeast of Otter Creek, Levy County, Florida.

Range.—Levy County and adjacent areas on the Gulf Coast of Florida.

Common name.—Gulf hammock mud siren.

Pseudobranchus striatus spheniscus Goin and Crenshaw

> *Pseudobranchus striatus spheniscus* Goin and Crenshaw, 1949, Ann. Carnegie Mus., **31**: 277.—Seven miles south of Smithville, Lee County, Georgia.

Range.—Southwestern Georgia (Baker and Lee counties) and adjacent Florida (Columbia, Gulf, Leon, and Liberty counties).

Common name.—Slender mud siren.

AMBYSTOMIDAE

Dicamptodon Strauch

> *Dicamptodon* Strauch, 1870, Mem. Acad. Sci. St. Petersbourg, (7), **16**, no. 4, p. 68.—Type: *ensatus* (by monotypy).
>
> *Chondrotus* Cope, 1887, Amer. Nat., **21**: 88.—Type: *tenebrosum = ensatus.*

Dicamptodon ensatus Eschscholtz

> *Triton ensatus* Eschscholtz, 1833, Zool. Atlas, pt. 5, p. 6, pl. 22.—Vicinity of the Bay of San Francisco, California.
>
> *Dicamptodon ensatus* Strauch, 1870, Mem. Acad. Sci. St. Petersbourg, (7), **16**, no. 4, p. 69.
>
> *Amblystoma tenebrosum* Baird and Girard, 1852, Proc. Acad. Nat. Sci. Phila., **6**: 174.—Oregon.
>
> *Amblystoma aterrimum* Cope, 1867, Proc. Acad. Nat. Sci. Phila., **19**: 201.—North Rocky Mountains.

Range.—Extreme southwest corner of British Columbia through western Washington, Oregon, and northwestern California to Santa Cruz County; an isolated area in northern Idaho.

Common name.—Pacific giant salamander.

Rhyacotriton Dunn

> *Rhyacotriton* Dunn, 1920, Proc. New England Zool. Club, **7**: 56.—Type: *olympicus.*

Rhyacotriton olympicus Gaige

> *Ranodon olympicus* Gaige, 1917, Occ. Papers Mus. Zool. Univ. Mich., **40**: 2, pl. 1.—Lake Cushman, Washington.
>
> *Rhyacotriton olympicus* Dunn, 1920, Proc. New England Zool. Club, **7**: 56.

Range.—Pacific coastal region from the Olympic Mountains south to southern Humboldt County, California.

Common name.—Mountain salamander.

Rhyacotriton olympicus olympicus Gaige

Rhyacotitron olympicus olympicus Stebbins and Lowe, 1951, Univ. Calif. Publ. Zool., **50**: 465, pl. 31, text fig. 1.

Range.—West of the crest of the Cascades in Washington from the Olympic Peninsula south to the Columbia River and probably along the Oregon coast to Tillamook County.

Common name.—Olympic mountain salamander.

Rhyacotriton olympicus variegatus Stebbins and Lowe

Rhyacotriton olympicus variegatus Stebbins and Lowe, 1951, Univ. Calif. Publ. Zool., **50**: 471, pl. 31, text fig. 1.—1.3 miles west of Burnt Ranch Post Office, Trinity County, California.

Range.—Coastal area in northwestern California, from southern Humboldt County to the Rogue River Valley, Curry County, Oregon; inland in California to extreme western Trinity County [intergradient with *olympicus olympicus* in the area intervening between the stated ranges of the subspecies].

Common name.—California mountain salamander.

Ambystoma Tschudi

Ambystoma Tschudi, 1838, Mém. Soc. Sci. Nat. Neuchâtel, **1838**: 92.—Type: *subviolacea* Barton (by monotypy) = *maculatum.*

Xiphonura Tschudi, 1838, Mém. Soc. Sci. Nat. Neuchâtel, **1838**: 95.—Type: *jeffersonianum.*

Salamandroidis Fitzinger, 1843, Syst. Rept., p. 33.—Type: *subviolacea* Barton (by monotypy).

Amblystoma Agassiz, 1846, Nomenclator Zool. Rept., p. 2.—Emendation.

Heterotriton Gray, 1850, Cat. Batr. Grad. Brit. Mus., p. 33.—Type: *ingens* Green (by monotypy) = *tigrinum.*

Plagiodon Duméril, Bibron, and Duméril, 1854, Erpét. Gén., **9**: 101.—Substitute name for *Ambystoma.*

Desmiostoma Sager, 1858, Penin. Jour. Med., **5**: 428.—Type: *maculatum.*

Camarataxis Cope, 1859, Proc. Acad. Nat. Sci. Phila., **11**: 122.—Type: *maculatum.*

Pectoglossa Mivart, 1867, Proc. Zool. Soc. London, **1867**: 698.—Type: *persimilis* = *jeffersonianum.*

Sirenodon Desor, 1870, Bull. Soc. Sci. Nat. Neuchâtel, **8**: 269.—Type: *lichenoides* Baird.

Linguaelapsus Cope, 1887, Amer. Nat., **21**: 88.—Type: not designated; here designated as *annulatum* Cope.

Ambystoma annulatum Cope

Amblystoma annulatum Cope, 1886, Proc. Amer. Phil. Soc., **23**: 525.—Locality unknown; here designated as vicinity of Hot Springs, Arkansas.
Ambystoma annulatum Stejneger and Barbour, 1917, Check list, ed. 1, p. 8.

Range.—Southern Missouri (north to Camden County), southward through Arkansas to eastern Oklahoma.

Common name.—Ringed salamander.

Ambystoma cingulatum Cope

Amblystoma cingulatum Cope, 1867, Proc. Acad. Nat. Sci. Phila., **19**: 205.—Grahamville, South Carolina.
Ambystoma cingulatum Stejneger and Barbour, 1917, Check list, ed. 1, p. 8.

Range.—Coastal plain of South Carolina, Georgia, Alabama, and northern Florida.

Common name.—Reticulated salamander.

Ambystoma cingulatum cingulatum Cope

Ambystoma cingulatum cingulatum Goin, 1950, Ann. Carnegie Mus., **31**: 307, pl. 1, text figs. 1, 2.
Ambystoma lepturum Cope, 1886, Proc. Amer. Phil. Soc., **23**: 524.—Locality unknown; designated as Jasper County, South Carolina.

Range.—Colleton County, South Carolina, and Jefferson County, Georgia, west and south to Lanier County, Georgia, and Duval County, Florida.

Common name.—Frosted salamander.

Ambystoma cingulatum bishopi Goin

Ambystoma cingulatum bishopi Goin, 1950, Ann. Carnegie Mus., **31**: 300, pl. 1, text figs. 1, 2.—About 5 miles north of Pensacola, Escambia County, Florida.

Range.—The Gulf coastal plain from Baker County, Georgia, and Calhoun County, Florida, to Mobile Bay, Alabama.

Common name.—Reticulated salamander.

Ambystoma gracile Baird

Siredon gracilis Baird, 1859, Pacif. R. R. Surv. Rept., 10, Williamson's Route, pt. 4, no. 4, p. 13, pl. 44, fig. 2.—Cascade Mountains, near 44° N. Lat. (Oregon).
Ambystoma gracile Dunn, 1926, Copeia, **154**: 136.

Range.—Southern Alaska to northern California.

Common name.—Northwestern salamander.

Ambystoma gracile gracile Baird

Ambystoma gracile gracile Dunn, 1944, Copeia, **1944**: 130.

Ambystoma paroticum Baird, 1867, Proc. Acad. Nat. Sci. Phila., **19**: 200.— Chiloweynck, British Columbia.

Range.—Vancouver Island and southwestern British Columbia through coastal Washington and Oregon to northern California.

Common name.—Oregon salamander.

Ambystoma gracile decorticatum Cope

Amblystoma decorticatum Cope, 1886, Proc. Amer. Phil. Soc., **23**: 522.— Port Simpson, British Columbia.

Ambystoma gracile decorticatum Dunn, 1944, Copeia, **1944**: 130.

Range.—Coastal British Columbia north of the Vancouver region to May Island, Alaska (54° 30′ N. Lat.).

Common name.—British Columbia salamander.

Ambystoma jeffersonianum Green

Salamandra jeffersoniana Green, 1827, Contr. Maclurean Lyc., **1**: 4, pl. 1, fig. 1.—Near Chartier's Creek in the vicinity of Jefferson College at Canonsburg, Washington County, Pennsylvania.

Ambystoma jeffersoniana Baird, 1849, Jour. Acad. Nat. Sci. Phila., (2), **1**: 283.

Amblystoma laterale Hallowell, 1858, Jour. Acad. Nat. Sci. Phila., (2), **3**: 352.—Borders of Lake Superior.

Amblystoma fuscum Hallowell, 1858, Jour. Acad. Nat. Sci. Phila., (2), **3**: 355.—Near Hanover College.

Plethodon persimilis Gray, 1859, Proc. Zool. Soc. London, **1859**: 230.— Siam [in error]; designated as vicinity of New York City.

Amblystoma platineum Cope, 1867, Proc. Acad. Nat. Sci. Phila., **19**: 198.— Cleveland, Ohio.

Amblystoma jeffersonianum jeffersonianum Cope, 1875, Bull. U. S. Nat. Mus., **1**: 26.

Range.—Northeastern United States and southern Canada, westward to northern Minnesota, Wisconsin, and Illinois, southward to Maryland, and through Virginia and West Virginia in the mountains; throughout Pennsylvania, Ohio, and Indiana; isolated occurrences in Missouri, Arkansas, and Tennessee.

Common name.—Jefferson's salamander.

Ambystoma mabeei Bishop

Ambystoma mabeei Bishop, 1928, Jour. Elisha Mitchell Sci. Soc., **43**: 157,
  pl. 23, figs. 1, 2.—Low grounds of the Black River near Dunn, Harnett
  County, North Carolina.

Range.—Southeastern coastal North Carolina through South Carolina to Liberty County, Georgia.

Common name.—Mabee's salamander.

Ambystoma macrodactylum Baird

Ambystoma macrodactyla Baird, 1849, Jour. Acad. Nat. Sci. Phila., (2),
  1: 299.—Astoria, Oregon.
Amblystoma krausei Peters, 1882, Sitzber. Ges. naturf. Freunde Berlin, **1882**:
  145.—Flathead River, Montana.
Amblystoma epixanthum Cope, 1883, Proc. Acad. Nat. Sci. Phila., **35**: 16.—
  South Boise River, Idaho.
Amblystoma stejnegeri Ruthven, 1912, Proc. U. S. Nat. Mus., **41**: 517.—
  Bloomfield, Davis County, Iowa [in error].

Range.—Southern British Columbia and Vancouver Island, south
to northern California, and eastward into Alberta, Idaho, and Montana.

Common name.—Long-toed salamander.

Ambystoma maculatum Shaw

Lacerta maculata Shaw, 1802, Gen. Zool., **3**, pt. 1, p. 304.—Carolina; restr.
  to vicinity of Charleston, South Carolina.
Ambystoma maculatum Stejneger, 1902, Proc. Biol. Soc. Wash., **15**: 239.
Lacerta punctata Linnaeus, 1766, Syst. Nat., ed. 12, **1**: 370.—Carolina; restr.
  to vicinity of Charleston, South Carolina [not of Linnaeus, 1758].
Salamandra palustris Bechstein, 1800, *in* Lacépède, Naturg. Amphib., **2**:
  544.—Carolina; restr. to vicinity of Charleston, South Carolina.
Salamandra venenosa Daudin, 1803, Hist. Nat. Rept., **8**: 229.—Vicinity of
  Philadelphia, Pennsylvania.
Lacerta subviolacea Barton, 1804, Trans. Amer. Phil. Soc., **6**: 109, pl. 4,
  fig. 6.—Philadelphia, Pennsylvania.
Ambystoma carolinae Gray, 1850, Cat. Batr. Grad. Brit. Mus., p. 35.—Substitute name for *maculatum* [reference not seen].
Ambystome argus Duméril, Bibron, and Duméril, 1854, Erpét. Gén., **9**: 103.
  —North America (lapsus for *Ambystoma*, substitute name).

Range.—Eastern North America: Southern Canada from the Gaspé
Peninsula and Nova Scotia west through southern Ontario to upper
Michigan and Wisconsin, south to the Gulf states, west to southeastern Kansas, eastern Oklahoma, and eastern Texas.

Common name.—Spotted salamander.

Ambystoma opacum Gravenhorst

Salamandra opaca Gravenhorst, 1807, Vergl. Uebersicht Zool. Syst., p. 431.—
New York.
Ambystoma opaca Baird, 1849, Jour. Acad. Nat. Sci. Phila., (2), **1**: 283.
Salamandra fasciata Green, 1818, Jour. Acad. Nat. Sci. Phila., (1), **1**: 350.—
Probably the vicinity of Princeton, New Jersey.

Range.—Eastern United States: New Hampshire to northern Florida, west to northwestern Indiana, southern Michigan, eastern Illinois, and to Missouri (west to Phelps County); southward to eastern Texas and the Gulf states.

Common name.—Marbled salamander.

Ambystoma talpoideum Holbrook

Salamandra talpoidea Holbrook, 1838, N. Amer. Herp., ed. 1, **3**: 117, pl. 29.
—Sea Islands on the border of South Carolina.
Ambystoma talpoideum Gray, 1850, Cat. Batr. Grad. Brit. Mus., p. 36.

Range.—Coastal plain of South Atlantic states southward from South Carolina, through the Gulf states to Louisiana; northward in the Mississippi Basin to eastern Oklahoma and southern Illinois.

Common name.—Mole salamander.

Ambystoma texanum Matthes

Salamandra texana Matthes, 1855, Allg. deutsche naturh. Zeitschr., (n.s.),
1: 266.—Rio Colorado and Cumming's Creek Bottom, Fayette County,
Texas; restr. to Rio Colorado bottom land.
Amblystoma microstomum Cope, 1861, Proc. Acad. Nat. Sci. Phila., **13**: 123.
—Wabash, Ohio [= Wabash River, Indiana; see Fowler and Dunn, Proc.
Acad. Nat. Sci. Phila., **69**: 11].

Range.—Kansas to Ohio, south to the Gulf states, east to West Virginia, Georgia, and North Carolina.

Common name.—Small-mouthed salamander.

Ambystoma tigrinum Green

Salamandra tigrina Green, 1825, Jour. Acad. Nat. Sci. Phila., (1), **5**: 116.—
Near Moorestown, Burlington County, New Jersey.
Ambystoma tigrina Baird, 1849, Jour. Acad. Nat. Sci. Phila., (2), **1**: 284.

Range.—Most of temperate North America, except the Pacific northwest.

Common name.—Tiger salamander.

Ambystoma tigrinum tigrinum Green

Ambystoma tigrinum tigrinum Dunn, 1940, Copeia, **1940**: 156.

89576

Salamandra ingens Green, 1830, Jour. Acad. Nat. Sci. Phila., (1), **6**: 254.—
Near New Orleans, Louisiana.

Salamandra lurida Sager, 1839, Amer. Jour. Sci., (1), **36**: 322.—No locality.

Ambystoma episcopus Baird, 1849, Jour. Acad. Nat. Sci. Phila., (2), **1**: 293.—
Kemper County, Mississippi.

Amblystoma bicolor Hallowell, 1858, Proc. Acad. Nat. Sci. Phila., **10**: 215.—
Near Beesley's Point [Cape May County], New Jersey.

Amblystoma conspersum Cope, 1859, Proc. Acad. Nat. Sci. Phila., **11**: 123.—
Londongrove, Chester County, Pennsylvania.

Amblystoma obscurum Baird, 1867, *in* Cope, Proc. Acad. Nat. Sci. Phila.,
19: 192.—Fort Des Moines, Iowa.

Amblystoma xiphias Cope, 1867, Proc. Acad. Nat. Sci. Phila., **19**: 192.—
Columbus, Franklin County, Ohio.

Amblystoma copeanum Hay, 1888, Proc. U. S. Nat. Mus., **8**: 209, pl. 14.—
Irvington, Marion County (near Indianapolis), Indiana.

Range.—Eastern United States from New York and New Jersey southward through the Atlantic and Gulf coastal plains, westward to Louisiana and Iowa; recorded from Essex County, Ontario, and southeastern Manitoba.

Common name.—Eastern tiger salamander.

Ambystoma tigrinum melanostictum Baird

Siredon lichenoides melanostictum Baird, 1860, Expl. Surv. R. R. Miss.
Pacific, **12**, pt. 2, p. 306.—Near Fort Union, Nebraska.

Ambystoma tigrinum melanostictum Bishop, 1942, Copeia, **1942**: 256.

Ambystoma tigrinum slateri Dunn, 1940, Copeia, **1940**: 159.—5 miles southeast of Coulee Dam, Grant County, Washington.

Range.—Eastern British Columbia and Alberta, southeastward through eastern Washington and Oregon, Idaho, Montana, Wyoming, North Dakota, South Dakota, and Nebraska.

Common name.—Blotched tiger salamander.

Ambystoma tigrinum diaboli Dunn

Ambystoma tigrinum diaboli Dunn, 1940, Copeia, **1940**: 160.—Devil's Lake,
Ramsey County, North Dakota.

Range.—North Dakota east and north of the Altamont Moraine, north into adjacent Saskatchewan and Manitoba.

Common name.—Gray tiger salamander.

Ambystoma tigrinum mavortium Baird

Ambystoma mavortia Baird, 1850, Jour. Acad. Nat. Sci. Phila., (2), **1**: 284.—
New Mexico.

Ambystoma tigrinum mavortium Dunn, 1940, Copeia, **1940**: 158.

Ambystoma proserpine Baird, 1852, Proc. Acad. Nat. Sci. Phila., **6**: 173.—
Salado, 4 miles from San Antonio, Texas.
Siredon harlanii Duméril, Bibron, and Duméril, 1854, Erpét. Gén., **9**: 181,
pl. 95, figs. 1, 1a.—Spring Lake, New Mexico.
Siredon lichenoides Baird, 1854, Proc. Acad. Nat. Sci. Phila., **6**: 68.—Lake
at head of Santa Fe Creek, New Mexico.
Amblystoma trisruptum Cope, 1868, Proc. Acad. Nat. Sci. Phila., **19**: 194.—
Ocate River, New Mexico.

Range.—Kansas and Oklahoma, southwestward through Texas
and eastern Colorado to eastern and central New Mexico.

Common name.—Yellow-barred tiger salamander.

Ambystoma tigrinum nebulosum Hallowell

Ambystoma nebulosum Hallowell, 1854, Proc. Acad. Nat. Sci. Phila., **6**: 209.
—San Francisco Mountains, Arizona.
Ambystoma tigrinum nebulosum Dunn, 1940, Copeia, **1940**: 158.

Range.—Colorado plateau in Utah, western Colorado, northwestern New Mexico and Arizona.[3]

Common name.—Clouded tiger salamander.

Ambystoma tigrinum californiense Gray

Ambyostoma californiense Gray, 1853, Proc. Zool. Soc. London, **1853**: 11,
pl. 7.—Monterey, California, in error designated as vicinity of San Francisco.
Ambystoma tigrinum californiense Dunn, 1940, Copeia, **1940**: 157.

Range.—Central western California, from Sonoma and Sacramento
counties southward in the Central Valley to Kern County, and coast-
wise to Monterey County.

Common name.—California tiger salamander.

SALAMANDRIDAE

Diemictylus[4] Rafinesque

Diemictylus Rafinesque, 1820, Ann. Nat., Lexington, no. 1, p. 5.—Type:
viridescens.
Notophthalmus Rafinesque, 1820, Ann. Nat., Lexington, no. 1, p. 5.—Type:
miniatus = *viridescens*.
Diemyctylus Hallowell, 1858, Jour. Acad. Nat. Sci. Phila., (2), **3**: 363
(emend.).

[3] *Ambystoma tigrinum*, possibly representing *nebulosum*, is recorded as abundant in the Huachuca Mountains by Reed (1951, Nat. Hist. Misc., **79**).

[4] Wolterstorff, Willy, and Wolf Herre, 1935. Die Gattungen der Wasser-
molche der Familie Salamandridae, Arch. Naturg., (n.f.), **4**, Heft 2, pp. 217–
229.

Diemictylus viridescens Rafinesque

Triturus viridescens Rafinesque, 1820, Ann. Nat., Lexington, no. 1, p. 5.—
Lake George, Lake Champlain.
Diemyctylus viridescens Cope, 1889, Bull. U. S. Nat. Mus., **34**: 207.

Range.—Eastern North America.

Common name.—Newt.

Diemictylus viridescens viridescens Rafinesque

Diemyctylus viridescens viridescens Cope, 1889, Bull. U. S. Nat. Mus., **34**:
207, illus.
Triturus miniatus Rafinesque, 1820, Ann. Nat., Lexington, no. 1, p. 5.—
Eastern United States; restr. to borders of Lake Champlain.
Salamandra symmetrica Harlan, 1825, Jour. Acad. Nat. Sci. Phila., (1),
5: 157.—Near Camden, South Carolina.
Salamandra greeni Gray, 1831, *in* Griffith's Anim. Kingd., **9**, Synopsis, p. 107.
—Substitute name (for *viridescens,* cf. Boulenger, 1882, Cat. Batr. Caud.,
p. 22).
Salamandra millepunctata Storer, 1840, Boston Jour. Nat. Hist., **2**: 60.—
Roxbury and Amherst, Massachusetts.
Triton punctatissimus Duméril, Bibron, and Duméril, 1854, Erpét. Gén.,
9: 154.—Substitute name for *millepunctata.*
Salamandra ventralis Provancher, 1875, Nat. Canadien, **7**: 251.—Yamaska,
Quebec.

Range.—Eastern North America, from the St. Lawrence Basin in
Quebec and southern Ontario to New Brunswick, south to South
Carolina, Georgia, and Alabama, and west to Michigan and Indiana.

Common name.—Red-spotted newt, red eft (for the land stage).

Diemictylus viridescens dorsalis Harlan

[New comb.]

Salamandra dorsalis Harlan, 1828, Jour. Acad. Nat. Sci. Phila., (1), **6**: 101.
—South Carolina; restr. to northeastern South Carolina.
Diemyctylus viridescens vittatus Garman, 1897, Jour. Cincinnati Soc. Nat.
Hist., **19**: 49.—Wilmington, New Hanover County, North Carolina.

Range.—Southeastern North Carolina and northeastern South Carolina.

Common name.—Broken-striped newt.

Diemictylus viridescens louisianensis Wolterstorff

Diemyctylus viridescens louisianensis Wolterstorff, 1914, Abh. Mus. Naturk.
Magdeburg, **2**: 383.—New Orleans, Orleans Parish, Louisiana.

Range.—Atlantic and Gulf coastal plains, from southeastern South
Carolina to eastern Texas and Oklahoma, north in the Mississippi

Basin to Iowa and through Illinois, northwestern Indiana, Wisconsin, the western Upper Peninsula of Michigan, and eastern Minnesota.

Common name.—Variable newt.

Diemictylus viridescens perstriatus Bishop
[New comb.]

> *Triturus perstriatus* Bishop, 1941, Occ. Papers Mus. Zool. Univ. Mich., **451**: 3.—Dedge Pond, 2 miles east of Chesser's Island, Charlton County, Georgia.

Range.—Southeastern Georgia and northeastern Florida.

Common name.—Striped newt.

Diemictylus meridionalis Cope

> *Diemyctylus miniatus meridionalis* Cope, 1880, Bull. U. S. Nat. Mus., **17**: 30.—Matamoros, Tamaulipas.
> *Diemictylus meridionalis* Smith, 1947, Bull. Chicago Acad. Sci., **8**: 6.

Range.—Gulf Coast of Texas from Houston to the Rio Grande and into adjacent Tamaulipas.

Common name.—Black-spotted newt.

Taricha Gray

> *Taricha* Gray, 1850, Cat. Batr. Grad. Brit. Mus., p. 25.—Type: *torosa* (by subsequent designation).

Taricha torosa Rathke

> *Triton torosus* Rathke, 1833, *in* Eschscholtz, Zool. Atlas, pt. 5, p. 12, pl. 21, fig. 15.—Vicinity of San Francisco, California.
> *Taricha torosa* Herre, 1934, Blätter Aquarien-Terr. Kunde, **45**: 250.

Range.—Coast ranges of California from Mendocino County to the vicinity of San Diego, and the Sierra Nevada.

Common name.—California newt.

Taricha torosa torosa Rathke

> *Taricha torosa torosa* Herre, Abh. Mus. Naturk. Magdeburg, **7**: 91, figs. 6, 7.
> *Triton ermani* Wiegmann, 1835, *in* Erman's Reise um die Erde, Naturk. Atlas, p. 24.—San Francisco, San Mateo County, California.
> *Taricha laevis* Baird and Girard, 1853, Proc. Acad. Nat. Sci. Phila., **6**: 302.—San Francisco.
> *Taricha torosa klauberi* Wolterstorff, 1935, Blätter Aquarien-Terr. Kunde, **46**: 179.—Boulder Creek, San Diego County, California.

Range.—Coastal California from the vicinity of San Diego north to middle Mendocino County, north of San Francisco.

Common name.—Coast Range newt.

Taricha torosa sierrae Twitty
[New comb.]

> *Triturus sierrae* Twitty, 1942, Copeia, **1942**: 65, pl. 1.—Cherokee Creek, in the hills above Chico, Butte County, California.

Range.—Sierra Nevada of California in Butte, Eldorado, Mariposa, Tuolumne, Placer, and Fresno counties, north to Shasta County.

Common name.—Sierra newt.

Taricha granulosa Skilton
[New comb.]

> *Salamandra (Triton) granulosa* Skilton, 1849, Amer. Jour. Sci. Arts, (2), 7: 202, pl. 1.—Oregon; restr. to Willamette Falls (= Oregon City), Clackamas County, Oregon.

Range.—The Pacific coastal region from southern Alaska to Santa Clara and Santa Cruz counties, California.

Common name.—Rough-skinned newt.

Taricha granulosa granulosa Skilton
[New comb.]

Range.—From the northern boundary of California northward through coastal Oregon, Washington, and British Columbia to Admiralty Island, Alaska.

Common name.—Rough-skinned newt.

Taricha granulosa mazamae Myers
[New comb.]

> *Triturus granulosus mazamae* Myers, 1942, Copeia, **1942**: 80, fig.—Higher slopes of Mount Mazama near Crater Lake, Klamath County, Oregon.

Range.—Vicinity of Crater Lake, Oregon.

Common name.—Crater Lake newt.

Taricha granulosa twittyi Bishop
[New comb.]

> *Triturus granulosus twittyi* Bishop, 1941, Occ. Papers Mus. Zool. Univ. Mich., **451**: 16.—Saratoga, Santa Clara County, California.

Range.—Santa Clara, Santa Cruz, Marin and southern Mendocino counties, California.

Common name.—Twitty's newt.

Taricha granulosa similans Twitty
[New comb.]

Triturus similans Twitty, 1935, Copeia, **1935**: 76.—Robinson Creek, Ukiah, Mendocino County, California.

Range.—Mendocino and Butte counties, California.

Common name.—Mendocino newt.

Taricha rivularis Twitty
[New comb.]

Triturus rivularis Twitty, 1935, Copeia, **1935**: 73.—Gibson Creek, about 1 mile west of Ukiah, Mendocino County, California.

Range.—Northern California, in Sonoma, Mendocino, Humboldt and probably Del Norte counties.

Common name.—Western red-bellied newt.

AMPHIUMIDAE
Amphiuma Garden

Amphiuma Garden, 1821, *in* Smith, Correspondence of Linnaeus, **1**: 333, 599.—Type: *means.*

Chrysodonta Mitchill, 1822, Amer. Med. Rec., **5**: 503.—Type: *larvaeformis* = *means.*

Sirenoidis Fitzinger, 1843, Syst. Rept., p. 34.—Type: *didactylum.*

Muraenopsis Fitzinger, 1843, Syst. Rept., p. 34.—Type: *tridactylum.*

Amphiuma means Garden

Amphiuma means Garden, 1821, *in* Smith, Correspondence of Linnaeus, **1**: 333, 599.—Type locality not stated; from the context either Charleston, South Carolina, or eastern Florida; restr. to Charleston, South Carolina.

Range.—Southeastern North America.

Common name.—Amphiuma, congo eel, lamp or lamper eel, mud eel.

Amphiuma means means Garden

Amphiuma means means Goin, 1938, Herpetologica, **5**: 128.

Chrysodonta larvaeformis Mitchill, 1822, Amer. Med. Rec., **5**: 503.—Savannah, Chatham County, Georgia.

Amphiuma didactylum Cuvier, 1827, Mem. Mus. Hist. Nat. Paris, **14**: 4.—
Substitute name for *means.*

Range.—Southeastern Virginia south through the Atlantic coastal plain, peninsular Florida, and west to southeastern Mississippi and extreme eastern Louisana (including the area of intergradation with *tridactylum,* according to Goin).

Common name.—Two-toed amphiuma, two-toed mud eel.

Amphiuma means tridactylum Cuvier

Amphiuma tridactylum Cuvier, 1827, Mem. Mus. Hist. Nat. Paris, **14**: 7.—
New Orleans.
Amphiuma means tridactylum Goin, 1938, Herpetologica, **1**: 128.

Range.—Gulf coastal plain from eastern Texas through Louisiana, Mississippi, and Alabama; north through Arkansas and western Tennessee to the adjacent areas of Missouri, Kentucky, and undoubtedly Illinois; Clark County, Indiana.

Common name.—Lamp eel, lamper eel [Louisiana], three-toed amphiuma.

PLETHODONTIDAE

DESMOGNATHINAE

Desmognathus Baird

Desmognathus Baird, 1850, Jour. Acad. Nat. Sci. Phila., (2), **1**: 282.—Type: *fuscus.*

Desmognathus aeneus Brown and Bishop

Desmognathus aeneus Brown and Bishop, 1947, Copeia, **1947**: 163, fig. 1.—
Seepage branch, 100 feet north of Peachtree Creek, 3½ miles south-southeast of Peachtree, Cherokee County, North Carolina.

Range.—Known only from the type locality.

Common name.—Cherokee salamander.

Desmognathus fuscus Green

Salamandra fusca Green, 1818, Jour. Acad. Nat. Sci. Phila., (1), **1**: 357.—
Probably the vicinity of Princeton, New Jersey.
Desmognathus fuscus Baird, 1849, Jour. Acad. Nat. Sci. Phila., (2), **1**: 285;
Grobman, 1950, Nat. Hist. Misc., **70**: 1–8, figs. 1, 2 [maps].

Range.—Eastern United States, west to eastern Oklahoma and Texas; southern New Brunswick and southern Ontario.

Common name.—Dusky salamander.

Desmognathus fuscus fuscus Rafinesque

Desmognathus fusca fusca Cope, 1889, Bull. U. S. Nat. Mus., **34**: 194.
Desmognathus fuscus fuscus Dunn, 1926, Plethodontidae, p. 81.
Salamandra nigra Green, 1818, Jour. Acad. Nat. Sci. Phila., (1), **1**: 352.—
  Probably vicinity of Princeton, New Jersey.
Salamandra sinciput-albida Green, 1818, Jour. Acad. Nat. Sci. Phila., (1),
  1: 352.—New Jersey.
Triturus nebulosus Rafinesque, 1820, Ann. Nat., Lexington, no. 1, p. 5.—
  Near New York, at Harlem and Long Island.
Salamandra picta Harlan, 1825, Jour. Acad. Nat. Sci. Phila., (1), **5**: 136.—
  Vicinity of Philadelphia.
Salamandra intermixta Green, 1825, Hall's Portfolio, **20**: 159.—Jefferson
  College, Pennsylvania.
Salamandra frontalis Gray, 1831, Syn. Rept., *in* Griffith's Anim. Kingd., **9**,
  Appendix, p. 107 (substitute name for *sinciput-albida*).
Salamandra phoca Matthes, 1855, Allg. deutsche naturh. Zeitschr., (n.s.),
  1: 273.—Taylor's Creek, opposite the town of Miami on the west bank
  of the Miami River, Ohio [about 14 miles northwest of Newport, Camp-
  bell County, Kentucky].

Range.—New Brunswick to eastern Ontario and through the
Appalachian region to Alabama and Georgia, westward to southern
Illinois. Interdigitating with *brimleyorum* on the Piedmont plateau.

Common name.—Northern dusky salamander.

Desmognathus fuscus welteri Barbour

Desmognathus fuscus welteri Barbour, 1950, Copeia, **1950**: 277.—Looney
  Creek, near Lynch, Harlan County, Kentucky.

Range.—Eastern Kentucky and adjacent Virginia.

Common name.—Black Mountain dusky salamander.

Desmognathus fuscus auriculatus Holbrook

Salamandra auriculata Holbrook, 1838, N. Amer. Herp., ed. 1, **3**: 115, pl.
  28.—Riceborough, Liberty County, Georgia.
Desmognathus fuscus auriculata Cope, 1869, Proc. Acad. Nat. Sci. Phila.,
  21: 116.

Range.—Southeastern South Carolina, southward to central Florida, and westward to southeastern Mississippi.

Common name.—Coastal plain dusky salamander.

Desmognathus fuscus brimleyorum Stejneger

Desmognathus brimleyorum Stejneger, 1895, Proc. U. S. Nat. Mus., **17**: 598.
  —Hot Springs, Garland County, Arkansas.
Desmognathus fuscus brimleyorum Dunn, 1926, Plethodontidae, p. 101.

Range.—Southeastern Virginia, southwestward to eastern Texas and northward through Arkansas. Interdigitating with *fuscus* on the Piedmont plateau.

Common name.—Brimley's dusky salamander.

Desmognathus fuscus carri Neill

> *Desmognathus fuscus carri* Neill, 1951, Publ. Res. Div. Allen's Rept. Inst., **1**: 25, figs. 1, 2.—Silver Glen Springs, in the Ocala National Forest, Marion County, Florida.

Range.—The Big Scrub region (the Ocala National Forest) of Marion County, Florida, southward through Hillsborough and Polk counties.

Common name.—Ocala dusky salamander.

Desmognathus ochrophaeus Cope

> *Desmognathus ochrophaea* Cope, 1839, Proc. Acad. Nat. Sci. Phila., **11**: 124. —Susquehanna County, Pennsylvania.

Range.—From the Hudson River Valley west to Lakes Ontario and Erie in New York and Pennsylvania, southward to Georgia.

Common name.—Allegheny mountain salamander.

Desmognathus ochrophaeus ochrophaeus Cope

> *Desmognathus ochrophaea ochrophaea* Dunn, 1917, Proc. U. S. Nat. Mus., **53**: 415.

Range.—Clinton County, New York, to Garrett County, Maryland, West Virginia and adjacent Ohio, southward into Kentucky.

Common name.—Allegheny mountain salamander.

Desmognathus ochrophaeus carolinensis Dunn

> *Desmognathus ochrophaea carolinensis* Dunn, 1916, Proc. Biol. Soc. Wash., **29**: 74.—Spring near top of Mount Mitchell, Buncombe County, North Carolina.
>
> *Desmognathus aureatagulus* Weller, 1930, Proc. Junior Soc. Nat. Sci. Cincinnati, **1**, no. 7, [not paged].—Trail between Newfound Gap and Indian Pass, 4,400 to 5,000 feet alt., Great Smoky Mountain National Park.
>
> *Desmognathus fuscus imitator* Dunn, 1927, Copeia, **164**: 84.—Indian Pass, Great Smoky Mountains, North Carolina.

Range.—Appalachian ranges from Virginia to northeastern Georgia.

Common name.—Blue Ridge mountain salamander.

Desmognathus ocoee Nicholls

Desmognathus ocoee Nicholls, 1949, Jour. Tenn. Acad. Sci., **24**: 127.—Ships Prow Rock, Ocoee Gorge, nine miles west of Ducktown, Polk County, Tennessee.

Range.—Known only from the type locality.

Common name.—Ocoee salamander.

Desmognathus perlapsus Neill

Desmognathus perlapsus Neill, 1950, Publ. Ross Allen Rept. Inst., **1**: 1, fig. 1.—Tallulah Gorge, near Tallulah Falls, Rabun County, Georgia.

Range.—Known only from the type locality.

Common name.—Tallulah salamander.

Desmognathus monticola Dunn

Desmognathus monticola Dunn, 1916, Proc. Biol. Soc. Wash., **29**: 73.— Elk Lodge, near Brevard, North Carolina; Grobman, 1945, Proc. Biol. Soc. Wash., **58**: 40, map.

Desmognathus phoca Dunn, 1923, Proc. New England Zool. Club, **8**: 39 (*nec* Matthes).

Range.—Southwestern Pennsylvania through the Appalachian highlands to northern Georgia.

Common name.—Seal salamander.

Desmognathus monticola monticola Dunn

Desmognathus monticola monticola Hoffman, 1951, Jour. Elisha Mitchell Sci. Soc., **66**: 251, pl. 17, fig. 2, map. 1.

Range.—Range of *monticola* exclusive of the Blue Ridge Province.

Common name.—Seal salamander.

Demognathus monticola jeffersoni Hoffman

Desmognathus monticola jeffersoni Hoffman, 1951, Jour. Elisha Mitchell Sci. Soc., **66**: 250, pl. 17, fig. 1, map 1.

Range.—Blue Ridge Province in Virginia.

Common name.—Blue Ridge seal salamander.

Desmognathus chermocki Bishop and Valentine

Desmognathus chermocki Bishop and Valentine, 1950, Copeia, **1950**: 39.— Hurricane Creek, Tuscaloosa County, Alabama.

Range.—Tuscaloosa County, Alabama.

Common name.—Alabama salamander.

Desmognathus quadramaculatus Holbrook

Salamandra quadra-maculata Holbrook, 1840, N. Amer. Herp., ed. 1, **4**: 121, pl. 26.—Georgia, Carolina and Pennsylvania; restr. to Great Smoky Mountains ["maculo-quadrata" in text reference].

Desmognathus quadrimaculata Stejneger, 1903, Proc. U. S. Nat. Mus., **26**: 557.

Desmognathus quadramaculatus amphileucus Bishop, 1941, Occ. Papers Mus. Zool. Univ. Mich., **451**: 12.—Demorest, Habersham County, Georgia; Pope, 1949, Nat. Hist. Misc., **44**: 1.

Range.—From Monroe County, West Virginia, eastward to Henry County, Virginia, and southward to northeastern Georgia, in the Appalachian Mountains.

Common name.—Black-bellied salamander.

Desmognathus wrighti King

Desmognathus wrighti King, 1936, Herpetologica, **1**: 57, pl. 5.—Mount Le Conte, Sevier County, Tennessee.

Range.—Spruce-fir forests of Great Smoky Mountains; White Top Mountain, Virginia.

Common name.—Pygmy salamander.

Leurognathus Moore

Leurognathus Moore, 1899, Proc. Acad. Nat. Sci. Phila., **51**: 316.—Type: marmoratus (by monotypy).

Leurognathus marmorata Moore

Leurognathus marmorata Moore, 1899, Proc. Acad. Nat. Sci. Phila., **51**: 316, pl. 14.—South flank of Grandfather Mountain, Avery County, North Carolina; Pope and Hairston, 1947, Fieldiana: Zoology, **31**: 155–162, figs. 28, 29 (map).

Range.—Southern part of the Blue Ridge Province, above 1,500 feet alt.

Common name.—Shovel-nosed salamander.

Leurognathus marmorata marmorata Moore

Leurognathus marmorata marmorata Stejneger and Barbour, 1939, Check list, ed. 4, p. 12.

Range.—Grandfather and Roan Mountains in North Carolina, southwestward to the valley of the French Broad River.

Common name.—Northern shovel-nosed salamander.

Leurognathus marmorata intermedia Pope

Leurognathus marmorata intermedia Pope, 1928, Amer. Mus. Nov., **306**: 1.
—Davis Gap, Waynesville, Davis County, North Carolina.

Range.—Southern part of the Blue Ridge Province, southwestward from the valley of the French Broad River to Rabun County, Georgia.

Common name.—Southern shovel-nosed salamander.

PLETHODONTINAE

Plethodon Tschudi

Plethodon Tschudi, 1838, Mém. Soc. Sci. Nat. Neuchâtel, **1838**: 92.—Type: *glutinosus;* for distribution maps see Grobman, 1944, Ann. New York Acad. Sci., **45**: 265–316, figs. 1–11.

Plethodon cinereus Green

Salamandra cinerea Green, 1818, Jour. Acad. Nat. Sci. Phila., (1), **1**: 356.—New Jersey; restr. to vicinity of Princeton, New Jersey.
Plethodon cinereus Tschudi, 1838, Mém. Soc. Sci. Nat. Neuchâtel, **1838**: 92.

Range.—Eastern North America.

Common name.—Red-backed salamander.

Plethodon cinereus cinereus Green

Plethodon cinereus cinereus Cope, 1889, Bull. U. S. Nat. Mus., **34**: 134, fig. 30.
Salamandra erythronota Green, 1818, Jour. Acad. Nat. Sci. Phila., (1), **1**: 356.—New Jersey; restr. to vicinity of Princeton, New Jersey.

Range.—Eastern North America, from Nova Scotia and New Brunswick through Quebec and Ontario to James Bay and to eastern Minnesota; south to Georgia, at higher altitudes southward.

Common name.—Red-backed salamander, lead-backed salamander (names for the two color phases).

Plethodon cinereus angusticlavius Grobman

Plethodon cinereus angusticlavius Grobman, 1944, Ann. N. Y. Acad. Sci., **45**: 302.—Mud Cave, near Fairy Cave, Stone County, Missouri.

Range.—Ozark plateau in southern Missouri and northern Arkansas.

Common name.—Narrow-striped red-backed salamander.

Plethodon cinereus serratus Grobman

Plethodon cinereus serratus Grobman, 1944, Ann. N. Y. Acad. Sci., **45**: 306.
—Rich Mountain, Polk County, Arkansas.

Range.—Ouachita Mountains (western Arkansas and eastern Oklahoma).

Common name.—Ouachita red-backed salamander.

Plethodon dorsalis Cope

Plethodon cinereus dorsalis Cope, 1889, Bull. U. S. Nat. Mus., **34**: 139.—Louisville, Kentucky.

Plethodon dorsalis Stejneger and Barbour, 1917, Check list, ed. 1, p. 15.

Range.—Southern Indiana and Illinois, through western Kentucky and central Tennessee to northern Alabama.

Common name.—Zigzag salamander.

Plethodon glutinosus Green

Salamandra glutinosa Green, 1818, Jour. Acad. Nat. Sci. Phila., (1), **1**: 357.—Vicinity of Princeton, New Jersey.

Plethodon glutinosus Tschudi, 1838, Mém. Soc. Sci. Nat. Neuchâtel, **1838**: 92.

Range.—Eastern United States, west to Texas.

Common name.—Slimy salamander.

Plethodon glutinosus glutinosus Green

Plethodon glutinosus glutinosus Dunn, 1920, Proc. Biol. Soc. Wash., **33**: 131

Salamandra variolata Gilliams, 1818, Jour. Acad. Nat. Sci. Phila., (1), **1**: 460, pl. 18, fig. 1.—Southern states; restr. to vicinity of Charleston, South Carolina.

Salamandra cylindracea Harlan, 1825, Jour. Acad. Nat. Sci. Phila., (1), **5**: 156.—South Carolina; restr. to vicinity of Charleston.

Salamandra melanoleuca Wied, 1865, Nova Acta Acad. Leop.—Carol., **32**: 130.—Nazareth, Northampton County, Pennsylvania.

Range.—Eastern United States, from New York through the Atlantic and Gulf states to eastern Texas; northward to central Illinois, Indiana, and eastern and southern Ohio, exclusive of ranges of southeastern coastal plain species.

Common name.—Slimy salamander.

Plethodon glutinosus albagula Grobman

Plethodon glutinosus albagula Grobman, 1944, Ann. N. Y. Acad. Sci., **45**: 283.—20 miles north of San Antonio, Bexar County, Texas.

Range.—Southern part of the Edwards Plateau in central Texas.

Common name.—White-throated slimy salamander.

Plethodon glutinosus grobmani Allen and Neill

Plethodon glutinosus grobmani Allen and Neill, 1949, Herpetologica, **5**: 112.
—Half-mile Creek Swamp, about a half-mile northeast of Silver Springs, Marion County, Florida.

Range.—Lower coastal plain of Georgia southward in Florida to Pinellas and Hillsborough counties.

Common name.—Grobman's slimy salamander.

Plethodon glutinosus chlorobryonis Mittleman

Plethodon glutinosus chlorobryonis Mittleman, 1951, Herpetologica, **7**: 108.
—13 miles north of New Bern, Craven County, North Carolina.

Range.—Eastern North Carolina, on the coastal plain.

Common name.—Carolina slimy salamander.

Plethodon dixi Pope and Fowler

Plethodon dixi Pope and Fowler, 1949, Nat. Hist. Misc., **47**: 1.—Dixie Caverns, Roanoke County, Virginia.

Range.—Dixie Caverns and near-by caves in Roanoke County, Virginia.

Common name.—Dunn's cave salamander, Dixie Caverns salamander.

Plethodon jordani Blatchley

Plethodon jordani Blatchley, 1901, 25th Ann. Rept. Dept. Geol. Indiana, p. 762.—Mount Collins and Indian Pass at 3,000 to 5,000 feet alt., Sevier County, Tennessee; Pope and Hairston, 1948, Evolution, **2**: 276, fig. 11 [map]; Hairston, 1950, Copeia, **1950**: 264, fig. 1 [map].

Range.—Southern Appalachian Mountains.

Common name.—Jordan's salamander.

Plethodon jordani jordani Blatchley

Plethodon jordani jordani Hairston, 1950, Copeia, **1950**: 262.

Range.—Great Smoky Mountains in North Carolina and Tennessee.

Common name.—Red-cheeked salamander.

Plethodon jordani metcalfi Brimley

Plethodon metcalfi Brimley, 1912, Proc. Biol. Soc. Wash., **25**: 138, pl. 6, figs. 1, 2, 4, 7–11.—Sunburst, Haywood County, and Grandfather Mountain, Avery County, North Carolina; restr. to Sunburst.
Plethodon jordani metcalfi Hairston, 1950, Copeia, **1950**: 266.

Range.—From Tazewell County, southwestern Virginia, southwestward through North Carolina and Tennessee to areas of intergradation with *jordani, shermani,* and *melaventris.*

Common name.—Metcalf's salamander.

Plethodon jordani clemsonae Brimley

Plethodon clemsonae Brimley, 1927, Copeia, **164**: 73.—Jocassee, Oconee County, South Carolina.
Plethodon jordani clemsonae Hairston, 1950, Copeia, **1950**: 272.

Range.—Vicinity of Jocassee, Oconee County, northwestern South Carolina.

Common name.—Clemson's salamander.

Plethodon jordani shermani Stejneger

Plethodon shermani Stejneger, 1906, Proc. U. S. Nat. Mus., **30**: 559, fig. 1. —Wayah Bald, North Carolina.
Plethodon jordani shermani Hairston, 1950, Copeia, **1950**: 271.

Range.—Nantahala Mountains, southwestern North Carolina.

Common name.—Red-legged salamander.

Plethodon jordani melaventris Pope and Hairston

Plethodon shermani melaventris Pope and Hairston, 1948, Copeia, **1948**: 107.—Highlands, Macon County, North Carolina.
Plethodon jordani melaventris Hairston, 1950, Copeia, **1950**: 272.

Range.—Western North Carolina (Beech Gap) southward to the junction of North and South Carolina with Georgia.

Common name.—Highlands salamander.

Plethodon jordani rabunensis Pope and Hairston

Plethodon shermani rabunensis Pope and Hairston, 1948, Copeia, **1948**: 106. —Rabun Bald, Rabun County, Georgia.
Plethodon jordani rabunensis Hairston, 1950, Copeia, **1950**: 272.

Range.—Rabun Bald, Rabun County, and Lumpkin County, northeastern Georgia.

Common name.—Rabun Bald salamander.

Plethodon jordani teyahalee Hairston

Plethodon jordani teyahalee Hairston, 1950, Copeia, **1950**: 269.—Teyahalee Bald (= Johanna Bald), Snowbird Mountains, Graham and Cherokee counties, North Carolina.

Range.—Snowbird Mountains in Graham and Cherokee counties, North Carolina.

Common name.—Teyahalee salamander.

Plethodon jordani kentucki Mittleman

Plethodon kentucki Mittleman, 1951, Herpetologica, **7**: 105, 1 fig.—Pine Mountain, Harlan County, Kentucky.

Range.—Pike and Harlan counties, Kentucky.

Common name.—Kentucky salamander.

Plethodon nettingi Green

Plethodon nettingi Green, 1938, Ann. Carnegie Mus., **27**: 295.—Barton Knob, Randolph County, West Virginia; Brooks, 1948, Copeia, **1948**: 239–244, fig. 1.

Range.—Southern Cheat Mountains, in eastern West Virginia.

Common name.—Cheat Mountain salamander.

Plethodon ouachitae Dunn and Heintze

Plethodon ouachitae Dunn and Heintze, 1933, Copeia, **1933**: 121.—Ouachita National Forest, Rich Mountain, Polk County, Arkansas; Pope and Pope, 1951, Bull. Chicago Acad. Sci., **9**: 129, figs. 1, 2 (maps).

Range.—Ouachita Mountains, in Polk County, Arkansas, and Le Flore County, Oklahoma.

Common name.—Rich Mountain salamander.

Plethodon caddoensis Pope and Pope

Plethodon caddoensis Pope and Pope, 1951, Bull. Chicago Acad. Sci., **9**: 148, fig. 1 (map).—Polk Creek Mountain at 1,200 feet alt., Caddo Mountains, Montgomery County, Arkansas.

Range.—Caddo Mountains, Montgomery County, Arkansas, 950 to 1,200 feet alt.

Common name.—Caddo Mountain salamander.

Plethodon richmondi Netting and Mittleman

Plethodon richmondi Netting and Mittleman, 1938, Ann. Carnegie Mus., **27**: 288, pl. 30, fig. 1.—Huntington, Cabell County, West Virginia.

Range.—From Centre County, Pennsylvania, southward to Wayne County, West Virginia, eastward into western Virginia; Carter and Fayette counties, Kentucky, and west to Cincinnati, Yellow Springs, and Montgomery County in southwestern Ohio.

Common name.—Ravine salamander.

Plethodon wehrlei Fowler and Dunn

Plethodon wehrlei Fowler and Dunn, 1917, Proc. Acad. Nat. Sci. Phila., **69**: 23, pl. 4.—Two Lick Hills, Indiana County, Pennsylvania.

Range.—Northern portion of Appalachian plateau; extreme southwestern New York through western Pennsylvania, most of West Virginia, and into southeastern Ohio.

Common name.—Wehrle's salamander.

Plethodon huldae Grobman

Plethodon huldae Grobman, 1949, Proc. Biol. Soc. Wash., **62**: 136.—Along foot trail to Hawksbill Mountain, Skyline Drive, Madison County, Virginia, 3,500 feet alt.

Range.—Blue Ridge Province in suitable habitats between Poor Mountain, Roanoke County, and Stony Man Mountain, Page and Madison counties.

Common name.—Northern Blue Ridge salamander.

Plethodon welleri Walker

Plethodon welleri Walker, 1931, Proc. Junior Soc. Nat. Sci. Cincinnati, **2**: 48. —Grandfather Mountain, above 5,000 feet, near Linville, North Carolina.

Range.—Grandfather and Flat Top mountains, northwestern North Carolina, and White Top Mountain, southwestern Virginia.

Common name.—Weller's salamander.

Pethodon yonahlossee Dunn

Plethodon yonahlossee Dunn, 1917, Bull. Amer. Mus. Nat. Hist., **37**: 598, pl. 57, figs. 1–3, text fig. 1.—Yonahlossee Road, about 1½ miles from Linville, North Carolina, at 4,200 feet alt.; Pope, 1950, Bull. Chicago Acad. Sci., **9**: 79, fig. 1 (map).

Range.—Blue Ridge Mountains in North Carolina from the valley of the French Broad River northeastward into Virginia and Tennessee.

Common name.—Yonahlossee salamander.

Plethodon dunni Bishop

Plethodon dunni Bishop, 1934, Proc. Biol. Soc. Wash., **47**: 169.—Vicinity of Portland, Clackamas County, Oregon.

Range.—Western Oregon and extreme southwestern Washington, southward to the lower Rogue River.

Common name.—Dunn's salamander.

Plethodon elongatus Van Denburgh

Plethodon elongatus Van Denburgh, 1916, Proc. Calif. Acad. Sci., (4), **6:** 216.—Requa, Del Norte County, California.

Range.—Del Norte and Humboldt counties, California, north to Curry County, Oregon.

Common name.—Del Norte salamander.

Plethodon vandykei Van Denburgh

Plethodon vandykei Van Denburgh, 1906, Proc. Calif. Acad. Sci., (4), **4:** 61. —Paradise Valley, Mount Rainier Park, Washington.

Range.—Olympic Mountains to the Cascades and to northern Idaho.

Common name.—Van Dyke's salamander.

Plethodon vandykei vandykei Van Denburgh

Plethodon vandykei vandykei Lowe, 1950, Copeia, **1950:** 93.

Range.—Cascade and Olympic Mountains, Washington.

Common name.—Washington salamander.

Plethodon vandykei idahoensis Slater and Slip

Plethodon idahoensis Slater and Slip, 1940, Occ. Papers Dept. Biol. Univ. Puget Sound, **8:** 38, figs. 1, 2.—Northeast corner of Coeur d'Alene Lake, Kootenai County, Idaho.
Plethodon vandykei idahoensis Lowe, 1950, Copeia, **1950:** 93.

Range.—Mountains of northern Idaho.

Common name.—Coeur d'Alene salamander.

Plethodon vehiculum Cooper

Ambystoma vehiculum Cooper, 1860, Rept. Expl. Surv. Miss. River to Pacific, **12,** pt. 2, viii, pl. 31, fig. 4.—Astoria, Oregon.
Plethodon vehiculum Bishop, 1934, Proc. Biol. Soc. Wash., **47:** 171, pl. 1, fig. 2.
Plethodon intermedius Baird, 1857, Proc. Acad. Nat. Sci. Phila., **8:** 207.— Fort Tejon, California.
Plethodon crassulus Cope, 1886, Proc. Amer. Phil. Soc., **23:** 521.—California.

Range.—Southwestern British Columbia and Vancouver Island, western Washington, and northwestern Oregon.

Common name.—Western red-backed salamander.

Plethodon neomexicanus Stebbins and Riemer

Plethodon neomexicanus Stebbins and Riemer, 1950, Copeia, **1950:** 73.-

12 miles west and 4 miles south of Los Alamos, 8,750 feet alt., Sandoval
County, New Mexico.

Range.—Jemez Mountains, northern New Mexico.

Common name.—Jemez Mountains salamander.

Batrachoseps Bonaparte

Batrachoseps Bonaparte, 1839, Icon. Fauna Ital., **2**: fasc. 26, fol. 131.***—
Type: *attenuatus.*
Plethopsis Bishop, 1937, Herpetologica, **1**: 93.—Type: *wrighti.*

Batrachoseps attenuatus Eschscholtz

Salamandrina attenuata Eschscholtz, 1833, Zool. Atlas, pt. 5, p. 1, pl. 21,
figs. 1–14.—Vicinity of Bay of San Francisco, California.
Batrachoseps attenuatus Cooper, 1858, Pac. R. R. Surv., **12**, pt. 3, Zool.,
p. viii, pl. 31, fig. 5.

Range.—Southwestern Oregon to coastal California, including
coastal islands, south into Lower California.

Common name.—California slender salamander.

Batrachoseps attenuatus attenuatus Eschscholtz

Batrachoseps attenuatus attenuatus Dunn, 1926, Plethodontidae, p. 224.
Batrachoseps nigriventris Cope, 1869, Proc. Acad. Nat. Sci. Phila., **21**: 98.—
Fort Tejon, Kern County, California.
Batrachoseps caudatus Cope, 1889, Bull. U. S. Nat. Mus., **34**: 126, pl. 81,
fig. 2, text fig. 27.—Hassler Harbor, Alaska [best regarded as an error of
museum records unless substantiated].

Range.—Southwestern Oregon through western California to Los
Angeles County and the slopes of the Sierra Nevada in California.

Common name.—Northern slender salamander.

Batrachoseps attenuatus leucopus Dunn

Batrachoseps leucopus Dunn, 1922, Copeia, **109**: 60.—North Island, Los
Coronados Islands.
Batrachoseps attenuatus leucopus Dunn, 1926, Plethodontidae, p. 241.

Range.—The Coronados Islands and the opposite mainland of
California and Lower California west of the Coast Range.

Common name.—Southern slender salamander.

Batrachoseps pacificus Cope

Hemidactylium pacificus Cope, 1865, Proc. Acad. Nat. Sci. Phila., **17**: 195.—
Santa Barbara, California = Santa Barbara Island.
Batrachoseps attenuatus pacificus Bishop, 1943, Salamanders, p. 323, fig. 93,
map 38.

Range.—Islands off Santa Barbara and Los Angeles counties, California; Los Angeles–Pasadena area on the mainland.

Common name.—Pacific slender salamander.

Batrachoseps pacificus pacificus Cope

Batrachoseps pacificus pacificus Campbell, 1931, Copeia, **1931**: 133.

Range.—Islands off the coast of Santa Barbara County, California (San Miguel, Santa Rosa, Santa Cruz, and Anacapa).

Common name.—Channel Islands slender salamander.

Batrachoseps pacificus catalinae Dunn

Batrachoseps catalinae Dunn, 1922, Copeia, **109**: 62.—Santa Catalina Island.
Batrachoseps pacificus catalinae Campbell, 1931, Copeia, **1931**: 133.

Range.—Santa Catalina Island, California.

Common name.—Santa Catalina slender salamander.

Batrachoseps pacificus major Camp

Batrachoseps major Camp, 1915, Univ. Calif. Publ. Zool., **12**: 327.—Sierra Madre, 1,000 feet alt., Los Angeles County, California.
Batrachoseps pacificus major Campbell, 1931, Copeia, **1931**: 133.

Range.—Scattered localities in Los Angeles, San Bernardino, Riverside, and Orange counties in southern California.

Common name.—Greater slender salamander.

Batrachoseps wrighti Bishop

Plethopsis wrighti Bishop, 1937, Herpetologica, **1**: 93.—8.7 miles southeast of Sandy, Clackamas County, Oregon.
[*Batrachoseps wrighti*] Stebbins and Lowe, 1949, Copeia, **1949**: 128.

Range.—Linn and Clackamas counties, northwestern Oregon.

Common name.—Oregon slender salamander.

Hemidactylium Tschudi

Hemidactylium Tschudi, 1838, Mém. Soc. Sci. Nat. Neuchâtel, **1838**: 59.—Type: *scutatum*.
Cotobotes Gistel, 1848, Naturgeschichte, p. 11.—Substitute name for *Hemidactylium*.
Desmodactylus Duméril, Bibron, and Duméril, 1854, Erpét. Gén., **9**: 117.—Substitute name for *Hemidactylium*.

Hemidactylium scutatum Schlegel

Salamandra scutata Schlegel, 1838, Fauna Japonica, p. 119.—Nashville, Davidson County, Tennessee.

Hemidactylium scutatum Tschudi, 1838, Mém. Soc. Sci. Nat. Neuchâtel, **1838**: 94.

Salamandra melanosticta Gibbes, 1844, Boston Jour. Nat. Hist., **5**: 89.— Abbeville County, Abbeville District, South Carolina.

Range.—Eastern United States and Canada, from southern New Brunswick and Nova Scotia to eastern Virginia; west through southern Ontario to Wisconsin and the Upper Peninsula of Michigan; southward, west of the Appalachians, to Alabama and Arkansas; an isolated area in South Carolina and northeastern Georgia.

Common name.—Eastern four-toed salamander.

Ensatina Gray

Ensatina Gray, 1850, Cat. Batr. Grad. Brit. Mus., p. 48.—Type: *eschscholtzi.*

Heredia Girard, 1856, Proc. Acad. Nat. Sci. Phila., **8**: 140.—Type: *oregonensis.*

Urotropis Espada, 1870, An. Soc. Españ. Hist. Nat., **4**: 70.—Type: *platensis.*

Ensatina eschscholtzi Gray

Ensatina eschscholtzii Gray, 1850, Cat. Batr. Grad. Brit. Mus., p. 48.—California; restr. to Monterey; Stebbins, 1949, Univ. Calif. Publ. Zool., **48**: 377–526, pls. 11–16, 16 text figs.

Range.—Pacific coastal region west of the Cascades and of the Sierra Nevada from southern British Columbia to southern California.

Common name.—Eschscholtz's salamander, Redwood salamander.

Ensatina eschscholtzi eschscholtzi Gray

Ensatina eschscholtzii eschscholtzii Wood, 1940, Univ. Calif. Publ. Zool., **42**: 426.

Range.—Southwestern California.

Common name.—Monterey salamandeı.

Ensatina eschscholtzi klauberi Dunn

Ensatina klauberi Dunn, 1929, Proc. U. S. Nat. Mus., **74**, Art. 25, p. 1.—· Descanso, San Diego County, California.

Ensatina eschscholtzii klauberi Stebbins, 1949, Univ. Calif. Publ. Zool., **48**: 467.

Range.—San Jacinto Mountains, Riverside County, south to Pine Valley, San Diego County, California, mostly in the Transition Life Zone.

Common name.—Klauber's blotched salamander.

Ensatina eschscholtzi croceater Cope

Plethodon croceater Cope, 1867, Proc. Acad. Nat. Sci. Phila., **19:** 210.—Fort Tejon, California.
Ensatina eschscholtzii croceater Stebbins, 1949, Univ. Calif. Publ. Zool., **48:** 457.

Range.—From near Keene, Tehachapi Mountains, south to Fort Tejon, Kern County, California.

Common name.—Yellow-blotched salamander.

Ensatina eschscholtzi platensis Espada

Urotropis platensis Espada, 1875, An. Soc. Españ. Hist. Nat., **4:** 71.—Near Montevideo, Uruguay, *in errore;* designated as Yosemite Valley, Mariposa County, California.
Ensatina eschscholtzii platensis Stebbins, 1949, Univ. Calif. Publ. Zool., **48:** 434.
Ensatina sierrae Storer, 1929, Univ. Calif. Publ. Zool., **30:** 448.—Yosemite Valley, Mariposa County, California.

Range.—Western slopes of the Sierra Nevada, mainly in the Upper Sonoran and Transition zones, from northern Tehama County south to southern Tulare County, California.

Common name.—Sierra Nevada salamander.

Ensatina eschscholtzi picta Wood

Ensatina eschscholtzii picta Wood, 1940, Univ. Calif. Publ. Zool., **42:** 425.—Klamath, Del Norte County, California.

Range.—A narrow coastal area from the vicinity of Weott, Humboldt County, California, north through Del Norte County to Port Orford, Curry County, Oregon.

Common name.—Painted salamander.

Ensatina eschscholtzi oregonensis Girard

Heredia oregonensis Girard, 1857, Proc. Acad. Nat. Sci. Phila., **8:** 140.—"Oregon"; restr. to Puget Sound region, Washington.
Ensatina eschscholtzii oregonensis Stebbins, 1949, Univ. Calif. Publ. Zool., **48:** 393.
Plethodon ensatus Cope, 1867, Proc. Acad. Nat. Sci. Phila., **19:** 167 (*in errore,* by confusion with *Dicamptodon ensatus* Eschscholtz).

Range.—Southwestern British Columbia and Vancouver Island, south through Washington and Oregon, west of the Cascade Range, south in coastal California, exclusive of the range of *picta*, to northern Sonoma County.

Common name.—Northern Pacific red salamander.

Ensatina eschscholtzi xanthoptica Stebbins

Ensatina eschscholtzii xanthoptica Stebbins, 1949, Univ. Calif. Publ. Zool.,
   48: 407, pl. 11, figs. 2, 12.—4.5 miles east of Schellville, Napa County,
   California.

Range.—Coast Range of California between the central valley and
San Francisco Bay, north to east central Sonoma County, and south
to Alum Rock Park near San Jose in northern Santa Clara County,
mostly in the Upper Sonoran Life Zone.

Common name.—Yellow-eyed salamander.

Stereochilus Cope

Stereochilus Cope, 1869, Proc. Acad. Nat. Sci. Phila., **21:** 100.—Type: *marginatus.*

Stereochilus marginatus Hallowell

Pseudotriton marginatus Hallowell, 1857, Proc. Acad. Nat. Sci. Phila., **8:**
   130.—Liberty County, Georgia.
Stereochilus marginatum Cope, 1869, Proc. Acad. Nat. Sci. Phila., **21:** 101.

Range.—Southeastern Virginia through the lower Atlantic coastal
plain to eastern Georgia.

Common name.—Margined salamander.

Haideotriton Carr

Haideotriton Carr, 1939, Occ. Papers Boston Soc. Nat. Hist., **8:** 334.—Type:
   wallacei.

Haideotriton wallacei Carr

Haideotriton wallacei Carr, 1939, Occ. Papers Boston Soc. Nat. Hist., **8:** 335.
   —Albany, Dougherty County, Georgia.

Range.—Known only from a 200-foot well at Albany, Dougherty
County, Georgia.

Common name.—Georgia blind salamander.

Typhlotriton Stejneger

Typhlotriton Stejneger, 1892, Proc. U. S. Nat. Mus., **15:** 115.—Type:
   spelaeus.

Typhlotriton spelaeus Stejneger

Typhlotriton spelaeus Stejneger, 1892, Proc. U. S. Nat. Mus., **15:** 116, pl. 9.
   —Rock House Cave, Missouri.

Range.—Ozark plateau in Missouri and Arkansas and adjacent Kansas and Oklahoma.

Common name.—Veil-eyed salamander.

Typhlotriton nereus Bishop

Typhlotriton nereus Bishop, 1944, Copeia, **1944**: 1, figs. 1–4.—York Spring, Imboden, Arkansas.

Range.—Southern Missouri and northern Arkansas, with adjacent Oklahoma.

Common name.—Spring blind salamander.

Typhlomolge Stejneger

Typhlomolge Stejneger, 1896, Proc. U. S. Nat. Mus., **18**: 620.—Type: *rathbuni.*

Typhlomolge rathbuni Stejneger

Typhlomolge rathbuni Stejneger, 1896, Proc. U. S. Nat. Mus., **18**: 620.— San Marcos, Hays County, Texas.

Range.—Underground waters in Hays, Kendall and Comal counties, central Texas.

Common name.—Texas blind salamander.

Gyrinophilus Cope

Gyrinophilus Cope, 1869, Proc. Acad. Nat. Sci. Phila., **21**: 108.—Type: *porphyriticus.*

Gyrinophilus porphyriticus Green

Salamandra porphyritica Green, 1827, Contr. Maclurean Lyc., **1**: 3, pl. 1, fig. 2.—French Creek, near Meadville, Crawford County, Pennsylvania.
Gyrinophilus porphyriticus Cope, 1869, Proc. Acad. Nat. Sci. Phila., **21**: 108.

Range.—Coastal New England to western New York, adjacent Ontario, and Pennsylvania; southward west of the Appalachians.

Common name.—Purple salamander.

Gyrinophilus porphyriticus porphyriticus Green

Gyrinophilus porphyriticus porphyriticus Stejneger and Barbour, 1933, Check list, ed. 3, p. 15.
Salamandra salmonea Storer, 1838, *in* Holbrook, N. Amer. Herp., ed. 1, **3**: 101, pl. 22.—Vermont.

Range.—New England states through New York and adjacent Quebec to the Niagara Falls region in Ontario, south through northern New Jersey, most of Pennsylvania, western Maryland, southeastern Ohio, West Virginia, eastern Kentucky, and central Tennessee.

Common name.—Northern purple salamander.

Gyrinophilus porphyriticus inagnoscus Mittleman

> *Gyrinophilus porphyriticus inagnoscus* Mittleman, 1942, Proc. New England Zool. Club, **20**: 27, pl. 5, fig. E, text fig. 2.—Salt Creek, 4 miles southeast of Bloomingville, Good Hope Township, Hocking County, Ohio.

Range.—Unglaciated southern Ohio but not found in the counties bordering the Ohio River.

Common name.—Ohio purple salamander.

Gyrinophilus porphyriticus duryi Weller

> *Pseudotriton duryi* Weller, 1930, Proc. Junior Soc. Nat. Sci. Cincinnati, **1**, nos. 5, 6, p. 7.—Cascade Caves, about 10 miles from Grayson, Carter County, Kentucky.
> *Gyrinophilus porphyriticus duryi* Stejneger and Barbour, 1933, Check list, ed. 3, p. 15.

Range.—Northeastern Kentucky, southern tier of counties in Ohio, and western West Virginia.

Common name.—Kentucky purple salamander.

Gyrinophilus lutescens Rafinesque

> *Triturus lutescens* Rafinesque, 1832, Atlantic Jour., **1**: 121.—West Kentucky.
> *Gyrinophilus lutescens* Mittleman, 1942, Proc. New England Zool. Club, **20**: 33, pl. 6, fig. D.

Range.—Limestone caves of Kentucky.

Common name.—Neotenic purple salamander.

Gyrinophilus danielsi Blatchley

> *Spelerpes danielsi* Blatchley, 1950, 25th Ann. Rept. Dept. Geol. Indiana, p. 60.—Mount Collins and Indian Pass, Sevier County, Tennessee.
> *Gyrinophilus danielsi* Fowler and Dunn, 1917, Proc. Acad. Nat. Sci. Phila., **69**: 19.

Range.—Southern Appalachians.

Common name.—Mountain purple salamander.

Gyrinophilus danielsi danielsi Bishop

> *Gyrinophilus danielsi danielsi* Bishop, 1943, Salamanders, p. 361.

Range.—Southern section of the Blue Ridge Mountains; through extreme eastern Tennessee.

Common name.—Blue Ridge purple salamander.

Gyrinophilus danielsi dunni Mittleman and Jopson

Gyrinophilus dunni Mittleman and Jopson, 1941, Smiths. Misc. Coll., **101**, no. 2, p. 2, pl. 1.—Clemson College campus, Clemson, Pickens County, South Carolina.

Gyrinophilus danielsi dunni Bishop, 1943, Salamanders, p. 365, fig. 108.

Range.—Northwestern South Carolina, northeastern Georgia, and western North Carolina.

Common name.—Carolina purple salamander.

Gyrinophilus danielsi polystictus Reese

Gyrinophilus danielsi polystictus Reese, 1950, Nat. Hist. Misc., **63**: 2, figs. 1A, 2 [map].—Mount Mitchell, Yancey County, North Carolina, 6,000 feet alt.

Range.—Known only from altitudes above 4,500 feet on Mount Mitchell and Blackstock Knob Mountain, Yancey County, North Carolina.

Common name.—Mount Mitchell purple salamander.

Pseudotriton Tschudi

Pseudotriton Tschudi, 1838, Mém. Soc. Sci. Nat. Neuchâtel, **1838**: 60.— Type: *subfusca* = *ruber* Sonnini.

Mycetoglossus Bonaparte, 1839, Icon. Fauna Ital., **2**: fasc. 131.—Substitute name.

Batrachopsis Fitzinger, 1843, Syn. Rept., p. 34.—Substitute name.

Pelodytes Gistel, 1848, Naturgeschichte, p. 11.—Substitute name; not *Pelodytes* Fitzinger.

Pseudotriton montanus Baird

Pseudotriton montanus Baird, 1849, Jour. Acad. Nat. Sci. Phila., (2), **1**: 293. —South Mountain, near Carlisle, Cumberland County, Pennsylvania.

Range.—Pennsylvania to Florida, westward into Kentucky and Tennessee, and to eastern Louisiana in the Gulf coastal plain.

Common name.—Mud salamander.

Pseudotriton montanus montanus Baird

Pseudotriton montanus montanus Stejneger and Barbour, 1923, Check list, ed. 2, p. 14.

Spelerpes ruber sticticeps Cope, 1869, Proc. Acad. Nat. Sci. Phila., **21**: 108.—
Georgia; restr. to Rabun County, Georgia.

Range.—Atlantic coastal plain and eastern Piedmont plateau, from
Cumberland County, Pennsylvania, and Delaware, southward to
South Carolina.

Common name.—Eastern mud salamander.

Pseudotriton montanus diastictus Bishop

Pseudotriton montanus diastictus Bishop, 1941, Occ. Papers Mus. Zool. Univ.
Mich., **451**: 14, pl. 2, figs. 1, 2.—Cascade Caverns, Carter County, Kentucky.

Range.—The unglaciated plateau region of southern Ohio, central
and eastern Kentucky, southwestern West Virginia, and eastern
Tennessee.

Common name.—Midland mud salamander.

Pseudotriton montanus flavissimus Hallowell

Pseudotriton flavissimus Hallowell, 1856, Proc. Acad. Nat. Sci. Phila., **8**: 130.
—Liberty County, Georgia.
Pseudotriton montanus flavissimus Stejneger and Barbour, 1923, Check list,
ed. 2, p. 14.

Range.—Liberty and Lowndes counties, Georgia, westward in the
coastal plain through the Florida panhandle, Alabama, Mississippi,
and extreme southeastern Louisiana.

Common name.—Gulf Coast mud salamander.

Pseudotriton montanus floridanus Netting and Goin

Pseudotriton montanus floridanus Netting and Goin, 1942, Ann. Carnegie
Mus., **29**: 175, pl. 1, fig. 5.—Seepage area along "C" Creek, University
of Florida campus, Gainesville, Florida.

Range.—Northern third of the Florida peninsula and adjacent
Georgia.

Common name.—Florida mud salamander.

Pseudotriton ruber Sonnini

Salamandra rubra Sonnini, *in* Sonnini and Latreille, 1802, Hist. Nat. Rept.,
4: 305.—United States; restr. to vicinity of Philadelphia.
Pseudotriton ruber Baird, 1849, Jour. Acad. Nat. Sci. Phila., (2), **1**: 286.

Range.—New York to the Gulf coastal plain; not in Atlantic coastal
plain.

Common name.—Red salamander.

Pseudotriton ruber ruber Sonnini

Pseudotriton ruber ruber Dunn, 1918, Bull. Mus. Comp. Zool., **62**: 466.

Salamandra subfusca Green, 1818, Jour. Acad. Nat. Sci. Phila., (1), **1**: 351. —Vicinity of Princeton, New Jersey.

Salamandra rubriventris Green, 1818, Jour. Acad. Nat. Sci. Phila., (1), **1**: 353.—Vicinity of Princeton, New Jersey.

Proteus neocaesariensis Green, 1818, Jour. Acad. Nat. Sci. Phila., (1), **1**: 358.—New Jersey; restr. to vicinity of Princeton.

Range.—Southern New York southwestward to northern Georgia and Alabama, exclusive of the ranges of the mountain subspecies.

Common name.—Northern red salamander.

Pseudotriton ruber schencki Brimley

Spelerpes ruber schencki Brimley, 1912, Proc. Biol. Soc. Wash., **25**: 139, pl. 7, figs. 12, 13, 15, 17, 18, 20–22.—Sunburst, Haywood County, North Carolina.

Pseudotriton ruber schencki Dunn, 1918, Bull. Mus. Comp. Zool., **62**: 467.

Range.—Southern part of the southern Blue Ridge Province, to above 5,000 feet alt.

Common name.—Black-chinned red salamander.

Pseudotriton ruber nitidus Dunn

Pseudotriton ruber nitidus Dunn, 1920, Proc. Biol. Soc. Wash., **33**: 133.— White Top Mountain, Virginia, at 4,000 feet alt.

Range.—The central part of the southern Blue Ridge Province up to 5,000 feet alt.

Common name.—Blue Ridge red salamander.

Pseudotriton ruber vioscai Bishop

Pseudotriton ruber vioscai Bishop, 1928, Occ. Papers Boston Soc. Nat. Hist., **5**: 247.—A spring run 10 miles west of Bogatusa, Washington Parish, Louisiana.

Range.—Gulf coastal plain from eastern Mississippi, southeastern Tennessee, and Louisiana to Georgia and northwestern Florida.

Common name.—Southern red salamander.

Aneides Baird

Aneides Baird, 1849, Icon. Encycl., **2**, Zool., p. 257.—Type: *lugubris*.

Anaides Baird, 1849, Icon. Encycl., **2**, Zool., p. 256.—Variant spelling.

Autodax Boulenger, 1887, Ann. Mag. Nat. Hist., (5), **19**: 67.—Substitute name.

Aneides aeneus Cope and Packard

Plethodon aeneus Cope and Packard, 1881, Amer. Nat., **15**: 878.—Nickajack Cave, southern Tennessee.

Aneides aeneus Dunn, 1923, Proc. New England Zool. Club, **8**: 39.

Range.—Appalachian system, exclusive of the Piedmont plateau, from Fayette County, southwestern Pennsylvania, and western West Virginia to southern Ohio, and to eastern Tennessee, northern Georgia, and northeastern Alabama.

Common name.—Green salamander.

Aneides ferreus Cope

Anaides ferreus Cope, 1869, Proc. Acad. Nat. Sci. Phila., **21**: 109.—Fort Umpqua, Oregon.

Aneides ferreus Stejneger and Barbour, 1917, Check list, ed. 1, p. 21.

Range.—Northern coastal California through coastal Oregon and northwestern Washington to Cracroft Island, British Columbia (50° 40′ N. Lat.).

Common name.—Clouded salamander.

Aneides flavipunctatus Strauch

Plethodon flavipunctatus Strauch, 1870, Mem. Acad. Sci. St. Petersbourg, (7), **16**: 71.—New Albion, California.

Aneides flavipunctatus Storer, 1925, Univ. Calif. Publ. Zool., **27**: 119.

Range.—Southern Cascades, in Washington, to central California.

Common name.—Black salamander.

Aneides flavipunctatus flavipunctatus Strauch

Aneides flavipunctatus flavipunctatus Myers and Maslin, 1948, Proc. Biol. Soc. Wash., **61**: 134.

Plethodon iëcanus Cope, 1883, Proc. Acad. Nat. Sci. Phila., **35**: 24.—Baird, Shasta County, California.

Range.—Coastal California north of San Francisco through Oregon, north to the Klamath Mountains and the southern Cascades.

Common name.—Shasta salamander.

Aneides flavipunctatus niger Myers and Maslin

Aneides flavipunctatus niger Myers and Maslin, 1948, Proc. Biol. Soc. Wash., **61**: 132.—Near the forks of Waddell Creek, Santa Cruz County, California.

Range.—Western Santa Clara County, northern Santa Cruz County, and the southernmost part of San Mateo County, California.

Common name.—Black salamander.

Aneides lugubris Hallowell

Salamandra lugubris Hallowell, 1849, Proc. Acad. Nat. Sci. Phila., **4**: 126.—Monterey, California.

Aneides lugubris Baird, 1849, Icon. Encycl., **2**, Zool., p. 257.

Range.—Central and southern California and the Farallon Islands.

Common name.—Arboreal salamander.

Aneides lugubris lugubris Hallowell[5]

Aneides lugubris lugubris Grinnell and Camp, 1917, Univ. Calif. Publ. Zool., **17**: 134.

Range.—Central and southern California west of the Sierra Nevada and south to San Diego County.

Common name.—Arboreal salamander.

Aneides lugubris farallonensis Van Denburgh

Autodax lugubris farallonensis Van Denburgh, 1895, Proc. Calif. Acad. Sci., (3), **4**: 5, pl. 2.—South Farallon Island, California.

Range.—The Farallon Islands.

Common name.—Farallon Island salamander.

Aneides hardyi Taylor

Plethodon hardii Taylor, 1941, Proc. Biol. Soc. Wash., **54**: 77.—Cloudcroft, New Mexico.

Aneides hardyi Lowe, 1950, Copeia, **1950**: 93, fig. 1.

Range.—Sacramento Mountains, southern New Mexico.

Common name.—Sacramento Mountains salamander.

Eurycea Rafinesque

Eurycea Rafinesque, 1822, Kentucky Gazette, Lexington, (n.s.), **1**, no. 9, p. 3.—Type: *lucifuga*.

Spelerpes Rafinesque, 1832, Atlantic Jour., **1**: 22.—Type: *lucifuga*.

[5] *Triton tereticauda* Eschscholtz, 1833, has long priority over *lugubris* Hallowell, 1849; and Storer (1925, Univ. Calif. Publ. Zool., **27**: 127) seems to have made a satisfactory allocation of the name without drawing the nomenclatural conclusion. I have asked the International Commission to suppress the name *tereticauda* to avoid changing a well-known name.

Cylindrosoma Tschudi, 1838, Mém. Soc. Sci. Nat. Neuchâtel, **1838**: 58.—
Type: *longicauda.*
Saurocercus Fitzinger, 1843, Syn. Rept., p. 34.—Type: *longicauda.*

Eurycea bislineata Green

Salamandra bislineata Green, 1818, Jour. Acad. Nat. Sci. Phila., (1), **1**: 352.
—Vicinity of Princeton, New Jersey.
Eurycea bislineata Stejneger and Barbour, 1917, Check list, ed. 1, p. 18;
Mittleman, 1949, Proc. Biol. Soc. Wash., **62**: 89, pl. 6 [map].

Range.—Eastern North America from the borders of the St. Lawrence to the Gulf of Mexico.

Common name.—Two-lined salamander.

Eurycea bislineata bislineata Green

Eurycea bislineata bislineata Dunn, 1920, Proc. Biol. Soc. Wash., **33**: 134.
Salamandra flavissima Harlan, 1826, Amer. Jour. Sci., **10**: 286.—Pennsylvania; restr. to vicinity of Philadelphia.
Salamandra haldemani Holbrook, 1840, N. Amer. Herp., ed. 1, **4**: 125,
pl. 28.—Susquehanna River, Pennsylvania; restr. to Harrisburg.
Salamandra dorsata Valenciennes, 1854, *in* Duméril, Bibron, and Duméril,
Erpét. Gén., **9**: 93.—No locality; designated as Harrisburg, Pennsylvania.
Spelerpes bilineatus borealis Baird, 1889, *in* Cope, Bull. U. S. Nat. Mus.,
34: 165.—Lake Oquassa, Maine = Lake Mooselookmeganticl, Franklin
County.
Eurycea bislineata major Trapido and Clausen, 1938, Copeia, **1938**: 118.—
Ouiatchouan River, Lake St. John County, Quebec.

Range.—New Brunswick, Maine, southern Quebec, and eastern Ontario; southward through Virginia and West Virginia.

Common name.—Northern two-lined salamander.

Eurycea bislineata rivicola Mittleman

Eurycea bislineata rivicola Mittleman, 1949, Proc. Biol. Soc. Wash., **62**: 93,
pl. 6.—Echo Canyon, McCormick's Creek State Park, Owen County,
Indiana.

Range.—Extreme western West Virginia at low altitudes, westward to central and northern Illinois and southwestern Michigan, southward to northern Alabama.

Common name.—Mid-west two-lined salamander.

Eurycea bislineata wilderae Dunn

Eurycea bislineata wilderae Dunn, 1920, Proc. Biol. Soc. Wash., **33**: 134.—
White Top Mountain, Virginia, 4,000 feet alt.

Range.—Southern Blue Ridge Province, from White Top Mountain, Virginia, southward to Georgia.

Common name.—Blue Ridge two-lined salamander.

Eurycea bislineata cirrigera Green

Salamandra cirrigera Green, 1830, Jour. Acad. Nat. Sci. Phila., (1), **6**: 253. —New Orleans, Orleans Parish, Louisiana.

Eurycea bislineata cirrigera Dunn, 1920, Proc. Biol. Soc. Wash., **33**: 135.

Range.—North Carolina south through most of South Carolina and Georgia, most of Alabama, northwestern Florida, southern Mississippi, and eastern Louisiana.

Common name.—Southern two-lined salamander.

Eurycea longicauda Green

Salamandra longicauda Green, 1818, Jour. Acad. Nat. Sci. Phila., (1), **1**: 351.—New Jersey; restr. to vicinity of Princeton.

Eurycea longicauda Stejneger and Barbour, 1917, Check list, ed. 1, p. 19.

Range.—Southern New York southwestward to Oklahoma and southward through the Atlantic and Gulf states.

Common name.—Long-tailed salamander.

Eurycea longicauda longicauda Green

Eurycea longicauda longicauda Bailey, 1937, Occ. Papers Mus. Zool. Univ. Mich., **364**: 8.

Range.—Appalachian highlands from southern New York into Tennessee, thence westward to southeastern Missouri.

Common name.—Long-tailed salamander.

Eurycea longicauda guttolineata Holbrook

Salamandra guttolineata Holbrook, 1838, N. Amer. Herp., **2**: 61, pl. 12.— Greenville, Greenville County, South Carolina.

Eurycea longicauda guttolineata Bailey, 1937, Occ. Papers Mus. Zool. Univ. Mich., **364**: 8.

Range.—Coastal plain and piedmont from Maryland southwestward to Mississippi and eastern Louisiana; absent in peninsular Florida.

Common name.—Three-lined salamander.

Eurycea longicauda melanopleura Cope

Spelerpes melanopleura Cope, 1893, Proc. Acad. Nat. Sci. Phila., **45**: 383.— Raley's Creek, head of White River, Missouri.

Eurycea longicauda melanopleura Bishop, 1941, Occ. Papers Mus. Zool. Univ. Mich., **451**: 20.

Spelerpes stejnegeri Eigenmann, 1901, Trans. Amer. Micro. Soc., **22**: 189, pl. 28.—Rock House Cave, Missouri.

Range.—Ozark plateau and Ouachita Mountains, in Missouri, Arkansas, and adjacent Oklahoma.

Common name.—Black-sided salamander.

Eurycea longicauda pernix Mittleman

Eurycea longicauda pernix Mittleman, 1942, Proc. New England Zool. Club, **21**, pl. 20.—Jimmie Strahl Creek, Brown County State Park, 2½ miles southeast of Nashville, Indiana.

Range.—Southern Indiana, adjacent Illinois and Kentucky to western Tennessee.

Common name.—Midland long-tailed salamander.

Eurycea lucifuga Rafinesque

Eurycea lucifuga Rafinesque, 1822, Kentucky Gazette, Lexington, (n.s.), **1**, no. 9, p. 3.—Near Lexington, Fayette County, Kentucky.

Gyrinophilus maculicaudus Cope, 1890, Amer. Nat., **24**: 967.—Brookville, Franklin County, Indiana.

Range.—Southern Indiana and extreme southern Ohio through Kentucky, southern West Virginia, western Virginia, Tennessee, and northern Alabama; isolated areas in southern Missouri, northeastern Oklahoma, northern Arkansas, and southeastern Kansas.

Common name.—Cave salamander.

Eurycea multiplicata Cope

Spelerpes multiplicatus Cope, 1869, Proc. Acad. Nat. Sci. Phila., **21**: 106.— Red River; restr. to vicinity of Fort Towson, Choctaw County, eastern Oklahoma.

Eurycea multiplicata Stejneger and Barbour, 1917, Check list, ed. 1, p. 20.

Range.—Southern Missouri, Arkansas, southeastern Kansas, and eastern Oklahoma.

Common name.—Many-ribbed salamander.

Eurycea multiplicata multiplicata Cope
[New comb.]

Range.—Southeastern Oklahoma and the Ouachita Mountain region of Arkansas.

Common name.—Many-ribbed salamander.

Eurycea multiplicata griseogaster Moore and Hughes

Eurycea griseogaster Moore and Hughes, 1941, Copeia, **1941**: 139.—Swimsner's Creek, near its junction with the Illinois River, 10 miles north of Gore, Sequoyah County, Oklahoma.

Eurycea multiplicata griseogaster Dundee (*in litt.*).

Range.—The Oklahoma Ozarks and southwestern Missouri, southward to the Arkansas River.

Common name.—Gray-bellied salamander.

Eurycea tynerensis Moore and Hughes

Eurycea tynerensis Moore and Hughes, 1939, Amer. Midl. Nat., **22**: 697, fig. 1.—Tyner Creek, tributary of Barron Folk Creek, near Procter, Adair County, Oklahoma.

Range.—Eastern Oklahoma.

Common name.—Oklahoma neotenic salamander.

Eurycea neotenes Bishop and Wright

Eurycea neotenes Bishop and Wright, 1937, Proc. Biol. Soc. Wash., **50**: 142.
—Culebra Creek, 5 miles north of Helotes, Bexar County, Texas.

Range.—Springs along the escarpment of the Edwards Plateau in Texas.

Eurycea neotenes neotenes Bishop and Wright
[New comb.]

Range.—Bexar County, Texas.

Common name.—Bexar County neotenic salamander.

Eurycea neotenes nana Bishop
[New comb.]

Eurycea nana Bishop, 1941, Occ. Papers Mus. Zool. Univ. Mich., **451**: 6, pl. 1, fig. 1.—Head of San Marcos River, Hays County, Texas.

Range.—Known only from the type locality.

Common name.—San Marcos neotenic salamander.

Eurycea neotenes latitans Smith and Potter
[New comb.]

Eurycea latitans Smith and Potter, 1946, Herpetologica, **3**: 105.—Cascade Cavern, 4.6 miles southeast of Boerne, Kendall County, Texas.

Range.—Kendall County, Texas.

Common name.—Cascade Cavern neotenic salamander.

Eurycea neotenes pterophila Burger, Smith, and Potter
[New comb.]

Eurycea pterophila Burger, Smith, and Potter, 1950, Proc. Biol. Soc. Wash., **63**: 51, pl. 5, fig. F, pl. 6, figs. D, E, pl. 7.—Fern Bank Spring, 6.3 miles northeast of Wimberley, Hays County, Texas.

Range.—Confined to the type locality, in Hays County, Texas.

Common name.—Fern Bank neotenic salamander.

Manculus Cope

Manculus Cope, 1869, Proc. Acad. Nat. Sci. Phila., **21**: 95.—Type: *quadridigitatus.*

Manculus quadridigitatus Holbrook

Salamandra quadridigitata Holbrook, 1942, N. Amer. Herp., ed. 2, **5**: 65, pl. 21.—South Carolina, Georgia, and Florida: restr. to vicinity of Charleston, South Carolina.

Manculus quadridigitatus Cope, 1869, Proc. Acad. Nat. Sci. Phila., **21**: 101.

Manculus remifer Cope, 1871, Rept. Peabody Acad. Salem, **1870**: 84.—Jacksonville, Florida.

Manculus quadridigitatus paludicolus Mittleman, 1947, Herpetologica, **3**: 220.—Pollock, Grant Parish, Louisiana.

Manculus quadridigitatus uvidus Mittleman, 1947, Herpetologica, **3**: 221, map.—Gayle, Caddo Parish, Louisiana.

Range.—Coastal plain of the Atlantic and Gulf states from North Carolina to eastern Texas, except southern Florida; north into southeastern Oklahoma and southwestern Arkansas.

Common name.—Dwarf four-toed salamander.

Hydromantes Gistel

Hydromantes Gistel, 1848, Naturg. Thiers., p. 11.—Type: *genei* Schlegel.

Geotriton Bonaparte, 1837, Icon. Fauna Ital., **2**, fasc. 19.—Type: *fuscus* (not of Bonaparte, 1832).

Hydromantes platycephalus Camp

Spelerpes platycephalus Camp, 1916, Univ. Calif. Publ. Zool., **17**: 11.—Head of Lyell Cañon, 10,800 feet alt., Yosemite National Park, California.

Hydromantes platycephalus Dunn, 1923, Proc. New England Zool. Club, **8**: 40.

Range.—High altitudes in the Sierra Nevada from Alpine County south to northern Tulare County, California.

Common name.—Mount Lyell salamander.

Order SALIENTIA

ASCAPHIDAE

Ascaphus Stejneger

Ascaphus Stejneger, 1899, Proc. U. S. Nat. Mus., **21**: 899.—Type: *truei.*

Ascaphus truei Stejneger

Ascaphus truei Stejneger, 1899, Proc. U. S. Nat. Mus., **21**: 900, pl. 89, text figs. 1–4.—Humptulips, Gray's Harbor County, Washington.

Range.—The Olympic peninsula, northern Cascades, and Rocky Mountains, southward from British Columbia to Humboldt County, California, and into Idaho and Montana in the Rockies.

Common name.—Tailed frog.

Ascaphus truei truei Stejneger

Ascaphus truei truei Mittleman and Myers, 1949, Proc. Biol. Soc. Wash., **62**: 62.

Range.—Oregon, Washington, and southern British Columbia, in the Cascade, Sierra, and Pacific border provinces.

Common name.—Olympic tailed frog.

Ascaphus truei californicus Mittleman and Myers

Ascaphus truei californicus Mittleman and Myers, 1949, Proc. Biol. Soc. Wash., **62**: 63.—Near Klamath, Del Norte County, California.

Range.—Del Norte, Humboldt, and Siskiyou counties, California.

Common name.—California tailed frog.

Ascaphus truei montanus Mittleman and Myers

Ascaphus truei montanus Mittleman and Myers, 1949, Proc. Biol. Soc. Wash., **62**: 64.—Tributary of Lincoln Creek, Glacier National Park, Flathead County, Montana.

Range.—Northern Rocky Mountains Province, in Idaho, western Montana, and adjacent British Columbia.

Common name.—Rocky Mountain tailed frog.

PELOBATIDAE

Scaphiopus Holbrook

Scaphiopus Holbrook, 1836, N. Amer. Herp., ed. 1, **1**: 85.—Type: *solitarius* = *holbrookii.*

Spea Cope, 1866, Jour. Acad. Nat. Sci. Phila., (2), **6**: 81.—Type: *bombifrons.*

Scaphiopus holbrooki Harlan

Rana holbrookii Harlan, 1835, Med. Phys. Res., p. 105.—South Carolina; restr. to Charleston.

Scaphiopus holbrookii Baird, 1859, Expl. Surv. R. R. Miss. Pacific, **10**, pt. 4, no. 4, p. 12.

Range.—Eastern United States, southward to Florida, and westward to Texas.

Common name.—Eastern spadefoot toad.

Scaphiopus holbrooki holbrooki Harlan

Scaphiopus holbrookii holbrookii Stejneger and Barbour, 1917, Check list, ed. 1, p. 26.

Scaphiopus solitarius Holbrook, 1836, N. Amer. Herp., ed. 1, **1**: 85, pl. 12.— Carolina, Georgia, Tennessee; restr. to Charleston, South Carolina.

Range.—Eastern United States, from Massachusetts to Florida, west to Louisiana, eastern Texas, and Arkansas, north in the midwest to West Virginia, and southern Ohio, Indiana, and Illinois.

Common name.—Spadefoot toad, eastern spadefoot.

Scaphiopus holbrooki albus Garman

Scaphiopus albus Garman, 1877, Proc. Amer. Assoc. Adv. Sci., Buffalo, **25**: 194.—Key West, Florida.

Scaphiopus holbrookii albus Stejneger and Barbour, 1917, Check list, ed. 1, p. 26.

Range.—Florida Keys, and extreme southern peninsular Florida.

Common name.—Key West spadefoot.

Scaphiopus holbrooki hurteri Strecker

Scaphiopus hurterii Strecker, 1910, Proc. Biol. Soc. Wash., **23**: 116.—Waco, Texas.

Scaphiopus holbrookii hurterii Wright and Wright, 1933, Frogs, p. 44.

Range.—Central and eastern Texas, eastern Oklahoma, and western Arkansas.

Common name.—Hurter's spadefoot.

Scaphiopus couchi Baird

Scaphiopus couchii Baird, 1854, Proc. Acad. Nat. Sci. Phila., **7**: 62.—Rio Nasas, Coahuila, and Matamoros, Tamaulipas; restr. to Matamoros, Tamaulipas.

Range.—The Great Plains, North Dakota west to Idaho, south to southern Texas and New Mexico.

Common name.—Great Plains spadefoot.

Scaphiopus bombifrons Cope

Scaphiopus bombifrons Cope, 1863, Proc. Acad. Nat. Sci. Phila., **15**: 53.—
Fort Union, Missouri River near 48° N. Lat., Platte River 200 miles west
of Fort Kearney, and the Llano Estacado of Texas; restr. to Fort Union.

Range.—Great Plains, west to Idaho and New Mexico, and from
the Dakotas to northwestern Texas.

Common name.—Central plains spadefoot.

Scaphiopus hammondi Baird

Scaphiopus hammondii Baird, 1839, Expl. Surv. R. R. Miss. Pacific, **10**,
pt. 4, no. 4, p. 12, pl. 28, fig. 2.—Fort Reading, California.

Range.—The Great Basin and Rocky Mountain regions eastward
to Oklahoma, westward to the interior valleys and coast of California, and southward on the Mexican plateau.

Common name.—Hammond's spadefoot.

Scaphiopus hammondi hammondi Baird

Spea stagnalis Cope, 1875, in Yarrow, U. S. Geol. Surv. W. 100th Meridian,
5: 525, pl. 25, figs. 6–8.—Northwestern New Mexico.

Range.—Western Texas to southwestern and western California,
north into Colorado; adjacent Mexico.

Common name.—Western spadefoot.

Scaphiopus hammondi intermontanus Cope

Scaphiopus intermontanus Cope, 1883, Proc. Acad. Nat. Sci. Phila., **35**: 15.
—Salt Lake City, Salt Lake County, Utah, and Pyramid Lake, Storey
County, Nevada; restr. to Salt Lake City.

Range.—Great Basin, north to Idaho and British Columbia, south
to northwestern Arizona.

Common name.—Great Basin spadefoot.

LEPTODACTYLIDAE

Leptodactylus Fitzinger

Leptodactylus Fitzinger, 1826, Neue Classif. Rept., p. 88.—Type: typhonia
(of South America).

Leptodactylus labialis Cope

Cystignathus labialis Cope, 1877, Proc. Amer. Phil. Soc., **17**: 90.—Mexico;
restr. to Tampico, Tamaulipas.
Leptodactylus labialis Brocchi, 1881, Miss. Sci. Mex., pt. 3, sec. 2, livr. 1,
p. 20, pl. 5, fig. 1.

Range.—Extreme southern Texas, south to Central America.

Common name.—Mexican white-lipped frog.

Eleutherodactylus Duméril and Bibron

Eleutherodactylus Duméril and Bibron, 1841, Erpét. Gén., **8**: 620.—Type: *martinicensis* (of the West Indies).

Eleutherodactylus latrans Cope

Lithodytes latrans Cope, 1880, Bull. U. S. Nat. Mus., **17**: 25.—Helotes, Bexar County, Texas.

Eleutherodactylus latrans Stejneger and Barbour, 1917, Check list, ed. 1, p. 34.

Range.—Border of the Edwards Plateau in central Texas, Bexar County to the Big Bend and southeastern New Mexico.

Common name.—Robber frog, barking frog.

Eleutherodactylus augusti Dugés

Hylodes augusti Dugés, 1879, *in* Brocchi, Bull. Soc. Phil. Paris, (7), **3**: 21. —Guanajuato, Mexico.

Eleutherodactylus augusti Slevin, 1931, Copeia, **1931**: 140.

Range.—Central Mexico north to southern Arizona in the highlands.

Common name.—Western barking frog.

Syrrhophus Cope

Syrrhophus Cope, 1878, Amer. Nat., **12**: 253.—Type: *marnockii.*

Syrrhophus campi Stejneger

Syrrhophus campi Stejneger, 1915, Proc. Biol. Soc. Wash., **28**: 131.—Brownsville, Texas.

Range.—The lower Rio Grande bottom lands.

Common name.—Camp's frog.

Syrrhophus marnocki Cope

Syrrhophus marnockii Cope, 1878, Amer. Nat., **12**: 253.—Near San Antonio, Bexar County, Texas.

Syrrhophus gaigeae Schmidt and Smith, 1944, Field Mus. Nat. Hist., Zool. Ser., **29**: 80.—The Basin, Big Bend National Park, Brewster County, Texas.

Range.—Western Texas, from San Marcos to the Big Bend region.

Common name.—Cliff frog.

BUFONIDAE
Bufo Laurenti

> *Bufo* Laurenti, 1768, Syn. Rept., p. 25.—Type: *Rana bufo* Linnaeus (by tautonymy).

Bufo alvarius Girard

> *Bufo alvarius* Girard, *in* Baird, U. S. Mex. Bound. Surv., **2**, pt. 2, p. 26, pl. 41, figs. 1–6.—Valley of the Gila and Colorado rivers; restr. to Colorado River bottom lands below Yuma, Arizona.

Range.—Lower Colorado River in California and Arizona, the Imperial Valley, southern Arizona, and south into Sonora.

Common name.—Colorado River toad.

Bufo boreas Baird and Girard

> *Bufo boreas* Baird and Girard, 1852, Proc. Acad. Nat. Sci. Phila., **6**: 174.—Columbia River and Puget Sound, Washington; restr. to vicinity of Puget Sound.

Range.—Western North America from southern Alaska to Lower California.

Common name.—Western toad.

Bufo boreas boreas Baird and Girard

> *Bufo boreas boreas* Stejneger and Barbour, Check list, ed. 1, p. 27.
>
> *Bufo columbiensis* Baird and Girard, 1853, Proc. Acad. Nat. Sci. Phila., **6**: 378.—Columbia River; restr. to vicinity of the mouth of the Columbia River.
>
> *Bufo pictus* Cope, 1875, *in* Yarrow, U. S. Geogr. Surv. W. 100th Meridian, **5**: 522, pl. 25, figs. 4, 5.—No type locality given; designated as Provo, Utah.

Range.—Western British Columbia and southern Alaska, south through Washington, Oregon, and Idaho, most of Montana and Wyoming, and into northern California, Nevada, Utah, and Colorado.

Common name.—Boreal toad, Columbian toad.

Bufo boreas exsul Myers

> *Bufo exsul* Myers, 1942, Occ. Papers Mus. Zool. Univ. Mich., **460**: 3, pls. 1, 2.—Deep Springs, Inyo County, California.

Range.—Deep Springs Valley, Inyo County, California.

Common name.—Black toad, Inyo County toad.

Bufo boreas nelsoni Stejneger

> *Bufo boreas nelsoni* Stejneger, 1893, N. Amer. Fauna, **7**: 220, pl. 3, figs. 4a, 4b.—Oasis Valley, Nye County, Nevada.

Range.—Southern and eastern Nye County, northern Lincoln County, Nevada, to Owens Valley, California.

Common name.—Amargosa toad.

Bufo boreas halophilus Baird and Girard

Bufo halophilus Baird and Girard, 1853, Proc. Acad. Nat. Sci. Phila., **6**: 301. —Benicia, Solano County, California.

Bufo boreas halophilus Stejneger and Barbour, 1917, Check list, ed. 1, p. 27.

Range.—Extreme western Nevada, the central valleys of California, and coastal California south to Lower California.

Common name.—Alkali toad.

Bufo canorus Camp

Bufo canorus Camp, 1916, Univ. Calif. Publ. Zool., **17**: 59.—Porcupine Flat, Yosemite National Park, California.

Range.—The high Sierra Nevada of California, from Alpine County to Fresno County.

Common name.—Yosemite toad.

Bufo cognatus Say

Bufo cognatus Say, 1823, *in* Long's Exped. Rocky Mts., **2**: 190.—Arkansas River, Powers County, Colorado.

Bufo dipternus Cope, 1879, Amer. Nat., **13**: 437.—North of Missouri River, east of Fort Benton, Chouteau County, Montana.

Range.—Great Plains, from southern Alberta and Saskatchewan to Texas; west into Montana, Wyoming, Colorado, Utah, Nevada, and Arizona; south into adjacent Mexico.

Common name.—Great Plains toad.

Bufo compactilis Wiegmann

Bufo compactilis Wiegmann, 1833, Isis, **1833**: 661.—Mexico; restr. to vicinity of city of Mexico.

Range.—Mexican plateau, central and southern Texas, western Oklahoma, and westward through New Mexico. [The typical subspecies confined to Mexico.]

Common name.—Sonora toad.

Bufo compactilis speciosus Girard

Bufo speciosus Girard, 1854, Proc. Acad. Nat. Sci. Phila., **7**: 85.—Rio Bravo [= Rio Grande] and New Leon.

Bufo compactilis speciosus Smith, 1947, Herpetologica, **4**: 8, fig. 1 (map).

Range.—Northern Nuevo León, northward to western Oklahoma and New Mexico.

Common name.—Northern Sonora toad.

Bufo debilis Girard

> *Bufo debilis* Girard, 1854, Proc. Acad. Nat. Sci. Phila., **7**: 87.—Lower part of the valley of the Rio Grande, Texas, and in Tamaulipas, Mexico; restr. to vicinity of Brownsville, Texas; Sanders and Smith, 1951, Field and Laboratory, **19**: 142, fig. 1 (map).

Range.—Southwestern Kansas and southeastern Colorado to central Texas and northern Tamaulipas, westward through southern Arizona and northern Mexico.

Common name.—Green toad.

Bufo debilis debilis Girard

> *Bufo debilis debilis* Smith, 1950, Misc. Publ. Univ. Kansas Mus. Nat. Hist., **2**: 75.

Range.—Southwestern Kansas southward through western Oklahoma (exclusive of the western Panhandle), and through central Texas to the lower Rio Grande region and adjacent Tamaulipas.

Common name.—Little green toad.

Bufo debilis insidior Girard

> *Bufo insidior* Girard, 1854, Proc. Acad. Nat. Sci. Phila., **7**: 88.—Chihuahua, Chihuahua.
>
> *Bufo debilis insidior* Smith, 1950, Misc. Publ. Univ. Kansas Mus. Nat. Hist., **2**: 75.

Range.—Southeastern Colorado and southwestern Kansas southward through Oklahoma and Texas, west of the range of *debilis debilis*, and through New Mexico to southeastern Arizona and adjacent Mexico.

Common name.—Western green toad.

Bufo debilis retiformis Sanders and Smith

> *Bufo debilis retiformis* Sanders and Smith, 1951, Field and Laboratory, **19**: 153, pl. 3, text fig. 1.—14.4 miles south of Ajo, Pima County, Arizona.

Range.—Southwestern Arizona, probably into adjacent Sonora.

Common name.—Pima green toad.

Bufo marinus Linnaeus[6]

> *Rana marina* Linnaeus, 1758, Syst. Nat., ed. 10, **1**: 211.—America; restr. to Surinam.
>
> *Bufo marinus* Schneider, 1799, Hist. Amph., **1**: 219.

Range.—Brownsville area in extreme southern Texas, ranging through the Gulf coastal plain of Mexico. Widespread in tropical America and widely introduced throughout the world where sugar cane is planted.

Common name.—Marine toad.

Bufo punctatus Baird and Girard

> *Bufo punctatus* Baird and Girard, 1852, Proc. Acad. Nat. Sci. Phila., **6**: 173. —Rio San Pedro (= Devil's River), Val Verde County, Texas.

Range.—Texas, Oklahoma, New Mexico, and Arizona, southern Nevada and southeastern California, into the adjacent states of Mexico.

Common name.—Red-spotted toad.

Bufo microscaphus Cope

> *Bufo microscaphus* Cope, 1867, Proc. Acad. Nat. Sci. Phila., **18**: 301.—Arizona and the upper Colorado region; restr. to Fort Mohave, Mohave County, Arizona, by Shannon.

Range.—Northwestern Arizona and adjacent Utah and Nevada; southwestern California.

Common name.—Southwestern toad.

Bufo microscaphus microscaphus Cope

> *Bufo microscaphus microscaphus* Stebbins, 1951, Amph. West. N. Amer., p. 274, pls. 18, 58, text fig. 29 [maps].

Range.—Northwestern Arizona, north of the Gila River, into adjacent Utah and Nevada.

Common name.—Fort Mojave toad, Arizona toad.

Bufo microscaphus californicus Camp

> *Bufo cognatus californicus* Camp, 1915, Univ. Calif. Publ. Zool., **12**: 331.— Santa Paula, Ventura County, California.

[6] The distinction by Smith and Taylor, 1948, of the Mexican *Bufo horribilis* Wiegmann from *Bufo marinus* Linnaeus (type locality restricted to Surinam) is unsupported by any review of the *Bufo marinus* complex. Contrary to their statement, abundant material of *marinus sensu lat.* is available in museum collections.

Bufo microscaphus californicus Stebbins, 1951, Amph. West. N. Amer., p. 274, pls. 18, 58 [map].

Range.—Coastal California from northern San Luis Obispo County into northern Lower California.

Common name.—California toad.

Bufo quercicus Holbrook

Bufo quercicus Holbrook, 1840, N. Amer. Herp., ed. 1, **4**: 109, pl. 22.—Charleston, South Carolina, and Smithville, North Carolina; restr. to Charleston, South Carolina.

Chilophryne dialopha Cope, 1862, Proc. Acad. Nat. Sci. Phila., **14**: 341.—Sandwich Islands, *in errore;* designated as Charleston, South Carolina.

Range.—Coastal North Carolina and through South Carolina and Georgia, throughout Florida, and into coastal Alabama, Mississippi, and Louisiana.

Common name.—Oak toad.

Bufo terrestris Bonnaterre

Rana terrestris Bonnaterre, 1789, Tabl. Encycl. Méth., Erp., p. 8.—Carolina; restr. to Charleston, South Carolina.

Bufo terrestris Stejneger and Barbour, 1917, Check list, ed. 1, p. 29.

Range.—Eastern North America.

Common name.—Common American toad, American toad.

Bufo terrestris terrestris Bonnaterre

Bufo terrestris terrestris Netting and Goin, 1946, Copeia, **1946**: 107.

Rana lentiginosa Shaw, 1802, Gen. Zool., **3**: 173, pl. 53.—Carolina and Virginia; restr. to Charleston, South Carolina.

Bufo musicus Sonnini and Latreille, 1802, Hist. Nat. Rept., **2**: 127.—Carolina; restr. to Charleston, South Carolina.

Range.—Extreme southeastern Virginia, south through the Atlantic and Gulf coastal plains to eastern Louisiana; throughout Florida.

Common name.—Southern toad.

Bufo terrestris americanus Holbrook

Bufo americanus Holbrook, 1836, N. Amer. Herp., ed. 1, **1**: 75, pl. 9.—Maine through all the Atlantic states; restr. to vicinity of Philadelphia.

Bufo terrestris americanus Netting and Goin, 1946, Copeia, **1946**: 107.

Range.—Eastern North America from the Maritime Provinces through Quebec and Ontario into Minnesota; southward to the northern borders of the Gulf states, except Louisiana and Texas; southwest into Arkansas, eastern Oklahoma, and eastern Kansas.

Common name.—American toad.

Bufo terrestris copei Yarrow and Henshaw

Bufo americanus copei Yarrow and Henshaw, 1878, Report Rept. Batr. Calif. Ariz. Nev., p. 207.—James Bay, Ontario.

Bufo terrestris copei Netting and Goin, 1946, Copeia, **1946**: 107.

Range.—Northern Ontario and Quebec.

Common name.—Hudson Bay toad.

Bufo valliceps Wiegmann

Bufo valliceps Wiegmann, 1833, Isis, **26**: 657.—Mexico; restr. to Vera Cruz, Vera Cruz.

Bufo granulosus Baird and Girard, 1852, Proc. Acad. Nat. Sci. Phila., **6**: 173. —Between Indianola and San Antonio, Texas; restr. to Indianola, Calhoun County, Texas (not of Spix).

Bufo nebulifer Girard, 1854, Proc. Acad. Nat. Sci. Phila., **7**: 87.—Substitute name for *granulosus* Baird and Girard.

Range.—Southern Arkansas, Louisiana, and coastal Texas; south into Mexico.

Common name.—Gulf Coast toad.

Bufo woodhousei Girard

Bufo woodhousii Girard, 1854, Proc. Acad. Nat. Sci. Phila., **7**: 86.—New Mexico; restr. to San Francisco Mountains, Coconimo County, Arizona.

Range.—The Great Plains region and eastward to the Atlantic coast, mainly in sandy areas.

Common name.—Woodhouse's toad.

Bufo woodhousei woodhousei Girard

Bufo woodhousii woodhousii Smith, 1934, Amer. Midl. Nat., **15**: 449; Shannon, 1949, Bull. Chicago Acad. Sci., **8**: 301, fig. 1 (map).

Bufo frontosus Cope, 1866, Proc. Acad. Nat. Sci. Phila., **18**: 301.—Territory of Arizona; restr. to Tucson, Pima County, Arizona.

Range.—The Great Plains, Rocky Mountain region, and eastern part of Great Basin, southward into the northern tier of states in Mexico.

Common name.—Woodhouse's toad.

Bufo woodhousei fowleri Hinckley

Bufo fowleri Hinckley, 1882, Proc. Boston Soc. Nat. Hist., **21**: 308.—Milton, Norfolk County, Massachusetts.

Bufo woodhousii fowleri Smith, 1934, Amer. Midl. Nat., **15**: 456.

Range.—Eastern North America from New Hampshire southward; absent from the lower coastal plain in the Carolinas, Georgia, and Florida; westward into eastern Texas, eastern Arkansas, and along the Missouri River to the Kansas border of Missouri; southeastern Ohio, southern Illinois, southern Michigan, and the enclosed states.

Common name.—Fowler's toad.

Bufo woodhousei hemiophrys Cope

[New comb.]

Bufo hemiophrys Cope, 1886, Proc. Amer. Phil. Soc., **23**: 515.—Northern boundary of Montana = Pembina, Pembina County, and Turtle Mountains, Rokette County, North Dakota; restr. to Turtle Mountains.

Range.—Extreme northern North Dakota; western Ontario, Manitoba, Saskatchewan, and eastern Alberta.

Common name.—Dakota toad.

Bufo woodhousei velatus Bragg and Sanders

Bufo woodhousii velatus Bragg and Sanders, 1951, Wasmann Jour. Biol., **9**: 366, figs. 1–4.—Elkhart, Anderson County, Texas.

Range.—Southeastern Texas and adjacent areas in Louisana, Arkansas, and Oklahoma.

Common name.—East Texas toad.

HYLIDAE

Acris Duméril and Bibron

Acris Duméril and Bibron, 1841, Erpét. Gén., **8**: 506.—Type: *gryllus.*

Acris gryllus Le Conte

Rana gryllus Le Conte, 1825, Ann. Lyc. Nat. Hist. New York, **1**: 282.—Not stated; designated as Riceboro, Liberty County, Georgia.

Acris gryllus Duméril and Bibron, 1841, Erpét. Gén., **8**: 506.

Range.—Eastern North America, west to the Rocky Mountains.

Common name.—Cricket frog.

Acris gryllus gryllus Le Conte

Acris gryllus gryllus Cope, 1875, Bull. U. S. Nat. Mus., **1**: 30.

Acris gryllus var. *bufonia* Boulenger, 1882, Cat. Batr. Sal. Brit. Mus., p. 337. —New Orleans, Louisiana.

Range.—Coastal plain of South Atlantic and Gulf states, Virginia to Louisiana, exclusive of peninsular Florida, north along the Mississippi to Tennessee.

Common name.—Coast marsh cricket frog.

Acris gryllus crepitans Baird

Acris crepitans Baird, 1854, Proc. Acad. Nat. Sci. Phila., **7**: 59.—Northern states; restr. to Potomac River at Harper's Ferry, West Virginia.

Acris gryllus crepitans Cope, 1875, Bull. U. S. Nat. Mus., **1**: 30.

Range.—Eastern United States, reaching the Atlantic coast from New England to Virginia, west to the Mississippi, south to Louisiana, mainly exclusive of the range of *Acris gryllus gryllus.*

Common name.—Short-legged cricket frog.

Acris gryllus blanchardi Harper

Acris gryllus blanchardi Harper, 1947, Proc. Biol. Soc. Wash., **60**: 39.— Smallen's Cave, at Ozark, Christian County, Missouri.

Range.—Interior plains and interior highlands of the United States, from South Dakota to southern Michigan, west to the Rockies, south to Texas, and west to Arizona.

Common name.—Blanchard's cricket frog.

Acris gryllus paludicola Burger, Smith, and Smith

Acris gryllus paludicola Burger, Smith, and Smith, 1949, Jour. Tenn. Acad. Sci., **24**: 131.—Sabine Pass, Jefferson County, Texas.

Range.—Known only from the type locality.

Common name.—Texas coast cricket frog.

Acris gryllus dorsalis Harlan

Rana dorsalis Harlan, 1827, Jour. Acad. Nat. Sci. Phila., (1), **5**: 340.—Lower 100 miles of St. John's River, Florida.

Acris gryllus dorsalis Netting and Goin, 1945, Quart. Jour. Florida Acad. Sci., **8**: 304, pl. 1.

Acris acheta Baird, 1854, Proc. Acad. Nat. Sci. Phila., **7**: 59.—Key West, Florida.

Range.—Peninsular Florida.

Common name.—Florida cricket frog.

Hyla Laurenti

Hyla Laurenti, 1768, Syn. Rept., p. 32.—Type: *viridis* = *arborea* (of Europe).

Hyla andersoni Baird

Hyla andersonii Baird, 1854, Proc. Acad. Nat. Sci. Phila., **7**: 60.—Anderson, Anderson County, South Carolina, *in errore;* designated as Aiken County, South Carolina.

Range.—Southern New Jersey; an isolated population at Southern Pines, North Carolina; occurrence at Anderson, South Carolina, doubted; coastal plain, Georgia.

Common name.—Pine Barrens tree frog.

Hyla arenicolor Cope

Hyla affinis Baird (*nec* Spix), 1854, Proc. Acad. Nat. Sci. Phila., **7**: 61.—Northern Sonora.

Hyla arenicolor Cope, 1866, Jour. Acad. Nat. Sci. Phila., (2), **6**: 84.—Substitute name for *affinis* Baird.

Hyla copii Boulenger, 1887, Ann. Mag. Nat. Hist., (5), **20**: 53.—El Paso, El Paso County, Texas.

Range.—Western Texas through New Mexico and Arizona to southern Nevada and southwestern California (north to San Luis Obispo County); south into adjacent Mexico.

Common name.—Canyon tree frog.

Hyla baudini Duméril and Bibron

Hyla baudinii Duméril and Bibron, 1841, Erpét. Gén., **8**: 564.—Mexico; restr. to Mexico City.

Hyla vanvlieti Baird, 1854, Proc. Acad. Nat. Sci. Phila., **7**: 61.—Brownsville, Texas.

Range.—Extreme southern Texas, south through eastern Mexico.

Common name.—Mexican tree frog.

Hyla cinerea Schneider[7]

Calamita cinereus Schneider, 1799, Hist. Amph., **1**: 174.—Carolina; restr. to Charleston, South Carolina.

Hyla cinerea Garman, 1891, Bull. Ill. State Lab. Nat. Hist., **3**: 189.

Range.—Southeastern United States.

Common name.—Green tree frog.

---

[7] I am unable to find *Calamita carolinensis* Pennant, listed by Schneider, Günther, Boulenger, and Cope. They refer to Arctic Zoology, vol. 2, p. 331. Sherborn's Index records no *Calamita carolinensis* Pennant.

Hyla cinerea cinerea Schneider

> *Hyla cinerea cinerea* Stejneger and Barbour, 1923, Check list, ed. 2, p. 30.
> *Hyla bilineata* Shaw, 1802, Gen. Zool., **3**: 136.—Warm parts of North America; restr. to Charleston, South Carolina.
> *Hyla lateralis* Daudin, 1802, *in* Sonnini and Latreille, Hist. Nat. Rept., **2**: 180.—Charleston, South Carolina.
> *Hyla semifasciata* Hallowell, 1856, Proc. Acad. Nat. Sci. Phila., **8**: 307.—Texas; restr. to vicinity of Houston, Texas.

Range.—Lowlands of the Atlantic and Gulf states from Virginia to Texas; north in the Mississippi Basin to southern Illinois.

Common name.—Green tree frog.

Hyla cinerea evittata Miller

> *Hyla evittata* Miller, 1899, Proc. Biol. Soc. Wash., **13**: 75.—Four Mile Run, Fairfax County, Virginia.
> *Hyla cinerea evittata* Stejneger and Barbour, 1923, Check list, ed. 2, p. 30.

Range.—The Delmarva Peninsula, eastern Maryland, and adjacent Virginia.

Common name.—Northern green tree frog.

Hyla crucifer Wied

> *Hyla crucifer* Wied, 1838, Reise Nord Amer., **1**, pt. 5, p. 275.—Leavenworth, Leavenworth County, Kansas.

Range.—Eastern North America.

Common name.—Spring peeper.

Hyla crucifer crucifer Wied

> *Hyla crucifer crucifer* Harper, 1939, Not. Nat. Acad. Nat. Sci. Phila., **27**: 1.
> *Hylodes pickeringii* Storer, 1839, Rep. Comm. Zool. Surv. Massachusetts, Reptiles, p. 240.—Danvers, Essex County, Massachusetts.

Range.—Eastern North America, from the lower St. Lawrence River west to Minnesota, south to eastern Texas and the northern half of Georgia; not recorded from Louisiana.

Common name.—Northern spring peeper.

Hyla crucifer bartramiana Harper

> *Hyla crucifer bartramiana* Harper, 1939, Not. Nat. Acad. Nat. Sci. Phila., **27**: 1.—Folkston, Charleston County, Georgia.

Range.—Southern Georgia and northern Florida.

Common name.—Southern spring peeper.

Hyla eximia Baird

Hyla eximia Baird, 1854, Proc. Acad. Nat. Sci. Phila., **7**: 61.—Valley of Mexico, Mexico.

Range.—Plateau of Mexico, north into Arizona.

Common name.—Baird's Mexican hyla.

Hyla eximia wrightorum Taylor

Hyla wrightorum Taylor, 1939, Univ. Kansas Sci. Bull., **25**: 436.—Eleven miles south of Springerville, Apache County, Arizona.

Range.—Arizona, south on the adjacent Mexican plateau.

Common name.—Arizona tree frog.

Hyla femoralis Sonnini and Latreille

Hyla femoralis Sonnini and Latreille, 1802, Hist. Nat. Rept., **2**: 181.—Carolina; restr. to Charleston, South Carolina.

Range.—Lower coastal plain from southeastern Virginia to eastern Louisiana; absent in southern Florida.

Common name.—Piny woods tree frog.

Hyla gratiosa Le Conte

Hyla gratiosa Le Conte, 1856, Proc. Acad. Nat. Sci. Phila., **8**: 146, pl. 6.—Lower country of Georgia; restr. to Liberty County, Georgia.

Range.—Lower coastal plain from North Carolina to eastern Louisiana; absent in southern Florida.

Common name.—Barking tree frog.

Hyla ocularis Bosc and Daudin

Hyla ocularis Bosc and Daudin, 1801, *in* Sonnini and Latreille, Hist. Nat. Rept., Deterville ed., **2**: 187.—Carolina; restr. to vicinity of Charleston, South Carolina; Harper, 1939, Amer. Midl. Nat., **22**: 134, figs. 1–5 (map).

Chorophilus angulatus Cope, 1875, Bull. U. S. Nat. Mus., **1**: 30.—South Carolina and Georgia; restr. to vicinity of Charleston, South Carolina.

Range.—Coastal plain from North Carolina to southern Florida and eastern Texas.

Common name.—Least tree frog.

Hyla phaeocrypta Cope

Hyla versicolor phaeocrypta Cope, 1889, Bull. U. S. Nat. Mus., **34**: 375.—Mount Carmel, Wabash County, Illinois.

Hyla phaeocrypta Viosca, 1923, Copeia, **122**: 96.

Range.—South Carolina and Georgia, west to eastern Louisiana, north through Alabama and Mississippi to southern Illinois and Indiana.

Common name.—Bird-voiced tree frog.

Hyla phaeocrypta phaeocrypta Cope

Hyla phaeocrypta phaeocrypta Neill, 1948, Herpetologica, **4**: 175.

Hyla avivoca Viosca, Proc. Biol. Soc. Wash., **41**: 89.—Mandeville, Louisiana.

Range.—Gulf coastal plain, north to southern Illinois and Indiana.

Common name.—Western bird-voiced tree frog.

Hyla phaeocrypta ogechiensis Neill

Hyla phaeocrypta ogechiensis Neill, 1948, Herpetologica, **4**: 175.—Ogeechee River, at Midville, Burke County, Georgia.

Range.—South Carolina to Jefferson, Emanuel, Richmond, and Burke counties in Georgia.

Common name.—Eastern bird-voiced tree frog.

Hyla regilla Baird and Girard

Hyla regilla Baird and Girard, 1852, Proc. Acad. Nat. Sci. Phila., **6**: 174.—Sacramento River, California, and Puget Sound; restr. to Sacramento County, California.

Hyla scapularis Hallowell, 1852, Proc. Acad. Nat. Sci. Phila., **6**: 183.—Oregon Territory; restr. to Vancouver, Washington.

Hyla nebulosa Hallowell, 1854, Proc. Acad. Nat. Sci. Phila., **7**: 96.—Tejon Pass, Kern County, California (not of Spix).

Hyla scapularis hypochondriaca Hallowell, 1854, Proc. Acad. Nat. Sci. Phila., **7**: 97.—Tejon Pass, Kern County, California.

Hyla cadaverina Cope, 1866, Jour. Acad. Nat. Sci. Phila., (2), **6**: 84.—Substitute name for *nebulosa* Hallowell.

Range.—Pacific coastal region, Cascades and Sierra Nevada; northern Rocky Mountains in Idaho; south into northern Lower California.

Common name.—Pacific tree frog.

Hyla squirella Sonnini and Latreille

Hyla squirella Sonnini and Latreille, 1802, Hist. Nat. Rept., **2**: 181.—Carolina; restr. to Charleston, South Carolina.

Hyla flavigula Glass, 1946, Herpetologica, **3**: 101.—Aransas National Wild Life Refuge, Aransas County, Texas.

Range.—Lower coastal plain from southern Virginia to Texas, north in the Mississippi Basin to southern Illinois and Indiana.

Common name.—Squirrel tree frog.

Hyla versicolor Le Conte

Hyla versicolor Le Conte, 1825, Ann. Lyc. Nat. Hist. New York, **1**: 281.—Northern states; restr. to vicinity of New York.

Range.—Eastern North America, westward to the Great Plains.

Common name.—Common tree frog, gray tree frog.

Hyla versicolor versicolor Le Conte

Hyla versicolor versicolor Stejneger and Barbour, 1923, Check list, ed. 2, p. 31.

Hyla richardi Baird, 1854, Proc. Acad. Nat. Sci. Phila., **7**: 60.—Cambridge, Essex County, Massachusetts.

Range.—Eastern North America, from southern Maine to northern Florida, west through Ontario to Manitoba and Minnesota, south through the tier of states west of the Mississippi to extreme southeastern Texas.

Common name.—Gray tree frog.

Hyla versicolor chrysoscelis Cope

Hyla femoralis chrysoscelis Cope, 1880, Bull. U. S. Nat. Mus., **17**: 29.—Dallas, Dallas County, Texas.

Hyla versicolor chrysoscelis Strecker, 1910, Proc. Biol. Soc. Wash., **23**: 117.

Range.—Eastern Texas.

Common name.—Southern gray tree frog.

Hyla versicolor sandersi Smith and Brown

Hyla versicolor sandersi Smith and Brown, 1947, Proc. Biol. Soc. Wash., **60**: 47.—Eight miles south of Somerset, Atascosa County, Texas.

Range.—Central Texas along the escarpment of the Edwards Plateau.

Common name.—Central Texas tree frog.

Pseudacris Fitzinger

Pseudacris Fitzinger, 1843, Syn. Rept., p. 31.—Type: *nigrita*.

Chorophilus Baird, 1854, Proc. Acad. Nat. Sci. Phila., **7**: 59.—Type: *nigritus*.

Helocaetes Baird, 1854, Proc. Acad. Nat. Sci. Phila., **7**: 59.—Type: not designated; here designated as *triseriata* Wied.

Pseudacris brachyphona Cope

Chorophilus feriarum brachyphonus Cope, 1889, Bull. U. S. Nat. Mus., **34**:
341.—West Pennsylvania near the Kiskiminitas River, Westmoreland
County.
Pseudacris brachyphona Walker, 1932, Ohio Jour. Sci., **32**: 379.

Range.—Eastern Ohio and Kentucky, western Pennsylvania, Maryland, Virginia, and West Virginia; south through Tennessee to northern Alabama and Mississippi.

Common name.—Mountain chorus frog, chorus frog.

Pseudacris brimleyi Brandt and Walker

Pseudacris brimleyi Brandt and Walker, 1933, Occ. Papers Mus. Zool. Univ.
Mich., **272**: 2.—Washington, North Carolina.

Range.—Lower coastal plain from southeastern Virginia to the
lower Ogeechee River, northern Georgia.

Common name.—Brimley's chorus frog, Dismal Swamp chorus
frog.

Pseudacris clarki Baird

Helocaetes clarkii Baird, 1854, Proc. Acad. Nat. Sci. Phila., **7**: 60.—Galveston
and Indianola, Texas; restr. to Galveston.
Pseudacris clarkii Smith, 1934, Amer. Midl. Nat., **15**: 462.

Range.—Central Kansas, south through Oklahoma and Texas to
the Gulf.

Common name.—Spotted chorus frog.

Pseudacris nigrita Le Conte

Rana nigrita Le Conte, 1825, Ann. Lyc. Nat. Hist. New York, **1**: 282.—No
locality stated; designated as Liberty County, Georgia.
Pseudacris nigrita Günther, 1858, Cat. Batr. Sal. Brit. Mus., p. 97.

Range.—Northwest Territory in Canada throughout the Great
Plains region; eastward in the United States to the Atlantic.

Common name.—Swamp tree frog, chorus frog.

Pseudacris nigrita nigrita Le Conte

Pseudacris nigrita nigrita Stejneger and Barbour, 1943, Check list, ed. 5,
p. 46.

Range.—Coastal plain from North Carolina south to northern
Florida and west to Mississippi.

Common name.—Southern chorus frog.

Pseudacris nigrita feriarum Baird

Helocaetes feriarum Baird, 1854, Proc. Acad. Nat. Sci. Phila., **7**: 60.–Carlisle County, Pennsylvania.

Pseudacris nigrita feriarum Stejneger and Barbour, 1933, Check list, ed. 3, p. 31.

Chorophilus triseriatus corporalis Cope, 1875, Bull. U. S. Nat. Mus., **1**: 30.– Nomen nudum [New Jersey].

Range.–Southern New Jersey and Pennsylvania through Maryland and the Delaware peninsula and the upper coastal plain to northern Georgia and to southwestern Georgia and northwestern Florida.

Common name.–Upland chorus frog.

Pseudacris nigrita triseriata Wied

Hyla triseriata Wied, 1838, Reise Nord Amer., **1**, pt. 4, p. 249.–Mount Vernon, Ohio River, Indiana.

Pseudacris nigrita triseriata Stejneger and Barbour, 1933, Check list, ed. 3, p. 32.

Hylodes maculatus Agassiz, 1850, Lake Superior . . . , p. 378, pl. 6, figs. 1–3. –Region of Lake Superior; restr. to vicinity of Sault Ste. Marie.

Range.–Western New York through the mid-western states to southern Canada and west to the Rocky Mountains and Colorado plateau; south into central Texas.

Common name.–Western chorus frog, swamp tree frog.

Pseudacris nigrita septentrionalis Boulenger

Chorophilus septentrionalis Boulenger, 1882, Cat. Batr. Sal. Brit. Mus., p. 335, pl. 23, fig. 1.–Great Bear Lake, Northwest Territory.

Pseudacris nigrita septentrionalis Stejneger and Barbour, 1943, Check list, ed. 5, p. 46.

Range.–Tundra border in northwestern Canada, southward in the adjacent taiga zone, presumably with a gradual transition to *triseriata.*

Common name.–Boreal chorus frog.

Pseudacris nigrita verrucosa Cope

Chorophilus verrucosus Cope, 1877, Proc. Amer. Phil. Soc., **17**: 87.–Volusia = National Gardens, Volusia County, Florida.

Pseudacris nigrita verrucosa Brady and Harper, 1935, Proc. Biol. Soc. Wash., **48**: 108.

Range.–Peninsular Florida.

Common name.–Florida chorus frog.

Pseudacris ornata Holbrook

Rana ornata Holbrook, 1836, N. Amer. Herp., ed. 1, **1**: 97, pl. 16.—Between the Cooper and Ashley rivers, four miles from Charleston, South Carolina.

Pseudacris ornata Stejneger and Barbour, 1917, Check list, ed. 1, p. 31.

Litoria occidentalis Baird and Girard, 1853, Proc. Acad. Nat. Sci. Phila., **6**: 301.—San Francisco, *in errore;* designated as Liberty County, Georgia.

Range.—Lower Atlantic and Gulf coastal plains, south through peninsular Florida, west to Mississippi.

Common name.—Ornate chorus frog.

Pseudacris streckeri Wright and Wright

Pseudacris streckeri Wright and Wright, 1933, Handbook of Frogs, ed. 1, p. 102, pl. 25.—Type locality not mentioned; designated as Waco, Mc-Lennan County, Texas.

Range.—Central Oklahoma southward through central Texas and into extreme southwestern Arkansas; southern Illinois.

Common name.—Strecker's chorus frog.

Pseudacris streckeri streckeri Wright and Wright

Pseudacris streckeri streckeri Smith, 1951, Bull. Chicago Acad. Sci., **9**: 191.

Range.—Central Oklahoma southward through central Texas and into southwestern Arkansas.

Common name.—Strecker's chorus frog.

Pseudacris streckeri illinoisensis Smith

Pseudacris streckeri illinoisensis Smith, 1951, Bull. Chicago Acad. Sci., **9**: 190, pl. 1.—3 miles north of Meredosia, Morgan County, Illinois.

Range.—Morgan and Cass counties, Illinois; presumably sand areas of southern Illinois and adjacent Missouri.

Common name.—Illinois chorus frog.

MICROHYLIDAE

Microhyla Tschudi

Microhyla Tschudi, 1839, Mém. Soc. Sci. Nat. Neuchâtel, **2**: 86.—Type: *achatina* (of Java).

Gastrophryne Fitzinger, 1843, Syst. Rept., p. 33.—Type: *rugosa* = *carolinensis.*

Microhyla carolinensis Holbrook

Engystoma carolinensis Holbrook, 1836, N. Amer. Herp., ed. 1, **1**: 83, pl. 2.—Charleston, South Carolina.

Microhyla carolinensis Parker, 1934, Monogr. Microhylidae, p. 146.

Range.—Southeastern United States westward through Texas and northern Mexico to Sonora.

Common name.—Narrow-mouthed toad.

Microhyla carolinensis carolinensis Holbrook

Microhyla carolinensis carolinensis Hecht and Matalas, 1946, Amer. Mus. Nov., **1315**: 7, figs. 2, 9–12.

Engystoma rugosum Duméril and Bibron, 1841, Erpét. Gén., **8**: 744.— Southern parts of North America; restr. to vicinity of Charleston, South Carolina.

Range.—Southeastern United States from Maryland to Key West, westward and northward to Illinois and Missouri (with extreme southern Iowa and extreme southeastern Kansas), and to Arkansas, eastern Oklahoma, and eastern Texas.

Common name.—Narrow-mouthed toad.

Microhyla carolinensis olivacea Hallowell

Engystoma olivaceum Hallowell, 1856, Proc. Acad. Nat. Sci. Phila., **8**: 252.— Kansas and Nebraska; restr. to vicinity of Lawrence, Kansas.

Microhyla carolinensis olivacea Hecht and Matalas, 1946, Amer. Mus. Nov., **1315**: 12, figs. 3, 4.

Engystoma areolata Strecker, 1909, Proc. Biol. Soc. Wash., **22**: 118.—Guadalupe River bottom, Victoria, Victoria County, Texas.

Range.—Extreme southeastern Nebraska through Kansas, Oklahoma, and central Texas; southward in northeastern Mexico.

Common name.—Great Plains narrow-mouthed toad.

Microhyla carolinensis mazatlanensis Taylor

Microhyla mazatlanensis Taylor, 1943, Univ. Kansas Sci. Bull., **29**: 355.— Two miles east of Mazatlan, Sinaloa.

Microhyla carolinensis mazatlanensis Hecht and Matalas, 1946, Amer. Mus. Nov., **1315**: 14, figs. 5, 6.

Range.—Extreme southeastern Arizona southward to Sinaloa.

Common name.—Sinaloa narrow-mouthed toad.

Hypopachus Keferstein

Hypopachus Keferstein, 1867, Nachr. Ges. Wiss. Göttingen, **1867**: 351.— Type: *seebachi* → *variolosus* [of Costa Rica].

Hypopachus cuneus Cope

Hypopachus cuneus Cope, 1889, Proc. U. S. Nat. Mus., **11**: 395.—San Diego, Duval County, Texas.

Range.—Southern Texas and Gulf coastal plain of Mexico.

Common name.—Mexican narrow-mouthed toad.

Hypopachus cuneus cuneus Cope

Hypopachus cuneus cuneus Taylor, 1940, Univ. Kansas Sci. Bull., **26**: 516, pl. 62, fig. A, pl. 63, figs. 7, 7a.

Range.—Southern Texas, south into adjacent Mexico. [A second subspecies in Mexico.]

Common name.—Brownsville narrow-mouthed toad.

RANIDAE

Rana Linnaeus

Rana Linnaeus, 1758, Syst. Nat., ed. 10, **1**: 210.—Type: *temporaria.*

Rana areolata Baird and Girard

Rana areolata Baird and Girard, 1852, Proc. Acad. Nat. Sci. Phila., **6**: 173.— Indianola, Texas.

Range.—Western Gulf coastal plain, north in the Mississippi Basin to southeastern Kansas, Illinois, and Indiana.

Common name.—Crawfish frog.

Rana areolata areolata Baird and Girard

Rana areolata areolata Goin and Netting, 1940, Ann. Carnegie Mus., **28**: 143.

Range.—Matagorda County, Texas, north to southwestern Arkansas and southeastern Oklahoma.

Common name.—Southern crawfish frog.

Rana areolata circulosa Rice

Rana areolata circulosa Rice, 1878, *in* Jordan, Man. Vert. N. Amer., ed. 2, p. 355.—Northern Illinois, *in errore;* restr. to vicinity of Olney, Richland County, Illinois.

Range.—Northern Louisiana north in the Mississippi lowlands on both sides of the river to central Illinois and Indiana; most of Arkansas and Missouri; southeastern Kansas and northeastern Oklahoma.

Common name.—Northern crawfish frog.

Rana capito Le Conte

Rana capito Le Conte, 1855, Proc. Acad. Nat. Sci. Phila., **7**: 425, pl. 5.— Riceborough, Liberty County, Georgia.

Range.—Atlantic coastal plain from North Carolina to Florida and westward to Louisiana.

Common name.—Gopher frog.

Rana capito capito Le Conte
[New comb.]

> *Rana areolata aesopus* Cope, 1886, Proc. Amer. Phil. Soc., **23**: 517.—Micanopy, Florida.

Range.—Central Florida, north in the lower coastal plain to southeastern North Carolina.

Common name.—Florida gopher frog.

Rana capito sevosa Goin and Netting
[New comb.]

> *Rana sevosa* Goin and Netting, 1940, Ann. Carnegie Mus., **28**: 137, pl. 12, figs. 1, 2.—Slidell, St. Tammany Parish, Louisiana.

Range.—Eastern Louisiana through southern Mississippi and Alabama.

Common name.—Dark gopher frog.

Rana catesbeiana Shaw

> *Rana catesbeiana* Shaw, 1802, Gen. Zool., **3**: 106, pl. 33.—South Carolina; restr. to vicinity of Charleston, South Carolina.
> *Rana mugiens* Merrem, 1820, Tent. Syst. Amphib., p. 175.—North America; restr. to vicinity of New York City.
> *Rana scapularis* Harlan, 1825, Amer. Jour. Sci., **10**: 59.—Pennsylvania; restr. to vicinity of Philadelphia.
> *Rana conspersa* Le Conte, 1855, Proc. Acad. Nat. Sci. Phila., **8**: 425.—Riceborough, Liberty County, Georgia.

Range.—Eastern North America, except southern third of Florida; north to the Maritime Provinces, Quebec, southern Ontario, and southeastern Manitoba; west through most of Kansas, Nebraska, and Oklahoma, and through Texas to the lower Rio Grande.

Common name.—Bullfrog.

Rana clamitans Latreille

> *Rana clamitans* Latreille, 1802, Hist. Nat. Rept., **2**: 157.—Charleston, South Carolina.
> *Rana fontinalis* Le Conte, 1825, Ann. Lyc. Nat. Hist. New York, **1**: 282.—Maine to Virginia; restr. to vicinity of New York City.
> *Ranaria melanota* Rafinesque, 1820, Ann. Nat., Lexington, no. 25.—Lake Champlain.

Rana flaviviridis Harlan, 1825, Amer. Jour. Sci., **10**: 58.—Vicinity of Philadelphia.

Rana horiconensis Holbrook, 1838, N. Amer. Herp., ed. 1, **3**: 91, pl. 18.—Outlet of Lake George, New York.

Rana nigricans Agassiz, 1850, Lake Superior, p. 379, pl. 6, figs. 4, 5.—Northern shores of Lake Superior.

Rana clamata Cope, 1889, Bull. U. S. Nat. Mus., **34**: 419, pl. 51, figs. 2, 3, pl. 75, figs. 19, 33, text fig. 107 (emendation).

Range.—Eastern United States from the Maritime Provinces of Canada and Newfoundland to eastern Minnesota, and south to the Gulf Coast, west to extreme eastern Kansas and Oklahoma; absent in southern Florida.

Common name.—Green frog.

Rana grylio Stejneger

Rana grylio Stejneger, 1901, Proc. U. S. Nat. Mus., **24**: 212.—Bay St. Louis, Mississippi.

Range.—Lower Gulf and Atlantic coastal plains from eastern Texas to peninsular Florida, southeastern Georgia, and adjacent South Carolina.

Common name.—Pig frog.

Rana heckscheri Wright

Rana heckscheri Wright, 1924, Proc. Biol. Soc. Wash., **37**: 143, pl. 11, pl. 12, fig. 2.—Alligator Swamp, Callahan, Florida.

Range.—Coastal South Carolina and Georgia, south into northern Florida and west to southern Mississippi.

Common name.—River swamp bullfrog.

Rana septentrionalis Baird

Rana septentrionalis Baird, 1854, Proc. Acad. Nat. Sci. Phila., **7**: 61.—Northern Minnesota; restr. to Lake Itasca.

Rana sinuata Baird, 1854, Proc. Acad. Nat. Sci. Phila., **7**: 61.—Sackett's Harbor, New York.

Range.—Eastern Canada through Quebec and Ontario to Hudson Bay and Manitoba; south into northern New York, Michigan, Wisconsin, and Minnesota.

Common name.—Mink frog.

Rana virgatipes Cope

Rana virgatipes Cope, 1891, Amer. Nat., **25**: 1017.—Mare Run, near Great Egg Harbor, Atlantic County, New Jersey.

Range.—Lower Atlantic coastal plain, southern New Jersey to southeastern Georgia.

Common name.—Carpenter frog.

Rana sylvatica Le Conte

Rana sylvatica Le Conte, 1825, Ann. Lyc. Nat. Hist. New York, **1**: 282.— Locality not stated; designated as vicinity of New York City.

Range.—Northern North America, south to Arkansas and Georgia.

Common name.—Wood frog.

Rana sylvatica sylvatica Le Conte

Rana sylvatica sylvatica Schmidt, 1938, Field Mus. Nat. Hist., Zool. Ser., **20**: 378.

Rana pennsylvanica Harlan, 1825, Amer. Jour. Sci., **10**: 58.—Nomen nudum.

Rana silvatica Cope, 1889, Bull. U. S. Nat. Mus., **34**: 447, fig. 115 (emendation).

Range.—Eastern North America, north to Labrador, south to Georgia in the Appalachians, west to southern Illinois and Arkansas.

Common name.—Eastern wood frog.

Rana sylvatica cantabrigensis Baird

Rana cantabrigensis Baird, 1854, Proc. Acad. Nat. Sci. Phila., **7**: 62.—Cambridge, Massachusetts, *in errore;* designated as Moose Jaw, Saskatchewan.

Rana sylvatica cantabrigensis Schmidt, 1938, Field Mus. Nat. Hist., Zool. Ser., **20**: 377.

Rana cantabrigensis latiremis Cope, 1886, Proc. Amer. Phil. Soc., **23**: 520.— Lake Alloknagic, Alaska.

Range.—Mouth of the Yukon and the Mackenzie delta to western Ontario; south into northern Minnesota, Wisconsin, and the Northern Peninsula of Michigan.

Common name.—Northern wood frog.

Rana tarahumarae Boulenger

Rana tarahumarae Boulenger, 1917, Ann. Mag. Nat. Hist., (8), **20**: 416.— Sierra Tarahumare, Sonora.

Range.—Southwestern New Mexico and southeastern Arizona; south in the Sierra Madre in Sonora and Chihuahua.

Common name.—Tarahumare frog.

Rana pipiens[8] Schreber

> *Rana pipiens* Schreber, 1782, Naturforscher, **18**: 185, pl. 4.—New York and
> Raccoon Landing, Gloucester County, New Jersey; restr. to White Plains,
> New York.

Range.—Eastern North America, north to 60° N. Lat. in the west,
west to the Rocky Mountains and Great Basin, south into eastern
Mexico and to Central America.

Common name.—Leopard frog.

Rana pipiens pipiens Schreber

> *Rana pipiens pipiens* Wright and Wright, 1933, Handbook of Frogs and
> Toads, pp. 34, 176, pl. 71.
> *Rana utricularius* Harlan, 1825, Amer. Jour. Sci., **10**: 60.—Pennsylvania and
> New Jersey; restr. to vicinity of Philadelphia.

Range.—Eastern North America, south to New Jersey and the
Ohio River.

Common name.—Northern leopard frog.

Rana pipiens sphenocephala Cope

> *Rana halecina sphenocephala* Cope, 1886, Proc. Amer. Phil. Soc., **23**: 517.—
> Near St. John's River, Florida.
> *Rana pipiens sphenocephala* Stejneger and Barbour, 1943, Check list, ed. 5,
> p. 58.
> *Rana oxyrhyncha* Hallowell, 1856, Proc. Acad. Nat. Sci. Phila., **9**: 142.—
> Florida (not of Sundevall, 1849, for an African species).

Range.—Southeastern United States on the Atlantic and Gulf
coastal plains, west into eastern Texas and Oklahoma, north to
southern Illinois and Indiana.

Common name.—Southern leopard frog.

---

[8] The nomenclature and classification of this species and its geographic forms
are insufficiently established. John A. Moore has shown that numerous populations of this species are genetically distinguishable within the continuous eastern range, a mosaic of minor geographic variants that obviously should not be
treated as subspecies. Aside from the rejection of the long current early names
virescens Kalm and *halecina* Kalm (as not binominal) even the now familiar
allocation of the name *pipiens* to the northern populations would be upset if the
type locality be designated as Raccoon Landing, Gloucester County, New Jersey. It seems possible to designate instead a locality in New York, as above. With
some deviation as to trinomials, and fully aware that the relations of the leopard
frogs west of the Mississippi are very inadequately clarified, I follow Wright and
Wright (1949, Handbook of Frogs, p. 498, maps 33 and 34). I reject *Rana
burnsi* and *Rana kandiyohi* as obviously based on mutations, not at all established
as subspecies.

Rana pipiens brachycephala Cope

> Rana virescens brachycephala Cope, 1889, Bull. U. S. Nat. Mus., **34**: 403, fig. 101.—Yellowstone River.
>
> Rana pipiens brachycephala Mittleman and Gier, 1942, Proc. New England Zool. Club, **22**: 7.
>
> Rana onca Cope, 1875, in Wheeler's Rept. Expl. W. 100th Meridian, p. 528.
>
> Rana burnsi Weed, 1922, Proc. Biol. Soc. Wash., **35**: 108.—New London, Kandiyohi County, Minnesota.
>
> Rana kandiyohi Weed, 1922, Proc. Biol. Soc. Wash., **35**: 109.—New London, Kandiyohi County, Minnesota.
>
> Rana noblei Schmidt, 1925, Amer. Mus. Nov., **175**: 1.—Yunnanfu, Yunnan, China, in errore.

Range.—Western Manitoba, Minnesota, Iowa, and Missouri, north to 60° N. Lat. and west to eastern British Columbia, Washington, and Oregon; south to meet the ranges of *fisheri* and *berlandieri*.

Common name.—Western leopard frog.

Rana pipiens berlandieri Baird

> Rana berlandieri Baird, 1854, U. S. Mex. Bound. Surv., **2**, pt. 2, Rept., p. 27, pl. 36, figs. 7–10.—Southern Texas.
>
> Rana pipiens berlandieri Schmidt, 1941, Field Mus. Nat. Hist., Zool. Ser., **22**: 487.
>
> Rana austricola Cope, 1889, Bull. U. S. Nat. Mus., **34**: 398.—No locality; type locality designated as Matamoros, Tamaulipas.

Range.—Rio Grande Basin, south in eastern Mexico to Central America.

Common name.—Rio Grande leopard frog.

Rana pipiens fisheri Stejneger

> Rana fisheri Stejneger, 1893, N. Amer. Fauna, **7**: 227.—Vegas Valley, Clark County, Nevada.

Range.—Vegas Valley, Clark County, Nevada.

Common name.—Vegas Valley leopard frog.

Rana palustris Le Conte

> Rana palustris Le Conte, 1825, Ann. Lyc. Nat. Hist. New York, **1**: 282.—Locality not stated; designated as vicinity of Philadelphia.
>
> Rana pardalis Harlan, 1825, Amer. Jour. Sci., **10**: 59.—"Middle states; common in the vicinity of Philadelphia."

Range.—Eastern North America, from Quebec through Ontario to Minnesota, south to northern South Carolina, Georgia, and Alabama, and south in Mississippi, Louisiana, and eastern Texas nearly to the Gulf.

Common name.–Pickerel frog.

Rana boyli Baird

> *Rana boylii* Baird, 1854, Proc. Acad. Nat. Sci. Phila., **7**: 62.–Eldorado County, California.

Range.–Eastern Oregon to California.

Common name.–Yellow-legged frog.

Rana boyli boyli Baird

> *Rana boylii boylii* Camp, 1917, Univ. Calif. Publ. Zool., **17**: 117.

Range.–Central and northern California north in eastern Oregon, south to Los Angeles County.

Common name.–California yellow-legged frog.

Rana boyli muscosa Camp

> *Rana boylii muscosa* Camp, 1917, Univ. Calif. Publ. Zool., **17**: 118.–Arroyo Seco Canyon, about 1,300 feet alt., near Pasadena, California.

Range.–San Gabriel, San Bernardino, and San Jacinto Mountains in California.

Common name.–San Bernardino yellow-legged frog.

Rana boyli sierrae Camp

> *Rana boylii sierrae* Camp, 1917, Univ. Calif. Publ. Zool., **17**: 120.–Matlack Lake, Sierra Nevada, Inyo County, California.

Range.–Southern half of the Sierra Nevada above 7,000 feet alt.

Common name.–Sierra Nevada yellow-legged frog.

Rana aurora Baird and Girard

> *Rana aurora* Baird and Girard, 1852, Proc. Acad. Nat. Sci. Phila., **6**: 174.–Puget Sound.

Range.–British Columbia to southern California.

Common name.–Red-legged frog.

Rana aurora aurora Baird and Girard

> *Rana aurora aurora* Camp, 1917, Univ. Calif. Publ. Zool., **17**: 123.

Range.–Coastal region and inland to the Rocky Mountains in southern British Columbia, south at lower altitudes west of the Columbia River and south through western Oregon to northern coastal California.

Common name.—Oregon red-legged frog.

Rana aurora cascadae Slater

> *Rana cascadae* Slater, 1939, Herpetologica, **1**: 1.—Elysian Fields, Rainier National Park, Washington, 5,700 feet alt.

Range.—Eastern Olympic peninsula and Cascade Mountains. Recorded from Pottsville, Idaho.

Common name.—Cascade Range frog.

Rana aurora draytoni Baird and Girard

> *Rana draytonii* Baird and Girard, 1852, Proc. Acad. Nat. Sci. Phila., **6**: 174. —San Francisco and the Columbia River; restr. to vicinity of San Francisco.
>
> *Rana aurora draytonii* Camp, 1917, Univ. Calif. Publ. Zool., **17**: 115.

Range.—Central and southern California; rare and local west of the Sierras.

Common name.—California red-legged frog.

Rana pretiosa Baird and Girard

> *Rana pretiosa* Baird and Girard, 1853, Proc. Acad. Nat. Sci. Phila., **6**: 378.— Puget Sound, Washington.

Range.—North central Utah, northern Nevada, and western Wyoming west and north to southern Alaska.

Common name.—Western spotted frog, red-bellied frog.

Rana pretiosa pretiosa Baird and Girard

> *Rana pretiosa pretiosa* Stejneger and Barbour, 1917, Check list, ed. 1, p. 38.

Range.—Northwestern California to southern Alaska, eastward in British Columbia to Alberta and Saskatchewan, south in the Rocky Mountains to western Wyoming and the Wasatch Mountains in Utah; north of the Columbia and Snake rivers in Washington and Idaho.

Common name.—Western spotted frog.

Rana pretiosa luteiventris Thompson

> *Rana pretiosa luteiventris* Thompson, 1913, Proc. Biol. Soc. Wash., **26**: 53, pl. 3, figs. 2–3.—Anne Creek, Elko County, Nevada.

Range.—Northern Great Basin, in Oregon, Idaho, and Nevada, reaching southeastern Washington and northeastern California.

Common name.—Great Basin spotted frog.

Class REPTILIA

Subclass ANAPSIDA

Order CHELONIA

Suborder THECOPHORA

CHELYDRIDAE

Chelydra Schweigger

> *Chelydra* Schweigger, 1812, Königsberg. Arch. Naturg. Math., **1**: 292.-Type: *serpentina*.

Chelydra serpentina Linnaeus

> *Testudo serpentina* Linnaeus, 1758, Syst. Nat., ed. 10, **1**: 199.—"Warmer regions" [of North America]; restr. to vicinity of New York City.
> *Chelydra serpentina* Schweigger, 1812, Königsberg. Arch. Naturg. Math., **1**: 292.

Range.—North America, east of the Rocky Mountains.

Common name.—Snapping turtle.

Chelydra serpentina serpentina Linnaeus

> *Chelydra serpentina serpentina* Stejneger, 1914, Copeia, **1914,** no. 6, p. [4].
> *Chelydra lacertina* Schweigger, 1812, Königsberg. Arch. Naturg. Math., **1**: 293.—Type locality unknown; designated as vicinity of New York City.
> *Testudo longicauda* Shaw, 1831, *in* Gray, Syn. Rept., pt. 1, p. 36 (in synonymy).—No type locality; designated as vicinity of Philadelphia.
> *Chelydra emarginata* Agassiz, 1857, Contr. Nat. Hist. U. S., **1**: 417.—Mobile, Alabama, and New Orleans, Louisiana; restr. to Mobile.

Range.—Eastern and central North America from Nova Scotia and Quebec westward through Ontario, Manitoba, Saskatchewan, and Alberta, and southward, east of the Rocky Mountains, to the Gulf and to northern Florida.

Common name.—Snapping turtle, common snapping turtle.

Chelydra serpentina osceola Stejneger

> *Chelydra osceola* Stejneger, 1918, Proc. Biol. Soc. Wash., **31**: 39.—Clearwater, Pinellas County, Florida.
> *Chelydra serpentina osceola* Rust, 1934, Blätter Aquarien-Terr. Kunde, **45**: 59.

Range.—Peninsular Florida.

Common name.—Florida snapping turtle.

Macrochelys Gray

Macrochelys Gray, 1856, Proc. Zool. Soc. London, **1855**: 200.—Type: *temminckii.*

Macrochelys temmincki Troost

Chelonura temminckii Troost, 1835, *in* Harlan's Med. Phys. Res., p. 158, footnote.—Tributary stream of the Mississippi above Memphis, Tennessee.

Macrochelys temminckii Gray, 1856, Proc. Zool. Soc. London, **1855**: 200.

Range.—Southern Georgia and northwestern Florida to southern Texas; northward in streams of the Mississippi Basin to southeastern Kansas, and the lower Missouri and Ohio rivers.

Common name.—Alligator snapping turtle.

KINOSTERNIDAE

Sternotherus Gray

Sternotherus Gray, 1825, Ann. Phil., (n.s.), **10**: 211.—Type: *odoratus.*

Sternotherus odoratus Latreille

Testudo odorata Latreille, 1801, Hist. Nat. Rept., **1**: 122.—Carolina; restr. to vicinity of Charleston, South Carolina.

Sternothaerus odoratus Bell, 1825, Zool. Jour., **2**: 307.

Testudo glutinata Daudin, 1802, Hist. Nat. Rept., **2**: 194, pl. 24, fig. 4.— North America; restr. to vicinity of Lancaster, Pennsylvania.

Terrapene boscii Merrem, 1820, Tent. Syst. Amph., p. 27.—North America; restr. to vicinity of Philadelphia, Pennsylvania.

Kinosternum guttatum Le Conte, 1854, Proc. Acad. Nat. Sci. Phila., **7**: 185.— Pennsylvania; restr. to vicinity of Philadelphia.

Ozotheca tristycha Agassiz, 1857, Contr. Nat. Hist. U. S., **1**: 425; **2**: pl. 5, figs. 20–22.—Osage River, Missouri, Williamson County, Texas, and between San Antonio and Medina River, Texas; restr. to San Antonio.

Range.—Eastern and southern United States from Quebec, Ontario, Michigan, Wisconsin, and Minnesota, southward through the tier of states west of the Mississippi to eastern and southern Texas, and southeast to Florida.

Common name.—Stink-pot, common musk turtle.

Sternotherus carinatus Gray

Aromochelys carinatus Gray, 1856, Proc. Zool. Soc. London, **1855**: 199.— Louisiana; restr. to vicinity of New Orleans.

Sternotherus carinatus Stejneger, 1923, Proc. U. S. Nat. Mus., **62,** Art. 6, p. 2.

Range.—Eastern United States, west to eastern Texas.

Common name.—Keel-backed musk turtle.

Sternotherus carinatus carinatus Gray

Goniochelys triquetra Agassiz, 1857, Contr. Nat. Hist. U. S., **1:** 423; **2:** 642. —Lake Concordia, Louisiana.

Range.—Arkansas, Oklahoma, eastern Texas and Louisiana; eastward into Mississippi and Tennessee.

Common name.—Mississippi musk turtle.

Sternotherus carinatus peltifer Smith and Glass

Sternotherus peltifer Smith and Glass, 1947, Jour. Wash. Acad. Sci., **37:** 22. —Bassfield, Jefferson Davis County, Mississippi.

Range.—Southern Mississippi, northward to eastern Tennessee.

Common name.—Tennessee musk turtle.

Sternotherus carinatus minor Agassiz

Goniochelys minor Agassiz, 1857, Contr. Nat. Hist. U. S., **1:** 424.—Mobile, Alabama, Columbus, Georgia, and New Orleans, Louisiana; restr. to Columbus, Georgia.

Sternotherus minor Stejneger, 1923, Proc. U. S. Nat. Mus., **62,** Art. 6, p. 2.

Range.—Central and northern Florida, westward to Mobile, and through Georgia and Alabama into Tennessee.

Common name.—Loggerhead musk turtle.

Kinosternon Spix

Kinosternon Spix, 1824, Test. Brasil, p. 17.—Type: *longicaudatum = scorpioides.*

Kinosternon bauri Garman

Cinosternum baurii Garman, 1891, Bull. Essex Inst., **23:** 141.—Key West, Florida.

Kinosternon baurii Stejneger and Barbour, 1917, Check list, ed. 1, p. 111.

Range.—Peninsular and northern Florida.

Common name.—Striped mud turtle.

Kinosternon bauri bauri Garman

Kinosternon baurii baurii Stejneger and Barbour, 1939, Check list, ed. 4, p. 155.

Range.—Florida, except the Panhandle, and exclusive of the range of *bauri palmarum.*

Common name.—Striped mud turtle.

Kinosternon bauri palmarum Stejneger

Kinosternon bauri palmarum Stejneger, 1925, Jour. Wash. Acad. Sci., **15**: 463.—Royal Palm State Park, Dade County, Florida.

Range.—Royal Palm State Park, northward into Collier County, Florida.

Common name.—Paradise Key mud turtle.

Kinosternon hirtipes Wagler

Cinosternon hirtipes Wagler, 1830, Nat. Syst. Amph., p. 137, pl. 5, figs. 29, 30.—Mexico; restr. to lakes near Mexico City.

Range.—The Mexican plateau, northward to western Texas.

Common name.—Mexican mud turtle.

Kinosternon hirtipes murrayi Glass and Hartweg

Kinosternon murrayi Glass and Hartweg, 1951, Copeia, **1951**: 50, fig. 1.— Harper Ranch, 37 miles south of Marfa, Presidio County, Texas.

Range.—Big Bend region of Texas.

Common name.—Big Bend mud turtle.

Kinosternon flavescens Agassiz

Platythyra flavescens Agassiz, 1857, Contr. Nat. Hist. U. S., **1**: 430; **2**: pl. 5, figs. 12–15.—Texas, Arizona; restr. to Waco, Texas.

Kinosternon flavescens Stejneger and Barbour, 1917, Check list, ed. 1, p. 111.

Range.—Texas to Arizona, northward to Utah and Colorado, and through Oklahoma and Kansas to Nebraska; southern Illinois.

Common name.—Yellow mud turtle.

Kinosternon flavescens flavescens Agassiz

Kinosternon flavescens flavescens Carr, 1952, Handbook N. Amer. Turtles, p. 94, pl. 15, map 5.

Range.—Texas, New Mexico, and Arizona, northward to southern Utah and Colorado, and through Oklahoma and Kansas to Nebraska.

Common name.—Yellow mud turtle.

Kinosternon flavescens spooneri Smith

Kinosternon flavescens spooneri Philip W. Smith, 1951, Bull. Chicago Acad. Sci., **9**: 195, pl. 2.—Henderson County State Forest, 7 miles north of Oquawka, Illinois.

Range.—Sand prairie region along the Illinois River, near Havana, Illinois.

Common name.—Illinois yellow mud turtle.

Kinosternon subrubrum Lacépède

Testudo subrubra Lacépède, 1788, Hist. Nat. Quadr. Ovip. Serp., **1**, synops. method. tabl., pp. 618, 619.—Pennsylvania; restr. to vicinity of Philadelphia.

Kinosternon subrubrum subrubrum Stejneger and Barbour, 1917, Check list, ed. 1, p. 112.

Range.—Eastern United States.

Common name.—Common mud turtle.

Kinosternon subrubrum subrubrum Lacépède

Kinosternon subrubrum subrubrum Stejneger and Barbour, 1917, Check list, ed. 1, p. 112.

Testudo pensilvanica Gmelin, 1789, Syst. Nat., **1**: 1042.—Pennsylvania; restr. to vicinity of Philadelphia.

Kinosternon oblongum Gray, 1844, Cat. Tort. Brit. Mus., p. 33.—America; restr. to vicinity of Philadelphia.

Kinosternon doubledayii Gray, 1844, Cat. Tort. Brit. Mus., p. 33.—California, *in errore;* designated as vicinity of Philadelphia.

Kinosternon punctatum Gray, 1855, Cat. Shield Rept. Brit. Mus., **1**: 45, pl. 20c, figs. 3, 4.—East Florida.

Swanka fasciata Gray, 1870, Suppl. Cat. Shield Rept. Brit. Mus., **1**: 68.— Origin unknown; type locality designated as vicinity of Philadelphia.

Range.—Eastern United States from Connecticut southward to northern Florida; westward through New York, Ontario, Michigan, and Wisconsin, and southward in the mid-west to Tennessee.

Common name.—Common mud turtle.

Kinosternon subrubrum steindachneri Siebenrock

Cinosternum steindachneri Siebenrock, 1906, Zool. Anz., **30**: 727, fig.— Orlando, Florida.

Kinosternon subrubrum steindachneri Carr, 1940, Univ. Fla. Publ., **3**, no. 1, p. 99.

Range.—Peninsular Florida.

Common name.—Florida mud turtle.

Kinosternon subrubrum hippocrepis Gray

Kinosternon hippocrepis Gray, 1856, Proc. Zool. Soc. London, **1855**: 198.—New Orleans.

Kinosternon subrubrum hippocrepis Stejneger and Barbour, 1917, Check list, ed. 1, p. 112.

Kinosternon louisianae Baur, 1893, Amer. Nat., **27**: 676.—New Orleans, Louisiana.

Range.—Alabama, Mississippi, Louisiana, and eastern Texas, northward through Oklahoma and Arkansas to southeastern Missouri, western Tennessee, and Kentucky.

Common name.—Mississippi mud turtle.

Kinosternon sonoriense Le Conte

Kinosternum sonoriense Le Conte, 1853, Proc. Acad. Nat. Sci. Phila., **6**: 184. —Tucson, Arizona.

Kinosternum henrici Le Conte, 1859, Proc. Acad. Nat. Sci. Phila., **11**: 4.— New Mexico; restr. to vicinity of Las Cruces.

Range.—Southwestern Texas through southern New Mexico and Arizona to southeastern California; adjacent states of Mexico.

Common name.—Sonora mud turtle.

EMYDIDAE

Clemmys Ritgen

Clemmys Ritgen, 1828, Nova Acta Acad. Leop.-Carol., **14**: 272.—Type: *punctata = guttata.*

Clemmys guttata Schneider

Testudo guttata Schneider, 1792, Schr. Ges. naturf. Freunde Berlin, **10**: 264. —Type locality not stated; designated as vicinity of Philadelphia.

Clemmys guttata Strauch, 1862, Mem. Acad. Sci. St. Petersbourg, (7), **5**, no. 7, p. 107.

Testudo anonyma Schneider, 1792, *in* Schoepff, Hist. Test., pt. 1, p. 28 [in synonymy].

Geoclemmys sebae Gray, 1869, Proc. Zool. Soc. London, **1869**: 188.—No type locality; designated as vicinity of Philadelphia.

Range.—Eastern North America from Quebec and Maine westward through Ontario, Michigan, and Wisconsin; in the east to West Virginia, and in the west through Ohio, Indiana, and Illinois.

Common name.—Spotted turtle.

Clemmys muhlenbergi Schoepff

Testudo muhlenbergii Schoepff, 1801, Hist. Test., pt. 6, p. 132, pl. 31.— Lancaster, Pennsylvania.

Clemmys muhlenbergii Fitzinger, 1835, Ann. Mus. Wien, **1**: 124.

Emys biguttata Say, 1824, Jour. Acad. Nat. Sci. Phila., **4**: 212.—Not stated;
   designated as vicinity of Philadelphia.

Clemmys nuchalis Dunn, 1917, Bull. Amer. Mus. Nat. Hist., **37**: 624, fig. 6.
   —Yonahlossee Road, about 3 miles from Linville, North Carolina, 4,200
   feet alt.

Range.—Rhode Island, Connecticut, New York, New Jersey, Pennsylvania, Maryland, and Virginia into western North Carolina, mainly in bogs.

Common name.—Muhlenberg's turtle; bog turtle.

Clemmys marmorata Baird and Girard

Emys marmorata Baird and Girard, 1852, Proc. Acad. Nat. Sci. Phila., **6**:
   177.—Puget Sound, Washington.

Clemmys marmorata Strauch, 1862, Mem. Acad. Sci. St. Petersbourg, (7),
   5, no. 7, p. 108.

Range.—Western United States, west of the Cascades and the Sierra Nevada.

Common name.—Pacific pond turtle.

Clemmys marmorata marmorata Baird and Girard

Clemmys marmorata marmorata Seeliger, 1945, Copeia, **1945**: 158, figs. 4, 5.

Emys nigra Hallowell, 1854, Proc. Acad. Nat. Sci. Phila., **7**: 91.—Poso Creek,
   Kern County, California.

Clemmys wosnessenskyi Strauch, 1862, Mem. Acad. Sci. St. Petersbourg, (7),
   5, no. 7, p. 114, pl.—Sacramento River, California.

Range.—Pacific coastal regions, from southern British Columbia southward to the San Francisco Bay region.

Common name.—Pacific pond turtle.

Clemmys marmorata pallida Seeliger

Clemmys marmorata pallida Seeliger, 1945, Copeia, **1945**: 158, figs. 4, 5.—
   Lower Coyote Creek, near Alamitos, Orange County, California.

Range.—San Francisco Bay region to San Diego County, with an intergradient population (with *m. marmorata*) on the western slopes of the Sierra Nevada.

Common name.—San Diego pond turtle, southern California pond turtle.

Clemmys insculpta Le Conte

Testudo insculpta Le Conte, 1830, Ann. Lyc. Nat. Hist. New York, **3**: 112.—
   Northern United States; restr. to vicinity of New York City.

Clemmys insculpta Fitzinger, 1835, Ann. Mus. Wien, **1**: 124.

Emys speciosa Gray, 1831, Syn. Rept., *in* Griffith's Anim. Kingd., p. 26.—New Jersey.

Emys inscripta "Le Conte" *in* Gray, 1831, Syn. Rept., pt. 1, p. 26.—Lapsus for *insculpta*.

Range.—Eastern North America from Nova Scotia to Virginia, westward through central Michigan and central Wisconsin to Iowa.

Common name.—Wood turtle.

Emys blandingi Holbrook

Cistudo blandingii Holbrook, 1838, N. Amer. Herp., ed. 1, **3**: 35, pl. 5.—Fox River, Illinois.

Emys blandingii Strauch, 1862, Mem. Acad. Sci. St. Petersbourg, (7), **5**, no. 7, p. 28.

Range.—A prairie peninsula endemic, ranging from Iowa and southern Minnesota through southern Wisconsin, northern Illinois and Indiana, southern Michigan and Ontario, eastward into Ohio, Pennsylvania, New York, Massachusetts, and New Jersey. Occurrence in the east in isolated colonies.

Common name.—Blanding's turtle; semibox turtle.

Terrapene Merrem

Terrapene Merrem, 1820, Tent. Syst. Amph., p. 27.—Type: *clausa = carolina*.

Terrapene carolina Linnaeus

Testudo carolina[9] Linnaeus, 1758, Syst. Nat., ed. 10, **1**: 198.—Carolina; restr. to vicinity of Charleston, South Carolina.

Terrapene carolina Bell, 1825, Zool. Jour., **2**: 309.

Range.—Eastern United States, west to the Great Plains.

Common name.—Box turtle, common box turtle.

Terrapene carolina carolina Linnaeus

Terrapene carolina carolina Stejneger and Barbour, 1917, Check list, ed. 1, p. 115.

Testudo carinata Linnaeus, 1758, Syst. Nat., **1**: 198.—"*In calidis regionibus*"; restr. to vicinity of Charleston, South Carolina.

Testudo incarcerata Bonnaterre, 1789, Tabl. Encycl. Méth., Erp., p. 29.—Philadelphia.

Testudo incarcerata-striata Bonnaterre, 1789, Tabl. Encycl. Méth., Erp., p. 29.—North America; restr. to vicinity of Philadelphia.

[9] With various emendations and misspellings: *carolinina, caroliniana, carolinae, carolinensis, "caritana."*

Testudo clausa Gmelin, 1789, Syst. Nat., ed. 13, **1**: 1042.—North America; restr. to vicinity of Philadelphia.

Testudo virgulata Latreille, 1801, Hist. Nat. Rept., **4**: 100, pl. 4, fig. 2.— Charleston, South Carolina.

Emys schneideri Schweigger, 1814, Königsberg. Arch. Naturg. Math., **1**: 317, 442.—Origin unknown; type locality restr. to vicinity of Philadelphia.

Monoclida kentukensis Rafinesque, 1822, Kentucky Gazette, Lexington, (n.s.), **1**, no. 21, p. 5, col. 5.—Kentucky.

Terrapene maculata Bell, 1825, Zool. Jour., **2**: 309.—Type locality unknown; designated as vicinity of Philadelphia.

Terrapene nebulosa Bell, 1825, Zool. Jour., **2**: 310.—Type locality unknown; designated as vicinity of Philadelphia.

Emys kinosternoides Gray, 1831, Syn. Rept., pt. 1, p. 32.—Type locality unknown; designated as vicinity of Philadelphia.

Cistudo virginea Agassiz, 1857, Contr. Nat. Hist. U. S., **1**: 445; **2**: pl. 4, figs. 17–19, pl. 7, figs. 10–14.—New England, westward as far as Michigan . . . ; restr. to vicinity of Cambridge, Massachusetts.

Range.—Eastern United States from Maine throughout the Atlantic states to Georgia; Ontario and Michigan to Ohio and Indiana, southern Illinois, Kentucky, and Tennessee.

Common name.—Eastern box turtle, common box turtle.

Terrapene carolina bauri Taylor

Terrapene bauri Taylor, 1895, Proc. U. S. Nat. Mus., **17**: 576.—Florida; restr. to Orlando, Florida.

Terrapene carolina bauri Carr, 1940, Univ. Fla. Publ., **3**, no. 1, p. 100.

Range.—Northeastern and peninsular Florida.

Common name.—Florida box turtle.

Terrapene carolina major Agassiz

Cistudo major Agassiz, 1857, Contr. Nat. Hist. U. S., **1**: 445.—Mobile, Alabama; Florida; restr. to Mobile.

Terrapene carolina major Carr, 1940, Univ. Fla. Publ., **3**, no. 1, p. 101.

Range.—Western Florida (the Panhandle) and southern Georgia along the Gulf Coast to eastern Texas.

Common name.—Gulf Coast box turtle.

Terrapene carolina triunguis Agassiz

Cistudo triunguis Agassiz, 1857, Contr. Nat. Hist. U. S., **1**: 445.—New Orleans, Louisiana.

Terrapene carolina triunguis Strecker, 1910, Proc. Biol. Soc. Wash., **23**: 121.

Range.—Southern South Carolina throughout the Atlantic and Gulf coastal plains to eastern Texas, exclusive of Florida; northward in the Mississippi Basin through Oklahoma and Arkansas to eastern Kansas and Missouri; Tennessee, Kentucky, and southern Illinois.

Common name.—Three-toed box turtle.

Terrapene ornata Agassiz

Cistudo ornata Agassiz, 1857, Contr. Nat. Hist. U. S., **1**: 445.—The upper Missouri River, and Iowa; restr. to junction of the Platte and Missouri rivers.

Terrapene ornata Baur, 1891, Science, **17**: 191.

Range.—Great Plains, eastward to Indiana, southward from Wyoming and South Dakota to northern Mexico.

Common name.—Ornate box turtle.

Terrapene ornata ornata Agassiz

Terrapene ornata ornata Smith and Ramsey, 1952, Wasman Jour. Biol., **10**: 48.

Terrapene ornata var. *cimarronensis* Cragin, 1894, Colorado College Studies, **5**: 37.—Red Beds of Cimarron Basin, Oklahoma.

Range.—Great Plains, with isolated populations eastward in Wisconsin, Illinois, and Indiana; northern limit in Wyoming and South Dakota, southward to the Gulf and westward in New Mexico and Arizona; adjacent northern Mexico (exclusive of the Trans-Pecos range of *Terrapene ornata luteola*).

Common name.—Ornate box turtle, Great Plains box turtle.

Terrapene ornata luteola Smith and Ramsey

Terrapene ornata luteola Smith and Ramsey, 1952, Wasman Jour. Biol., **10**: 45, pl. 1.—17 miles south of Van Horn, Culberson County, Texas.

Range.—An area in Trans-Pecos Texas, limited on the west by the Hueco Mountains, on the east by the Guadalupe, Delaware, and Davis Mountains, on the south by the Finlay, Eagle, and Van Horn Mountains and the Sierra Blanca and Sierra Vieja, and on the north by the Sierra Diablo.

Common name.—Salt Basin box turtle.

Malaclemys Gray

Malaclemys Gray, 1844, Cat. Tort. Brit. Mus., p. 28.—Type: *concentrica*.

Malaclemys terrapin Schoepff

Testudo terrapin Schoepff, 1793, Hist. Test., Fasc. 3, p. 64, pl. 15.—Philadelphia market and coastal waters of Long Island; restr. to coastal waters of Long Island.

Malaclemys terrapin Bangs, 1896, Proc. Boston Soc. Nat. Hist., **27**: 159.

Range.—Coastal marshes from New England to Texas.

Common name.—Diamondback terrapin.

Malaclemys terrapin terrapin Schoepff

Malaclemys terrapin terrapin Lindholm, 1929, Zool. Anz., **81**: 294 [cited for combination only].

Testudo concentrica Shaw, 1802, Gen. Zool., **3**: 43, pl. 9.—Philadelphia markets.

Testudo ocellata Link, 1807, Naturh. Samml. Rostuck, pt. 2, p. 52.—North America; restr. to "Philadelphia markets."

Emys macrocephala Gray, 1844, Cat. Tort. Brit. Mus., p. 26.—Type locality unknown; designated as Philadelphia markets.

Malaclemys tuberculifera Gray, 1844, Cat. Tort. Brit. Mus., p. 29.—California, *in errore;* designated as Philadelphia market.

Range.—Coastal strip, mainly in brackish water, from Buzzards Bay, Massachusetts, to Cape Hatteras, North Carolina, including Delaware and Chesapeake bays.

Common name.—Northern diamondback terrapin.

Malaclemys terrapin centrata Latreille

Testudo centrata Latreille, 1802, Hist. Nat. Rept., **1**: 145.—Carolina; restr. to vicinity of Charleston, South Carolina.

Malaclemmys terrapin centrata Mittleman, 1945, Copeia, **1944**: 248.

Emys concentrica and *livida* Gray, 1831, Syn. Rept., p. 27.—North America; restr. to vicinity of Charleston, South Carolina.

Range.—Coastal waters, Cape Hatteras, North Carolina, to Florida.

Common name.—Southeastern diamondback terrapin, southern diamondback terrapin.

Malaclemys terrapin rhizophorarum Fowler

Malaclemys littoralis rhizophorarum Fowler, 1906, Proc. Acad. Nat. Sci. Phila., **58**: 112, pl. 4.—Boca Grande Key, Lee County, Florida.

M[alaclemmys] terrapin rhizophorarum Carr, 1946, Copeia, **1946**: 171, fig. 1.

Range.—Florida Keys.

Common name.—Mangrove terrapin, Florida Key diamondback terrapin.

Malaclemys terrapin macrospilota Hay

Malaclemmys macrospilota Hay, 1904, Bull. U. S. Bur. Fisheries, **24**: 16, pls. 6, 7, 11, text fig. 1.—Charlotte Harbor, Florida.

Malaclemys terrapin macrospilota Carr, 1952, Handbook of Turtles, p. 178.

Range.—West coast of Florida.

Common name.—Florida diamondback terrapin.

Malaclemys terrapin pileata Wied

Emys pileata Wied, 1865, Nova Acta Acad. Leop.–Carol., **32**: 17, pl. 1, figs. 2, 3.—New Orleans, Louisiana.

Malaclemmys pileata Hay, 1904, Bull. U. S. Bur. Fisheries, **24**: 17.

Malaclemys terrapin pileata Carr, 1952, Handbook of Turtles, p. 182.

Range.—Gulf coast from the mouths of the Mississippi eastward to the Panhandle of Florida.

Common name.—Mississippi diamondback terrapin.

Malaclemys terrapin littoralis Hay

Malaclemmys litoralis Hay, 1904, Bull. U. S. Bur. Fisheries, **24**: 18, pls. 8, 9, 12, figs. 2, 3.

Malaclemys terrapin littoralis Carr, 1952, Handbook of Turtles, p. 184.

Range.—Gulf coast, from the mouths of the Mississippi westward along the coast of Texas.

Common name.—Texas diamondback terrapin.

Graptemys Agassiz

Graptemys Agassiz, 1857, Contr. Nat. Hist. U. S., **1**: 436.—Type: *geographica*.

Graptemys geographica Le Sueur

Testudo geographica Le Sueur, 1817, Jour. Acad. Nat. Sci. Phila., **1**: 86, pl. 5.—Marsh on border of Lake Erie.

Graptemys geographica Agassiz, 1857, Contr. Nat. Hist. U. S., **1**: 436.

Range.—Mississippi and St. Lawrence basins, from Iowa through southern Wisconsin, Michigan, and Ontario to Lake George, New York, and Vermont; southeastern Kansas, Missouri, Illinois, Indiana, Ohio, and Pennsylvania; eastern Virginia, West Virginia, and eastern Tennessee; eastern Oklahoma and Texas.

Common name.—Geographic turtle, common map turtle.

Graptemys pulchra Baur

Graptemys pulchra Baur, 1893, Amer. Nat., **27**: 675.—Lake near Montgomery, Alabama.

Range.—Vicinity of Montgomery, Alabama.

Common name.—Alabama map turtle, Alabama sawback turtle.

Graptemys oculifera Baur

Malacoclemmys oculifera Baur, 1890, Science, (1), **16**: 262.—Mandeville, Louisiana.
Graptemys oculifera Baur, 1893, Amer. Nat., **27**: 675.

Range.—Southeastern Louisiana.

Common name.—Ringed sawback turtle.

Graptemys pseudogeographica Gray

Emys pseudogeographica Gray, 1831, Syn. Rept., p. 31.—Wabash River, New Harmony, Indiana.
Graptemys pseudogeographica Gray, 1863, Ann. Mag. Nat. Hist., (3), **12**: 180.

Range.—Central United States.

Common name.—False map turtle.

Graptemys pseudogeographica pseudogeographica Gray

Graptemys pseudogeographica pseudogeographica Stejneger and Barbour, 1917, Check list, ed. 1, p. 117.
Emys lesueurii Gray, 1831, Syn. Rept., p. 31.—Wabash River, New Harmony, Indiana.

Range.—Mississippi Basin; Louisiana, Mississippi, Alabama, Tennessee, Kentucky, Ohio, and Indiana; Illinois, southern Wisconsin, and Iowa; eastern Kansas, Missouri, and Arkansas to eastern Oklahoma.

Common name.—False map turtle, Le Sueur's map turtle, midland sawback turtle.

Graptemys pseudogeographica kohni Baur

Malacoclemmys kohnii Baur, 1890, Science, (1), **16**: 263.—Bayou Lafourche, Bayou Teche, and St. Martinsville, Louisiana.
Graptemys pseudogeographica kohnii Stejneger and Barbour, 1917, Check list, ed. 1, p. 117.

Range.—Gulf strip from Pensacola to eastern Texas.

Common name.—Bayou map turtle, Mississippi sawback turtle.

Graptemys pseudogeographica versa Stejneger

Graptemys pseudogeographica versa Stejneger, 1925, Jour. Wash. Acad. Sci., **15**: 463.—Austin, Texas.

Range.—Central Texas, Austin to Edwards County.

Common name.—Texas map turtle, Texas sawback turtle.

Graptemys barbouri Carr and Marchand

> Graptemys barbouri Carr and Marchand, 1942, Proc. New England Zool. Club, **20**: 98, pls. 14, 15.—Chipola River, near Marianna, Jackson County, Florida.

Range.—Jackson and Calhoun counties, Florida, in the Chipola River.

Common name.—Barbour's map turtle, Chipola map turtle, Barbour's sawback turtle.

Chrysemys Gray

> Chrysemys Gray, 1844, Cat. Tort. Brit. Mus., p. 27.—Type: *picta.*

Chrysemys picta Schneider

> *Testudo picta* Schneider, 1783, Naturg. Schildkr., p. 348.—England, *in errore;* designated as vicinity of New York City.
>
> Chrysemys picta Gray, 1856, Cat. Shield Rept. Brit. Mus., pt. 1, p. 32.

Range.—Eastern United States, northwestward to the Puget Sound region.

Common name.—Painted turtle.

Chrysemys picta picta Schneider

> Chrysemys picta picta Bishop and Schmidt, 1931, Field Mus. Nat. Hist., Zool. Ser., **18**: 136.
>
> Chrysemys cinerea Bonnaterre, 1789, Encycl. Méth., Erp., p. 25.—Type locality unknown; designated as vicinity of Philadelphia.

Range.—Eastern North America, from New Brunswick and Quebec throughout New England, eastern New York, and the Atlantic states to Florida.

Common name.—Eastern painted turtle.

Chrysemys picta marginata Agassiz

> Chrysemys marginata Agassiz, 1857, Contr. Nat. Hist. U. S., **1**: 439; **2**: pl. 1, fig. 6, pl. 5, figs. 1–4.—Wisconsin, Iowa, Michigan, and Indiana; restr. to northern Indiana.
>
> Chrysemys picta marginata Bishop and Schmidt, Field Mus. Nat. Hist., Zool. Ser., **18**: 136.

Range.—Western New York and Pennsylvania through Ohio and Indiana to northern Illinois and southeastern Wisconsin.

Common name.—Midland painted turtle.

Chrysemys picta belli Gray

Emys bellii Gray, 1831, Syn. Rept., p. 31.—Type locality not stated; designated as Puget Sound, Washington.

Chrysemys picta bellii Bishop and Schmidt, 1931, Field Mus. Nat. Hist., Zool. Ser., **18**: 136.

Emys oregoniensis Harlan, 1837, Amer. Jour. Sci., **31**: 382, pl.—Near Columbia River. [Various emendations and misspellings.]

Chrysemys nuttalli Agassiz, 1857, Contr. Nat. Hist. U. S., **2**: 642.—Junction of the Yellowstone and Missouri rivers.

Chrysemys pulchra Gray, 1873, Ann. Mag. Nat. Hist., (4), **11**: 147.—North America; restr. to upper Mississippi River.

Range.—Northwestern Illinois, northern Wisconsin, and Upper Peninsula of Michigan westward to British Columbia, Washington, and Oregon; southwestward to Texas and New Mexico.

Common name.—Western painted turtle.

Chrysemys picta dorsalis Agassiz

Chrysemys dorsalis Agassiz, 1857, Contr. Nat. Hist. U. S., **1**: 440.—Mississippi and Louisiana; restr. to vicinity of New Orleans.

Chrysemys picta dorsalis Bishop and Schmidt, 1931, Field Mus. Nat. Hist., Zool. Ser., **18**: 136.

Range.—Mississippi Basin, northward to southern Illinois.

Common name.—Southern painted turtle.

Pseudemys Gray

Pseudemys Gray, 1856, Proc. Zool. Soc. London, **1855**: 197.—Type: *concinna.*

Pseudemys floridana Le Conte

Testudo floridana Le Conte, 1830, Ann. Lyc. Nat. Hist. New York, **3**: 100.—St. John's River, Florida.

Pseudemys floridana Baur, 1893, Proc. Amer. Phil. Soc., **31**: 223.

Range.—Eastern North America, west to Texas.

Common name.—Southern terrapin.

Pseudemys floridana floridana Le Conte

Pseudemys floridana floridana Carr, 1935, Copeia, **1935**: 147.

Range.—Northern Florida and adjacent Atlantic coastal plain.

Common name.—Florida terrapin, coastal plain turtle.

Pseudemys floridana concinna Le Conte

Testudo concinna Le Conte, 1830, Ann. Lyc. Nat. Hist. New York, **3**: 106.—
Rivers of Georgia and Carolina above Augusta and Columbia; restr. to
vicinity of Columbia, South Carolina.

Pseudemys floridana concinna Carr, 1951, Handbook N. Amer. Turtles, p.
286, pl. 53, text figs. 18, 19, map 19.

Emys annulifera Gray, 1831, Syn. Rept., p. 32.—No locality stated; type
locality designated as Columbia, South Carolina.

Emys conemna Holbrook, N. Amer. Herp., ed. 2, **1**: pl. 19 [err. sculp.].

Pseudemys elonae Brimley, 1928, Jour. Elisha Mitchell Sci. Soc., **44**: 67,
pl. 1, pl. 2, fig. 1.—Cape Fear drainage near Elon College, Guilford
County, North Carolina.

Range.—Atlantic coastal plain from Maryland to Alabama, mostly
above the fall line, and into eastern Tennessee.

Common name.—Le Conte's terrapin, river turtle.

Pseudemys floridana hieroglyphica Holbrook

Emys hieroglyphica Holbrook, 1836, N. Amer. Herp., ed. 1, **1**: 47, pl. 2.—
Cumberland River, Tennessee.

Pseudemys floridana hieroglyphica Carr, 1851, Handbook N. Amer. Turtles,
p. 304, pl. 57, map 19.

Emys labyrinthica Duméril, 1851, Cat. Meth. Rept., p. 13.—Wabash River.

Range.—Mississippi Valley, northward to southern Illinois and
Indiana.

Common name.—Hieroglyphic terrapin, midwest terrapin, hieroglyphic turtle.

Pseudemys floridana hoyi Agassiz

Ptychemys hoyi Agassiz, 1851, Contr. Nat. Hist. U. S., **1**: 433.—Southwestern Missouri; restr. to vicinity of Springfield, Missouri.

Pseudemys floridana hoyi Carr, 1951, Handbook N. Amer. Turtles, p. 307,
pl. 58, text figs. 19, 20, map 19.

Range.—Southeastern Kansas, Missouri south of the Missouri River, southward to northeastern Texas and Louisiana.

Common name.—Missouri terrapin, Hoy's turtle.

Pseudemys floridana mobilensis Holbrook

Emys mobilensis Holbrook, 1838, N. Amer. Herp., ed. 1, **2**: 53, pl. 9.—
Mobile, Alabama.

Pseudemys floridana mobilensis Carr, 1951, Handbook N. Amer. Turtles,
p. 301, pl. 56, text fig. 18, map 19.

Pseudemys alabamensis Baur, 1893, Proc. Amer. Phil. Soc., **31**: 224.—
Mobile Bay, Alabama.

Pseudemys vioscana Brimley, 1928, Jour. Elisha Mitchell Sci. Soc., **44**: 66, pl. 2, fig. 2.—Lake Des Allemands, Louisiana.

Range.—Gulf coastal plain, from Florida to eastern Texas.

Common name.—Mobile terrapin, Mobile turtle.

Pseudemys floridana suwannensis Carr

Pseudemys floridana suwannensis Carr, 1937, Occ. Papers Mus. Zool. Univ. Mich., **348**: 4, pl. 1.—Suwannee River at Manatee Springs, Levy—Dixie County line, Florida.

Range.—Suwanee River drainage, Florida.

Common name.—Suwanee terrapin, Suwanee turtle.

Pseudemys floridana peninsularis Carr

Pseudemys floridana peninsularis Carr, 1938, Copeia, **1938**: 105.—Crystal Springs, Pasco County, Florida.

Range.—Peninsular Florida, from southern Marion County to Key Largo.

Common name.—Florida peninsula terrapin, peninsular turtle.

Pseudemys floridana texana Baur

Pseudemys texana Baur, 1893, Proc. Amer. Phil. Soc., **31**: 223.—San Antonio, Texas.

Pseudemys floridana texana Carr, 1951, Handbook N. Amer. Turtles, p. 312, pl. 60, text figs. 18, 19, map 19.

Range.—Central and southwestern Texas.

Common name.—Texan terrapin, Texas turtle.

Pseudemys scripta Schoepff

Testudo scripta Schoepff, 1792, Hist. Test., pts. 1, 2, p. 16, pl. 3, figs. 4, 5.— No locality stated; designated type locality, Charleston, South Carolina.

Pseudemys scripta Jordan, 1899, Man. Vert. Anim. U. S., ed. 8, p. 209.

Range.—Southeastern North America.

Common name.—Pond terrapin.

Pseudemys scripta scripta Schoepff

Pseudemys scripta scripta Carr, 1937, Herpetologica, **1**: 76, pl. 7, figs. 1, 2.

Emys sanguinolenta Gray, 1856, Cat. Shield Rept. Brit. Mus., pt. 1, pp. 26, 81, pl. 15.—North America; restr. to Charleston, South Carolina.

Trachemys scabra Agassiz, 1857, Contr. Nat. Hist. U. S., **1**: 434; **2**: pl. 2, figs. 13–15 (not of Linnaeus).

Range.—Northern Florida to Princess Anne County, Virginia.

Common name.—Yellow-bellied turtle, pond terrapin.

Pseudemys scripta troosti Holbrook

Emys troostii Holbrook, 1836, N. Amer. Herp., ed. 1, **1**: 55, pl. 4.—Cumberland River, Tennessee.

Pseudemys scripta troostii Carr, 1937, Herpetologica, **1**: 76, pl. 7, figs. 5, 6.

Emys cumberlandensis Holbrook, 1840, N. Amer. Herp., ed. 1, **4**: 35, pl. 8. —Cumberland River, Tennessee.

Range.—Upper reaches of Cumberland and Tennessee rivers.

Common name.—Troost's terrapin, Cumberland turtle.

Pseudemys scripta elegans Wied

Emys elegans Wied, 1838, Reise Nord Amer., **1**: 213.—Fox River at New Harmony, Indiana.

Pseudemys scripta elegans Carr, 1951, Handbook N. Amer. Turtles, p. 248.

Emys holbrookii Gray, 1844, Cat. Tort. Brit. Mus., p. 23.—Louisiana.

Trachemys lineata Gray, 1873, Ann. Mag. Nat. Hist., (4), **11**: 147.—North America; restr. to New Harmony, Posey County, Indiana.

Range.—Mississippi Basin, westward into Texas, northward to Kansas, Iowa, Illinois, Indiana, and southeastern Ohio.

Common name.—Painted terrapin, elegant terrapin, red-eared turtle.

Pseudemys scripta gaigeae Hartweg

Pseudemys scripta gaigeae Hartweg, 1938, Occ. Papers Mus. Zool. Univ. Mich., **397**: 1.—Boquillas, Brewster County, Texas.

Range.—Middle Rio Grande Basin.

Common name.—Big Bend terrapin, Rio Grande turtle.

Pseudemys rubriventris Le Conte

Testudo rubriventris Le Conte, 1830, Ann. Lyc. Nat. Hist. New York, **3**: 101. —Delaware River, near Trenton, New Jersey.

Pseudemys rubriventris Jordan, 1899, Man. Vert. Anim. U. S., ed. 8, p. 209.

Range.—Massachusetts to Virginia in the coastal plain.

Common name.—Red-bellied turtle, red-bellied terrapin.

Pseudemys rubriventris rubriventris Le Conte

Pseudemys rubriventris rubriventris Babcock, 1937, Occ. Papers Boston Soc. Nat. Hist., **8**: 293.

Emys irrigata Duméril and Bibron, 1835, Erpét. Gén., **2**: 276.—United States; restricted to vicinity of Trenton, New Jersey.

Emys rivulata Gray, 1844, Cat. Tort. Brit. Mus., p. 22.—North America; restricted to vicinity of Trenton, New Jersey.

· *Range.*—The Atlantic coastal plain from New York to south central Virginia.

Common name.—Red-bellied turtle.

Pseudemys rubriventris bangsi Babcock

Pseudemys rubriventris bangsi Babcock, 1937, Occ. Papers Boston Soc. Nat. Hist., **8**: 293.—Boot Pond, Plymouth County, Massachusetts.

Range.—Confined to Plymouth County, Massachusetts.

Common name.—Plymouth turtle, Plymouth terrapin.

Pseudemys nelsoni Carr

Pseudemys nelsoni Carr, 1938, Occ. Papers Boston Soc. Nat. Hist., **8**: 307.— Fellsmere, Indian River County, Florida.

Range.—Peninsular Florida.

Common name.—Florida red-bellied turtle, Florida red-bellied terrapin.

Deirochelys Agassiz

Deirochelys Agassiz, 1857, Contr. Nat. Hist. U. S., **1**: 441.—Type: *reticulata = reticularia.*

Deirochelys reticularia Latreille

Testudo reticularia Latreille, 1802, Hist. Nat. Rept., **1**: 124.—Carolina; restr. to vicinity of Charleston, South Carolina.
Deirochelys reticularia Gray, 1870, Suppl. Cat. Shield Rept. Brit. Mus., p. 39.
Testudo reticulata Daudin, 1802, Hist. Nat. Rept., **2**: 144, pl. 21, fig. 3.— Carolina; restr. to vicinity of Charleston, South Carolina.

Range.—Atlantic and Gulf coastal plains from Beaufort, North Carolina, to eastern Texas; northward in the Mississippi Valley to Tennessee, Arkansas, and eastern Oklahoma.

Common name.—Chicken turtle.

TESTUDINIDAE

Gopherus Rafinesque

Gopherus Rafinesque, 1832, Atlantic Jour., **1**: 64.—Type: *polyphemus.*

Gopherus polyphemus Daudin

Testudo polyphemus Daudin, 1803, Hist. Nat. Rept., **2**: 256.—Borders of the Savannah and Alatamaba rivers; restr. to vicinity of Savannah, Georgia.
Gopherus polyphemus Stejneger, 1893, N. Amer. Fauna, **7**: 161.

Testudo depressa Guerin, 1829, Icon. Regne Anim., Rept., pl. 1, fig. 1.—North America; restr. to vicinity of Savannah, Georgia.

Testudo gopher Gray, 1844, Cat. Tort. Brit. Mus., p. 4.—North America; restr. to vicinity of Savannah, Georgia.

Range.—Coastal plain from South Carolina to Florida, westward to the Mississippi River and northward into southern Arkansas.

Common name.—Gopher turtle, "gopher," gopher tortoise.

Gopherus berlandieri Agassiz

Xerobates berlandieri Agassiz, 1857, Contr. Nat. Hist. U. S., **1**: 447; **2**: pl. 3, figs. 17–19.—Brownsville, Cameron County, Texas.

Gopherus berlandieri Stejneger, 1893, N. Amer. Fauna, **7**: 161.

Range.—Southern Texas and adjacent Mexico.

Common name.—Berlandier's gopher turtle, Berlandier's tortoise.

Gopherus agassizi Cooper

Xerobates agassizii Cooper, 1863, Proc. Calif. Acad. Sci., **2**: 120.—Mountains near Fort Mojave, California.

Gopherus agassizii Stejneger, 1895, N. Amer. Fauna, **7**: 161.

Range.—Southeastern California, western Arizona, and southern Nevada.

Common name.—Western gopher turtle, desert tortoise.

CHELONIDAE

Chelonia Latreille

Chelonia Latreille, 1801, Hist. Nat. Rept., **1**: 22.—Type: *mydas.*

Chelonia mydas Linnaeus

Testudo mydas Linnaeus, 1758, Syst. Nat., ed. 10, **1**: 197.—Ascension Island, etc.; restr. to Ascension Island.

Chelonia mydas Schweigger, 1812, Königsberg. Arch. Naturg. Math., **1**: 412.

Range.—Tropical oceans in littoral waters.

Common name.—Green turtle.

Chelonia mydas mydas Linnaeus

Chelonia mydas mydas Carr, 1951, Handbook N. Amer. Turtles, p. 345. [Synonymy omitted.]

Range.—Tropical and subtropical Atlantic, in coastal waters; breeding on sea beaches in Florida, straying northward along the temperate coasts.

Common name.—Atlantic green turtle.

Chelonia mydas agassizi Bocourt

Chelonia agassizii Bocourt, 1868, Ann. Sci. Nat., (5), **10**: 122.—Mouth of Nagualate River, Pacific coast of Guatemala.

Chelonia mydas agassizii Carr, 1951, Handbook N. Amer. Turtles, p. 357, pl. 66.

Range.—Tropical Pacific coasts of the Americas, straying northward to the California coast.

Common name.—East Pacific green turtle.

Eretmochelys Fitzinger

Eretmochelys Fitzinger, 1843, Syst. Rept., p. 30.—Type: *imbricata.*

Eretmochelys imbricata Linnaeus

Testudo imbricata Linnaeus, 1766, Syst. Nat., ed. 12, **1**: 350.—American seas; restr. to Belize, British Honduras.

Eretmochelys imbricata Agassiz, 1857, Contr. Nat. Hist. U. S., **1**: 381.

Range.—Tropical oceans, in littoral waters.

Common name.—Hawksbill turtle.

Eretmochelys imbricata imbricata Linnaeus

Eretmochelys imbricata imbricata Carr, 1951, Handbook N. Amer. Turtles, p. 366, text figs. 22–24, 27–29.
[Synonymy omitted.]

Range.—Florida and Gulf coasts, occasionally (as waifs) as far north as Massachusetts.

Common name.—Atlantic hawksbill turtle.

Eretmochelys imbricata squamata Agassiz

Eretmochelys squamata Agassiz, 1857, Contr. Nat. Hist. U. S., **1**: 382.—Indian and Pacific oceans; restr. to coasts of Ceylon.

Eretmochelys imbricata squamata Carr, 1942, Proc. New England Zool. Club, **21**: 4.

Eretmochelys imbricata [subsp.] Schmidt, 1945, Marine Life Occ. Papers, **1**: 9.

Range.—Tropical Pacific coasts of the Americas, northward to California waters as waifs.

Common name.—Pacific hawksbill turtle.

Lepidochelys Fitzinger

Lepidochelys Fitzinger, 1843, Syst. Rept., p. 30.—Type: *olivacea.*

Lepidochelys olivacea Eschscholtz

Chelonia olivacea Eschscholtz, 1829, Zool. Atlas, pt. 1, p. 2, pl. 3.—Manila Bay, Philippines.

Lepidochelys olivacea Girard, 1858, U. S. Expl. Exped., Herp., p. 435.

Range.—Tropical oceans, in littoral waters.

Common name.—Bastard turtle, ridley.

Lepidochelys olivacea remivaga Hay
[New comb.]

Caretta remivaga Hay, 1908, Proc. U. S. Nat. Mus., **34**: 194, pl. 10, figs. 1–3, pl. 11, fig. 5.—Ventosa Bay, Gulf of Tehuantepec, Mexico.

Range.—Tropical Pacific coasts of the Americas, straggling to California waters.

Common name.—Pacific ridley.

Lepidochelys olivacea kempi Garman

Thalassochelys (Colpochelys) kempi Garman, 1880, Bull. Mus. Comp. Zool., **6**: 123.—Gulf of Mexico; restr. to Key West, Florida.

Lepidochelys kempii Baur, 1890, Amer. Nat., **24**: 487.

Range.—Tropical Atlantic coasts of the Americas, straggling as far north as Massachusetts.

Common name.—Ridley, Atlantic ridley, bastard turtle.

Caretta caretta Linnaeus

Testudo caretta Linnaeus, 1758, Syst. Nat., ed. 10, **1**: 197.—About the American Islands; restr. to Bimini, British Bahamas.

Caretta caretta Stejneger, 1904, Ann. Rept. U. S. Nat. Mus., **1902**: 715.

Range.—Tropical oceans, in littoral waters.

Common name.—Loggerhead.

Caretta caretta caretta Linnaeus

Caretta caretta caretta Carr, 1951, Handbook N. Amer. Turtles, p. 382. [Synonymy omitted.]

Range.—Atlantic and Gulf coasts of the United States, breeding as far north as Beaufort, North Carolina; the Atlantic Ocean.

Common name.—Atlantic loggerhead turtle.

Caretta caretta gigas Deraniyagala

Caretta gigas Deraniyagala, 1933, Ceylon Jour. Sci., (B), **18**: 66, pl. 5, text figs. 4–6.—Ceylon.

Caretta caretta gigas Schmidt, 1945, Marine Life Occ. Papers, **1**: 9.

Range.—Coasts of tropical America, presumably as a straggler to the California coast; the tropical Pacific and Indian oceans.

Common name.—Pacific loggerhead.

TRIONYCHIDAE

Trionyx Geoffroy St. Hilaire

Trionyx Geoffroy St. Hilaire, 1809, Ann. Mus. Hist. Nat. Paris, **14**: 1.— Type: aegyptiacus = triunguis.[10]

Trionyx ferox Schneider

Testudo ferox Schneider, 1783, Naturg. Schildkr., p. 330.—Savannah River, Georgia.

Trionyx ferox Schweigger, 1812, Königsberg. Arch. Naturg. Math., **1**: 285.

Range.—Eastern North America, westward to the Rocky Mountains.

Common name.—Soft-shelled turtle.

Trionyx ferox ferox Schneider

Amyda ferox ferox Neill, 1951, Publ. Res. Div. Allen's Rept. Inst., **1**: 15, fig. 1.

Testudo mollis Lacépède, 1788, Hist. Nat. Quadr. Ovip. Serp., **1**, Synops. Meth. Quadr. Ovip., table between pp. 618 and 619.—No type locality; designated (following Stejneger, 1944) as eastern Florida.

Testudo verrucosa Schoepff, 1795, Hist. Test., pt. 5, p. 90.—Rivers, lakes, and ponds of eastern Florida.

Trionyx bartrami Daudin, 1802, Hist. Nat. Rept., **2**: 74.—Rivers of eastern Florida.

Trionyx carinatus Geoffroy St. Hilaire, 1809, Ann. Mus. Hist. Nat. Paris, **14**: 14, pl. 4.—Type locality unknown; designated as Savannah River, Georgia.

Trionyx georgianus Geoffroy St. Hilaire, 1809, Bull. Soc. Phil. Paris, **1**: 367.— Substitute name for ferox.

[10] The argument that Geoffroy St. Hilaire did not designate a type species of the genus Trionyx, in the paper describing the genus, rests on the desire to change the name current for nearly 100 years for the widespread Holarctic genus of soft-shelled turtles. St. Hilaire's words (op. cit., p. 20): "Le trionyx d'Egypte ... nous donnant une idee exacte du port et des charactères génériques des trionyx ..." are an entirely adequate designation of the type of Trionyx. The attempt of Stejneger and others to require of St. Hilaire the use of the exact words of the 1930 rules regarding designation of type provides a wonderful example of the legalistic and in this case specious reasoning of nomenclaturists. As in many other changes from current nomenclature of amphibians and reptiles, Stejneger's proposal appears to have been motivated by his known personal animus against Boulenger, rather than by any concern for a stable nomenclature.

Trionyx georgicus Geoffroy St. Hilaire, 1809, Ann. Mus. Hist. Nat. Paris, **14**: 17.—Rivers of Georgia and the Carolinas; restr. to Savannah River, Georgia.

Trionyx brongniarti Schweigger, 1812, Königsberg. Arch. Naturg. Math., **1**: 288.—Type locality unknown; designated as St. John's River, Florida.

Trionyx harlani Harlan, 1835, Med. Phys. Res., p. 159.—East Florida.

Range.—Southern Georgia and all of peninsular Florida.

Common name.—Southern soft-shelled turtle.

Trionyx ferox agassizi Baur

Platypeltis agassizi Baur, 1888, Amer. Nat., **22**: 1121.—Georgia.

Amyda ferox agassizii Neill, 1951, Publ. Res. Div. Allen's Rept. Inst., **1**: 15, fig. 1.

Range.—East central Georgia, to southern North Carolina.

Common name.—Agassiz's soft-shelled turtle.

Trionyx ferox aspera Agassiz

Aspidonectes asper Agassiz, 1857, Contr. Nat. Hist. U. S., **1**: 405.—Lake Concordia, Louisiana.

Amyda ferox asper Neill, 1951, Publ. Res. Div. Allen's Rept. Inst., **1**: 15, fig. 1.

Range.—Louisiana and eastward to include western Florida (the Florida Panhandle).

Common name.—Gulf Coast soft-shelled turtle, southern spiny soft-shelled turtle.

Trionyx ferox emoryi Agassiz

Aspidonectes emoryi Agassiz, 1857, Contr. Nat. Hist. U. S., **1**: 407; **2**: pl. 6, figs. 4, 5.

Amyda ferox emoryi Neill, 1951, Publ. Res. Div. Allen's Rept. Inst., **1**: 15, fig. 1.

Range.—Gulf drainage of Texas, and the Red River Basin. Introduced in the Colorado River.

Common name.—Texas soft-shelled turtle, Emory's soft-shelled turtle.

Trionyx ferox spinifera Le Sueur

Trionyx spiniferus Le Sueur, 1827, Mem. Mus. Hist. Nat. Paris, **15**: 258, pl. 6.—Wabash River at New Harmony, Posey County, Indiana.

Amyda ferox spinifera Neill, 1951, Publ. Res. Div. Allen's Rept. Inst., **1**: 15, fig. 1.

Trionyx ocellatus Le Sueur, 1827, Mem. Mus. Hist. Nat. Paris, **15**: 261.— New Harmony, Posey County, Indiana.

Trionyx annulifer Wied, 1838, Reise Nord Amer., **1**, pt. 3, p. 140.—Ohio River at Pittsburgh.

Tyrse argus Gray, 1844, Cat. Tort. Brit. Mus., p. 48.—West Africa, Sierra Leone(?), *in errore;* type locality designated as New Harmony, Indiana.

Aspidonectes nuchalis Agassiz, 1857, Contr. Nat. Hist. U. S., **1**: 406.—Cumberland and Tennessee rivers; restr. to Cumberland River, near Nashville.

Gymnopus olivaceus Wied, 1865, Nova Acta Acad. Leop.–Carol., **32**: 55, pl. 5.—New Harmony, Indiana.

Range.—Northward from Tennessee, and from the Mississippi to the Appalachians; the southern Great Lakes to Montreal.

Common name.—Midland soft-shelled turtle, eastern spiny soft-shelled turtle.

Trionyx ferox hartwegi Conant and Goin

Amyda spinifera hartwegi Conant and Goin, 1948, Occ. Papers Mus. Zool. Univ. Mich., **510**: 1, map 1.

Amyda ferox hartwegi Neill, 1951, Publ. Res. Div. Allen's Rept. Inst., **1**: 15, fig. 1.

Range.—Drainages of the western affluents of the Mississippi, from the Arkansas River northward.

Common name.—Western soft-shelled turtle, western spiny soft-shelled turtle.

Trionyx muticus Le Sueur

Trionyx muticus Le Sueur, 1827, Mem. Mus. Hist. Nat. Paris, **15**: 263, pl. 7. —Wabash River at New Harmony, Posey County, Indiana.

Potamochelys microcephala Gray, 1864, Proc. Zool. Soc. London, **1864**: 87.— Sarawak, Borneo, *in errore;* designated as New Harmony, Indiana.

Range.—Mississippi Basin, from Pennsylvania to South Dakota and southward to the northern headwaters of streams in the Gulf drainage.

Common name.—Le Sueur's soft-shelled turtle, spineless soft-shelled turtle.

Suborder ATHECAE

DERMOCHELIDAE

Dermochelys Blainville

Dermochelys Blainville, 1816, Bull. Soc. Phil. Paris, **1816**: 111 *bis* [= 119]. —Type: *coriacea.*

Dermochelys coriacea Linnaeus

Testudo coriacea Linnaeus, 1766, Syst. Nat., ed. 12, **1**: 350.—Mediterranean Sea.
Dermochelys coriacea Boulenger, 1889, Cat. Chelon. Brit. Mus., p. 10.

Range.—Tropical oceans, probably pelagic as well as littoral.

Common name.—Leatherback turtle.

Dermochelys coriacea coriacea Linnaeus

Dermochelys coriacea coriacea Carr, 1951, Handbook N. Amer. Turtles, p. 442.
[Synonymy omitted.]

Range.—Atlantic and Gulf coasts, occasional as far north as Nova Scotia.

Common name.—Leatherback turtle.

Dermochelys coriacea schlegeli Garman

Sphargis coriacea var. *schlegelii* Garman, 1884, Bull. U. S. Nat. Mus., **25**: 303.—Tropical Pacific and Indian oceans; restr. to coasts of Ceylon.
Dermochelys coriacea subsp. Schmidt, 1945, Marine Life Occ. Papers, **1**: 9.

Range.—Tropical Pacific coasts of the Americas; occasional as far north as British Columbia.

Common name.—Pacific leatherback turtle.

Subclass ARCHOSAURIA
Order CROCODILIA[11]
CROCODILIDAE

Crocodylus Laurenti

Crocodylus Laurenti, 1768, Syn. Rept., p. 53.—Type: *niloticus* = *Lacerta crocodilus* Linnaeus, in part.

Crocodylus acutus Cuvier

Crocodilus acutus Cuvier, 1807, Ann. Mus. Hist. Nat. Paris, **10**: 55, pl. 1, fig. 3, pl. 2, fig. 5.—San Domingo [actually L'Etang Saumatre, Haiti].
Crocodilus floridanus Hornaday, 1875, Amer. Nat., **9**: 504, figs. 211-213.—Vicinity of Biscayne Bay, southeast Florida.

[11] The ordinal name "Crocodilia" is to be preferred over "Loricata" of the earlier editions of the *Check list* because of various other uses of this term (for example, in Mammalia, for the pangolins) and more especially because the relation to the vernacular word "crocodile" makes the meaning of this term obvious.

Crocodylus acutus Stejneger and Barbour, 1917, Check list, ed. 1, p. 41.

Range.—Southern Florida and the Florida Keys; recorded from Volusia, Palm Beach, Collier, Dade, and Monroe counties. Native also in Hispaniola, Jamaica, and Cuba, swimming freely to off-shore cays from the main islands; along the Pacific coast of the Americas from Sinaloa, Mexico, to Guayaquil, Ecuador, and on the Caribbean coast from Yucatan to northern Colombia and the Magdalena Basin.

Common name.—American crocodile.

Alligator Cuvier

Alligator Cuvier, 1807, Ann. Mus. Hist. Nat. Paris, **10**: 25.—Type: *lucius* = *Lacerta alligator* Blumenbach, 1788, in part = *mississipiensis.*

Alligator mississipiensis Daudin

Crocodilus mississipiensis Daudin, 1803, Hist. Nat. Rept., **2**: 412.—Borders of the Mississippi.

Alligator missisipensis [sic] Gray, 1831, Syn. Rept., p. 62.

Alligator mississipiensis Stejneger and Barbour, Check list, ed. 1, p. 41.

Crocodilus lucius Cuvier, 1807, Ann. Mus. Hist. Nat. Paris, **10**: 28.—"Mississipi" River.

Crocodilus cuvieri Leach, 1815, Zool. Misc., **2**: 117, pl. 102.—Dauphin Island, Alabama.

Range.—Rivers and swamps of the Atlantic and Gulf coastal plains, from Tyrrell County, North Carolina, to the Texas coast at Corpus Christi; formerly to the lower Rio Grande; northward in the Mississippi Basin to Arkansas and southeastern Oklahoma.

Common name.—Alligator, American alligator.

Subclass SYNAPTOSAURIA
Order SAURIA
GEKKONIDAE

Coleonyx Gray

Coleonyx Gray, 1845, Ann. Mag. Nat. Hist., **16**: 162.—Type: *elegans.*

Coleonyx variegatus Baird

Stenodactylus variegatus Baird, 1858, Proc. Acad. Nat. Sci. Phila., **10**: 254. —Colorado Desert.

Coleonyx variegatus Cope, 1866, Proc. Acad. Nat. Sci. Phila., **18**: 125, 310.

Range.—Desert areas of the southwestern United States and adjacent parts of Mexico.

Common name.—Banded gecko.

Coleonyx variegatus variegatus Baird

Coleonyx variegatus variegatus Klauber, 1945, Trans. San Diego Soc. Nat. Hist., **10**: 138.

Range.—Deserts of southeastern California from northern Inyo County southward; southern Nye County and southwestern Clark County, Nevada; Arizona from the central mountain area west and south, west of a line drawn from Casa Grande to Covered Wells. Ranging into extreme northeastern Lower California and northwestern Sonora.

Common name.—Desert banded gecko.

Coleonyx variegatus abbotti Klauber

Coleonyx variegatus abbotti Klauber, 1945, Trans. San Diego Soc. Nat. Hist., **10**: 154.—Proctor Valley, San Diego County, California.

Range.—Coastal and cismontane southern California, from the San Gabriel Mountains, Los Angeles County, through Riverside County and all of the western part of San Diego County; an outlying occurrence in Kern County. Extending into northwestern Lower California, with an apparently isolated population on Cedros Island and indications of its occurrence in the central part of the peninsula.

Common name.—San Diegan banded gecko.

Coleonyx variegatus utahensis Klauber

Coleonyx variegatus utahensis Klauber, 1945, Trans. San Diego Soc. Nat. Hist., **10**: 171.—Watercress Spring, about one mile northwest of St. George, Washington County, Utah.

Range.—Washington County, Utah, extreme northwestern Mohave County, Arizona, and northeastern Clark County, Nevada; intergrading with *variegatus variegatus* in the southern and western periphery of this range.

Common name.—Utah banded gecko.

Coleonyx variegatus bogerti Klauber

Coleonyx variegatus bogerti Klauber, 1945, Trans. San Diego Soc. Nat. Hist., **10**: 176.—Xavier, Pima County, Arizona, about 10 miles south of Tucson.

Range.—Southeastern Arizona from the vicinity of Casa Grande, Pinal County, southward to the Mexican border, northeastward to the Roosevelt Reservoir, and thence southeastward to the New Mexican border at Duncan, Greenlee County, Arizona. Presumably present in extreme southwestern New Mexico. Intergrading with *v. variegatus* to the west, about on a line drawn from Casa Grande to Covered Wells.

Common name.—Tucson banded gecko.

Coleonyx variegatus brevis Stejneger
[New comb.]

> *Coleonyx brevis* Stejneger, 1893, N. Amer. Fauna, **7**: 163.—Helotes, Bexar County, Texas.

Range.—Central New Mexico, southward throughout the Trans-Pecos region of Texas, and along the Rio Grande to Kleberg County, with a northeastward extension to Bexar County. Adjacent parts of Mexico in northern Tamaulipas, Nuevo León, and Coahuila, and southwestward into northeastern Durango.

Common name.—Texas banded gecko.

Phyllodactylus Gray

> *Phyllodactylus* Gray, 1830, Spicileg. Zool., p. 3.—Type: *pulcher* (Dutch West Indies).

Phyllodactylus tuberculosus Wiegmann

> *Phyllodactylus tuberculosus* Wiegmann, 1835, Nova Acta Acad. Leop.-Carol., **17**: 241, pl. 18, figs. 2, 2a.—"California"; restr. to San Diego County, California.

Range.—Rocky desert areas in San Diego and Imperial counties, California. Widely distributed in Lower California and in western Mexico generally.

Common name.—Mexican leaf-fingered gecko.

IGUANIDAE

Anolis Daudin

> *Anolis* Daudin, 1803, Hist. Nat. Rept., **4**: 50.—Type: *bullaris = carolinensis* (*fide* Stejneger and Barbour, 1917).

Anolis carolinensis Voigt

> *Anolius carolinensis* Voigt, 1832, Cuvier's Thierreich, **2**: 71.—Carolina; restricted to Charleston, South Carolina.

Range.—Southeastern United States, Bahama Islands, and Cuba.

Common name.—Green anolis, green anole, "chameleon."

Anolis carolinensis carolinensis Voigt

Anolis carolinensis [carolinensis] Oliver, 1948, Amer. Mus. Nov., **1383**: 13.

Range.—Atlantic and Gulf coastal plain, from North Carolina to Florida and westward to eastern Texas; northward in the Mississippi Valley to Arkansas and Tennessee.

Common name.—Anolis, anole, "chameleon."

Anolis sagrei Cocteau

Anolis sagrei Cocteau, 1837, in Duméril and Bibron, Erpét. Gén., **4**: 149.— Cuba.

Range.—Island of Cuba to Central American coast, Bahamas, and Florida Keys.

Common name.—De La Sagra's anolis.

Anolis sagrei stejnegeri Barbour

Anolis stejnegeri Barbour, 1931, Copeia, **1931**: 88.—Key West, Florida.
Anolis sagrei stejnegeri Oliver, 1948, Amer. Mus. Nov., **1383**: 25.

Range.—Key West and adjacent keys, Monroe County, Florida.

Common name.—Stejneger's anolis, Key West anole.

Dipsosaurus Hallowell

Dipso-saurus Hallowell, 1854, Proc. Acad. Nat. Sci. Phila., **7**: 92.—Type: dorsalis.

Dipsosaurus dorsalis Baird and Girard

Crotaphytus dorsalis Baird and Girard, 1852, Proc. Acad. Nat. Sci. Phila., **6**: 126.—Colorado Desert, California.

Range.—Southwestern United States and adjacent Mexico.

Common name.—Crested lizard.

Dipsosaurus dorsalis dorsalis Baird and Girard

Dipsosaurus dorsalis dorsalis Stejneger and Barbour, 1923, Check list, ed. 2, p. 43.

Range.—Colorado and Mojave deserts, southern Nevada and Utah; extending into southwestern and south central Arizona.

Common name.—Crested lizard, desert iguana.

Crotaphytus Holbrook

Crotaphytus Holbrook, 1842, N. Amer. Herp., ed. 2, **2**: 79.—Type: collaris.

Crotaphytus collaris Say

Agama collaris Say, 1823, *in* Long's Exped. Rocky Mts., **2**: 252.—Verdigris River near its union with the Arkansas River [Oklahoma].
Crotaphytus collaris Holbrook, 1842, N. Amer. Herp., ed. 2, **2**: 79, pl. 10.

Range.—Missouri, south of the Missouri River, westward and southward to southern California; northward in the Great Basin to Idaho. Northern states of Mexico along the border.

Common name.—Collared lizard, mountain boomer.

Crotaphytus collaris collaris Say

[*Crotaphytus collaris collaris*] Stone and Rehn, 1903, Proc. Acad. Nat. Sci. Phila., **55**: 30.

Range.—Southern Missouri and northern Arkansas to southeastern Colorado; eastern New Mexico and northern and central Texas.

Common name.—Eastern collared lizard, mountain boomer.

Crotaphytus collaris baileyi Stejneger

Crotaphytus baileyi Stejneger, 1890, N. Amer. Fauna, **3**: 103, pl. 12, fig. 1.—Painted Desert, Arizona.
Crotaphytus collaris baileyi Stone and Rehn, 1903, Proc. Acad. Nat. Sci. Phila., **55**: 30.

Range.—Southern and western Texas, westward to southwestern California and northward through the Great Basin to Idaho and Oregon.

Common name.—Western collared lizard.

Crotaphytus collaris auriceps Fitch and Tanner

Crotaphytus collaris auriceps Fitch and Tanner, 1951, Trans. Kansas Acad. Sci., **54**: 533, figs. 1, 2 [map].—3½ miles north-northeast of Dewey, west side of the Colorado River, Grand County, Utah.

Range.—Upper Colorado and Green River basins in western Colorado and eastern Utah.

Common name.—Yellow-headed collared lizard.

Crotaphytus reticulatus Baird

Crotaphytus reticulatus Baird, 1858, Proc. Acad. Nat. Sci. Phila., **10**: 253.—Laredo and Ringgold Barracks, Texas.

Range.—Southwestern Texas, ranging into adjacent Mexico in Tamaulipas and Nuevo León.

Common name.—Reticulated lizard.

Crotaphytus wislizeni Baird and Girard

Crotaphytus wislizenii Baird and Girard, 1852, Stansbury's Expl. Surv. Vall. Great Salt Lake, p. 340, pl. 3.—Near Santa Fe, New Mexico.

Range.—The Great Basin and adjacent arid areas, southward into Mexico, and the San Joaquin Valley in California.

Common name.—Leopard lizard.

Crotaphytus wislizeni wislizeni Baird and Girard
[New comb.]

Range.—Idaho, through the Great Basin, southward into eastern California, Arizona, New Mexico, and western Texas. Adjacent Mexico.

Common name.—Leopard lizard.

Crotaphytus wislizeni silus Stejneger
[New comb.]

Crotaphytus silus Stejneger, 1890, N. Amer. Fauna, **3**: 105.—Fresno, California.

Gambelia wislizenii silus Smith, 1946, Handbook of Lizards, p. 164.

Range.—San Joaquin Valley, California.

Common name.—San Joaquin leopard lizard.

Sauromalus Duméril

Sauromalus Duméril, 1856, Arch. Mus. Hist. Nat. Paris, **8**: 535.—Type: *ater.*

Sauromalus obesus Baird

Sauromalus obesus Baird, 1858, Proc. Acad. Nat. Sci. Phila., **10**: 253.—Fort Yuma, Arizona.

Range.—Rocky terrain in the southern Colorado Desert region, southeastern California to Arizona, southern Nevada, and southwestern Utah.

Common name.—Chuckwalla.

Sauromalus obesus obesus Baird

Sauromalus obesus obesus Shaw, 1945, Trans. San Diego Soc. Nat. Hist., **10**: 295, map.

Range.—Southeastern California, southern Nevada, and western Arizona (south to the range of *S. o. tumidus*).

Common name.—Chuckwalla.

Sauromalus obesus tumidus Shaw

> *Sauromalus obesus tumidus* Shaw, 1945, Trans. San Diego Soc. Nat. Hist.,
> **10**: 292.—Telegraph Pass, Gila Mountains, Yuma County, Arizona.

Range.—Yuma, Pima, and Pinal counties, Arizona.

Common name.—Gila Mountain chuckwalla.

Callisaurus Blainville

> *Callisaurus* Blainville, 1835, Ann. Mus. Hist. Nat. Paris, **4**: 286.—Type:
> *draconoides*.

Callisaurus draconoides Blainville

> *Callisaurus draconoides* Blainville, 1835, Ann. Mus. Hist. Nat. Paris, **4**: 286,
> pl. 24, fig. 2.—California; restr. to southern Lower California.

Range.—Colorado Desert region, southward through Lower California.

Common name.—Gridiron-tailed lizard.

Callisaurus draconoides gabbi Cope

> *Callisaurus ventralis gabbii* Cope, 1900, Ann. Rept. U. S. Nat. Mus., **1898**:
> 272.—Northern Lower California.
> *Callisaurus draconoides gabbii* Linsdale, 1940, Proc. Amer. Acad. Arts, Sci.,
> **73**: 220–221.

Range.—Central Colorado Desert, from southern Nevada and western Arizona through southeastern California. Also adjacent Lower California.

Common name.—Colorado Desert gridiron-tailed lizard.

Callisaurus draconoides myurus Richardson

> *Callisaurus ventralis myurus* Richardson, 1915, Proc. U. S. Nat. Mus., **48**:
> 408.—Pyramid Lake Indian Agency, Nevada.
> *Callisaurus draconoides myurus* Linsdale, 1940, Proc. Amer. Acad. Arts, Sci.,
> **73**: 221–222.

Range.—Western Nevada.

Common name.—Nevada gridiron-tailed lizard.

Callisaurus draconoides ventralis Hallowell

> *Homalosaurus ventralis* Hallowell, 1852, Proc. Acad. Nat. Sci. Phila., **6**: 179.
> —New Mexico west of the Rio Grande.
> *Callisaurus draconoides ventralis* Cope, 1900, Ann. Rept. U. S. Nat. Mus.,
> **1898**: 272, fig. 25.

Range.—Central southern Arizona. Southward in Sonora to the Guaymas region.

Common name.—Arizona gridiron-tailed lizard.

Uma Baird

Uma Baird, 1858, Proc. Acad. Nat. Sci. Phila., **10**: 253.—Type: *notata.*

Uma notata Baird

Uma notata Baird, 1858, Proc. Acad. Nat. Sci. Phila., **10**: 253.—Mojave Desert, *in errore;* corrected to Colorado Desert, California; Heifetz, 1941, Copeia, **1941**: 99–111, 7 figs., [map].

Range.—Colorado and Mojave desert regions and the Coachella Valley, Riverside County, California.

Common name.—Fringe-toed lizard.

Uma notata notata Baird

Uma notata notata Heifetz, 1941, Copeia, **1941**: 101.
Uma rufopunctata Cope, 1895, Amer. Nat., **29**: 939.—Yuma Desert, Arizona.

Range.—Colorado Desert in sand dune areas from the Coast Range in San Diego County, California, through Imperial County, California, into adjacent extreme southwestern Arizona in Yuma County. Adjacent Lower California.

Common name.—Colorado Desert fringe-toed lizard.

Uma notata inornata Cope
[New comb.]

Uma inornata Cope, 1895, Amer. Nat., **29**: 939.—Colorado Desert, San Diego County, California, *in errore;* corrected to Riverside County, California.

Range.—Coachella Valley, Riverside County, California.

Common name.—Coachella Valley fringe-toed lizard.

Uma notata scoparia Cope
[New comb.]

Uma scoparia Cope, 1894, Amer. Nat., **28**: 435, figs. 3, 4.—Fort Buchanan, Arizona, *in errore;* corrected to Mojave Desert, California.

Range.—Mojave Desert dune areas, California.

Common name.—Mojave fringe-toed lizard.

Holbrookia Girard

Holbrookia Girard, 1851, Proc. Amer. Assoc. Adv. Sci., **4**: 201.—Type: *maculata.*

Holbrookia lacerata Cope

Holbrookia lacerata Cope, 1880, Bull. U. S. Nat. Mus., **17:** 15.—Erath
County; west of the upper Brazos, Comanche County, Guadalupe River,
Kendall or Comal County, Texas.

Range.—Eastern border of the Edwards Plateau in Texas. Southwestward into adjacent Coahuila in Mexico.

Common name.—Spot-tailed earless lizard.

Holbrookia maculata Girard

Holbrookia maculata Girard, 1851, Proc. Amer. Assoc. Adv. Sci., **4:** 201.—
Opposite Grand Island, Platte River [Nebraska].

Range.—Great Plains, southwestward to the Colorado Desert and
southward in northern Mexico.

Common name.—Earless lizard.

Holbrookia maculata maculata Girard

Holbrookia maculata maculata Cope, 1900, Ann. Rept. U. S. Nat. Mus.,
1898: 293, fig. 33.

Range.—Southeastern Wyoming and southern border of South
Dakota through Nebraska and Kansas to northwestern Oklahoma,
the Texas Panhandle, and northeastern New Mexico.

Common name.—Northern earless lizard.

Holbrookia maculata elegans Bocourt

Holbrookia elegans Bocourt, 1874, Miss. Sci. Mex., Rept., p. 164, pl. 27 *bis,*
figs. 8, 8a.—Mazatlan, Sinaloa.

Holbrookia maculata elegans Smith and Taylor, 1950, Bull. U. S. Nat. Mus.,
199: 84 [cited for comb. only].

Holbrookia thermophila Barbour, 1921, Proc. New England Zool. Club,
7: 79.—San José de Guaymas, Sonora.

Range.—Desert border of the mountains in southern Arizona,
Tucson area to Nogales. Southward on the coastal plain of the Gulf
of California through Sonora and Sinaloa.

Common name.—Western earless lizard.

Holbrookia maculata pulchra Schmidt

Holbrookia pulchra Schmidt, 1921, Amer. Mus. Nov., **22:** 1.—Carr Canyon,
Huachuca Mountains, southeastern Arizona.

Holbrookia maculata pulchra Smith, 1946, Handbook of Lizards, p. 124,
pl. 19.

Range.—Montane grassland region of southeastern Arizona, above about 5,000 feet alt.

Common name.—Huachuca earless lizard.

Holbrookia maculata approximans Baird

Holbrookia approximans Baird, 1858, Proc. Acad. Nat. Sci. Phila., **10**: 253.— Lower Rio Grande, *in errore;* here designated "Upper Rio Grande."

Holbrookia maculata approximans Stejneger, 1890, N. Amer. Fauna, **3**: 109.

Holbrookia maculata flavilenta Cope, 1883, Proc. Acad. Nat. Sci. Phila., **36**: 10.—Lake Valley, southern New Mexico.

Holbrookia maculata campi Schmidt, 1921, Amer. Mus. Nov., **22**: 1-2.— About 8 miles northwest of Adamana, Apache County, Arizona.

Range.—Eastern Arizona and most of New Mexico, northward into adjacent Utah and Colorado, southward through Trans-Pecos Texas. Adjacent northern Mexico.

Common name.—Speckled earless lizard.

Holbrookia maculata ruthveni Smith

Holbrookia maculata ruthveni Smith, 1943, Field Mus. Nat. Hist., Zool. Ser., **24**: 342.—White Sands, about 12 miles southwest of Alamogordo, New Mexico.

Range.—The White Sands region, near Alamogordo, Otero County, New Mexico.

Common name.—Bleached earless lizard.

Holbrookia propinqua Baird and Girard

Holbrookia propinqua Baird and Girard, 1852, Proc. Acad. Nat. Sci. Phila., **6**: 126.—Between Indianola and San Antonio, Texas.

Holbrookia propinqua stonei Harper, 1932, Proc. Biol. Soc. Wash., **45**: 15.— Padre Island, Texas.

Range.—Gulf coastal plain, from Refugio County southward to the Rio Grande and inland to San Antonio. Adjacent coastal plain in Mexico.

Common name.—Keel-scaled earless lizard.

Holbrookia texana Troschel

Cophosaurus texanus Troschel, 1852, Arch. Naturg., **16,** Band 1, p. 389, pl. 6.—Neubraunfels, Comal County, Texas.

Holbrookia texana Baird and Girard, 1852, Proc. Acad. Nat. Sci. Phila., **6**: 124.

Range.—Central and southeastern Arizona, southern New Mexico, and western Texas; southward in Mexico.

Common name.—Greater earless lizard.

Holbrookia texana texana Troschel

Holbrookia texana texana Peters, 1951, Occ. Papers Mus. Zool. Univ. Mich., **537**: 5, map 1.

Holbrookia affinis Baird and Girard, 1852, Proc. Acad. Nat. Sci. Phila., **6**: 125.—Rio San Pedro = Devils River, Val Verde County, Texas.

Range.—Southeastern New Mexico, central Texas, mainly on the Edwards Plateau, and southward along the Rio Grande; northeastern Mexico.

Common name.—Texas earless lizard.

Holbrookia texana scitula Peters

Holbrookia texana scitula Peters, 1951, Occ. Papers Mus. Zool. Univ. Mich., **537**: 8, map 1.—Mouth of a small arroyo entering the Canada del Oro, 16 miles north of Tucson, Pima County, Arizona.

Range.—Trans-Pecos Texas and southwestern New Mexico through southeastern and central Arizona.

Common name.—Arizona earless lizard.

Sceloporus Wiegmann

Sceloporus Wiegmann, 1828, Isis, **21**: 369.—Type: *torquatus;* Smith, 1939, Field Mus. Nat. Hist., Zool. Ser., **26**: 1–397, 31 pls., 59 text figs.

Lopherpes Rafinesque, 1832, Atlantic Jour., **1**: 144.—Type: *Lopherpes dicyanelis* Rafinesque = *Lacerta hyacinthina* Green.

Sceloporus variabilis Wiegmann

Sceloporus variabilis Wiegmann, 1834, Herp. Mex., p. 51.—Mexico; restr. to Vera Cruz.

Range.—Southern Texas; southward throughout Mexico.

Common name.—Rose-bellied lizard.

Sceloporus variabilis marmoratus Hallowell

Sceloporus marmoratus Hallowell, 1852, Proc. Acad. Nat. Sci. Phila., **6**: 178.—San Antonio, Texas.

Sceloporus variabilis marmoratus Smith, 1934, Proc. Biol. Soc. Wash., **47**: 121.

Sceloporus delicatissimus Hallowell, 1852, Proc. Acad. Nat. Sci. Phila., **6**: 178.—San Antonio, Texas.

Range.—Southern Texas; southward into northeastern Mexico.

Common name.—Texas rose-bellied lizard.

Sceloporus merriami Stejneger

Sceloporus merriami Stejneger, 1904, Proc. Biol. Soc. Wash., **17**: 17.—East Painted Cave, near mouth of Pecos River, Texas.

Range.—Trans-Pecos Texas, eastward to the Devils River, and adjacent Mexico.

Common name.—Canyon lizard.

Sceloporus merriami merriami Stejneger

Sceloporus merriami merriami Smith, 1937, Proc. Biol. Soc. Wash., **50**: 86.

Range.—Along the Rio Grande and the Pecos and Devils rivers, on rock cliffs, and in near-by rocky terrain, from Boquillas, Brewster County, eastward.

Common name.—Merriam's canyon lizard.

Sceloporus merriami annulatus Smith

Sceloporus merriami annulatus Smith, 1937, Proc. Biol. Soc. Wash., **50**: 83.—East slope of Chisos Mountains, Brewster County, Texas.

Range.—Big Bend region of Trans-Pecos Texas; eastern Coahuila, Mexico.

Common name.—Big Bend canyon lizard.

Sceloporus scalaris Wiegmann

Sceloporus scalaris Wiegmann, 1828, Isis, **21**: 370.—Mexico; restr. to Mexico City.

Range.—Northern and central Mexico and southern Arizona.

Common name.—Patterned swift.

Sceloporus scalaris slevini Smith

Sceloporus scalaris slevini Smith, 1937, Occ. Papers Mus. Zool. Univ. Mich., **361**: 3.—Miller Peak, Huachuca Mountains, Arizona.

Range.—Southeastern Arizona montane grassland region; southward to Durango and eastward in southern Coahuila and Nuevo León.

Common name.—Bunch grass lizard.

Sceloporus grammicus Wiegmann

Sceloporus grammicus Wiegmann, 1828, Isis, **21**: 370.—Mexico; restr. to southern Oaxaca.

Range.—Most of Mexico, northward to southern Texas.

Common name.—Mesquite lizard.

Sceloporus grammicus disparilis Stejneger

Sceloporus disparilis Stejneger, 1916, Proc. Biol. Soc. Wash., **29**: 227.—
Lomita Ranch, 6 miles north of Hidalgo, Hidalgo County, Texas.
Sceloporus grammicus disparilis Smith, 1946, Handbook of Lizards, p. 193.

Range.—Extreme southern Texas; widely distributed in Mexico, southward to Hidalgo and Guanajuato.

Common name.—Mesquite lizard.

Sceloporus jarrovi Cope

Sceloporus jarrovii Cope, 1875, *in* Wheeler's Rept. Surv. W. 100th Meridian,
5: 569, pl. 23, fig. 2.—Southern Arizona.

Range.—Southern Arizona and New Mexico; southward to central Vera Cruz.

Common name.—Yarrow's lizard.

Sceloporus jarrovi jarrovi Cope

Sceloporus jarrovii jarrovii Smith, 1938, Univ. Kansas Sci. Bull., **24**: 624.—
Southern Arizona; restr. to Huachuca Mountains.

Range.—Southeastern Arizona grassland region; eastward to Hidalgo County, New Mexico; southward in Mexico to Durango.

Common name.—Yarrow's scaly lizard.

Sceloporus poinsetti Baird and Girard

Sceloporus poinsettii Baird and Girard, 1852, Proc. Acad. Nat. Sci. Phila.,
6: 126.—Rio San Pedro, affluent of the Rio Grande, and Sonora; restr.
to Rio San Pedro.

Range.—Southern New Mexico, central and western Texas; in Mexico, through western Nuevo León and Coahuila to Durango.

Common name.—Red scaly lizard.

Sceloporus cyanogenys Cope

Sceloporus torquatus cyanogenys Cope, 1885, Proc. Amer. Phil. Soc., **22**:
402.—Monterrey, Nuevo León.
Sceloporus cyanogenys Smith, 1938, Univ. Kansas Sci. Bull., **24**: 599.

Range.—Southern Texas, along the lower Rio Grande; southward in Mexico to central Tamaulipas and Nuevo León.

Common name.—Blue scaly lizard.

Sceloporus olivaceus Smith

Sceloporus olivaceus Smith, 1934, Trans. Kansas Acad. Sci., **37**: 263.— Arroyo los Olmos, 3 miles southeast of Rio Grande City, Starr County, Texas.

Range.—South central Oklahoma southward through the Texan prairie region to the lower Rio Grande; in Mexico to southeastern Coahuila and southern Tamaulipas.

Common name.—Texas spiny lizard.

Sceloporus clarki Baird and Girard

Sceloporus clarkii Baird and Girard, 1852, Proc. Acad. Nat. Sci. Phila., **6**: 127.—Province of Sonora; restr. to Santa Rita Mountains, southern Arizona.

Range.—Arizona and northwestern Mexico.

Common name.—Clark's swift, Clark's spiny lizard.

Sceloporus clarki clarki Baird and Girard

Sceloporus clarkii clarkii Cope, 1875, Bull. U. S. Nat. Mus., **1**: 49.

Range.—Southeastern Arizona and adjacent New Mexico; southward in Mexico to Guaymas.

Common name.—Clark's spiny lizard.

Sceloporus orcutti Stejneger

Sceloporus orcutti Stejneger, 1893, N. Amer. Fauna, **7**: 181, pl. 1, fig. 4.— Milquatay Valley, San Diego County, California.

Range.—Southern California; southward in Lower California to the Sierra de la Gigantea.

Common name.—Granite spiny lizard.

Sceloporus magister Hallowell

Sceloporus magister Hallowell, 1854, Proc. Acad. Nat. Sci. Phila., **7**: 93.— Fort Yuma, California.

Range.—Southwestern United States and northwestern Mexico.

Common name.—Desert spiny lizard.

Sceloporus magister magister Hallowell

Sceloporus magister magister Linsdale, 1932, Univ. Calif. Publ. Zool., **38**: 365.

Range.—Southern California, exclusive of the western slopes, Arizona and New Mexico, northward to southern Nevada and Utah, and southwestern Colorado, eastward to extreme western Texas; southward in Mexico to southern Sonora and northern Durango.

Common name.—Desert spiny lizard.

Sceloporus undulatus Latreille

Stellio undulatus Latreille, Hist. Nat. Rept., **2**: 40.—"Les grands bois de la Caroline"; restr. (Smith, 1938) to Charleston, South Carolina.

Sceloporus undulatus Wiegmann, 1828, Isis, **21**: 369.

Range.—The eastern United States, west to the Great Basin, southward into northern Mexico.

Common name.—Fence lizard.

Sceloporus undulatus undulatus Latreille

Sceloporus undulatus undulatus Burt, 1937, Papers Mich. Acad. Sci., **22**: 538.

Sceloporus floridanus Baird, 1858, Proc. Acad. Nat. Sci. Phila., **10**: 254.—Pensacola, Florida.

Range.—Atlantic coastal plain from southeastern South Carolina to central Florida and westward in the Gulf coastal plain through southeastern Louisiana.

Common name.—Southern fence lizard.

Sceloporus undulatus hyacinthinus Green

Lacerta hyacinthina Green, 1818, Jour. Acad. Nat. Sci. Phila., **1**: 349.—Vicinity of Princeton, New Jersey.

Sceloporus undulatus hyacinthinus Smith, 1948, Nat. Hist. Misc., **24**: 1.

Lacerta fasciata (*nec* Linnaeus) Green, 1818, Jour. Acad. Nat. Sci. Phila., **1**: 349.—Vicinity of Princeton, New Jersey.

Lopherpes dicyanelus Rafinesque, 1832, Atlantic Jour., **1**: 145.—Knobhills, near Mammoth Cave, western Kentucky.

Sceloporus thayeri Baird and Girard, 1852, Proc. Acad. Nat. Sci. Phila., **6**: 127.—Indianola, Calhoun County, Texas.

Range.—Extreme southeastern New York, southward to northern South Carolina; westward through Pennsylvania, southern Ohio, Indiana, and Illinois, and through Missouri; southward west of the range of *undulatus undulatus* to the Gulf Coast of Texas and Louisiana.

Common name.—Northern fence lizard.

Sceloporus undulatus garmani Boulenger

Sceloporus garmani Boulenger, 1882, Proc. Zool. Soc. London, **1882**: 762.—Pine Ridge, South Dakota.

Sceloporus undulatus garmani Smith, 1938, Occ. Papers Mus. Zool. Univ. Mich., **387**: 14, map 1.

Range.—Southern South Dakota through Nebraska and Kansas to central Oklahoma.

Common name.—Northern prairie lizard.

Sceloporus undulatus consobrinus Baird and Girard

Sceloporus consobrinus Baird and Girard, 1853, Marcy's Expl. Red River, p. 237, pl. 10, figs. 5–12.—Red River, Beckham County, Oklahoma.

Sceloporus undulatus consobrinus Cope, 1900, Ann. Rept. U. S. Nat. Mus., **1898**: 377, fig. 60; Smith, 1938, Occ. Papers Mus. Zool. Univ. Mich., **387**: 10, map 1.

Range.—Central and western Texas, through southern New Mexico into the southeastern Arizona grasslands; southward into northeastern Mexico.

Common name.—Southern prairie lizard.

Sceloporus undulatus elongatus Stejneger

Sceloporus elongatus Stejneger, 1890, N. Amer. Fauna, **3**: 111.—Mohave, Painted Desert, Arizona.

Sceloporus undulatus elongatus Burt, 1933, Amer. Midl. Nat., **14**: 241; Smith, 1938, Occ. Papers Mus. Zool. Univ. Mich., **387**: 15, map 1.

Range.—Northwestern New Mexico, northeastern Arizona through eastern Utah and most of Colorado to southern Wyoming.

Common name.—Northern plateau lizard.

Sceloporus undulatus tristichus Cope

Sceloporus tristichus Cope, 1875, *in* Wheeler, Expl. Surv. W. 100th Meridian, Zool., **5**: 571.—Taos, New Mexico.

Sceloporus undulatus tristichus Cope, 1900, Ann. Rept. U. S. Nat. Mus., **1898**: 376; Smith, 1938, Occ. Papers Mus. Zool. Univ. Mich., **387**: 15, map 1.

Range.—Central New Mexico and northern Arizona, adjoining the range of *elongatus,* into southern Utah.

Common name.—Southern plateau lizard.

Sceloporus undulatus virgatus Smith

Sceloporus undulatus virgatus Smith, 1938, Occ. Papers Mus. Zool. Univ. Mich., **387**: 11, map 1.—Santa Maria Mine, El Tigre Mountains, Sonora, Mexico.

Range.—Southeastern Arizona, into extreme southwestern New Mexico; southward into adjacent Mexico.

Common name.—Striped plateau lizard.

Sceloporus occidentalis Baird and Girard

Sceloporus occidentalis Baird and Girard, 1852, Proc. Acad. Nat. Sci. Phila., **6**: 175.—Benicia, California.

Range.—The Pacific coastal region and the Great Basin.

Common name.—Western fence lizard.

Sceloporus occidentalis occidentalis Baird and Girard

Sceloporus occidentalis occidentalis Camp, 1916, Univ. Calif. Publ. Zool., **17**: 65.

Range.—Central and northern California, through western Oregon into western Washington.

Common name.—Pacific fence lizard.

Sceloporus occidentalis becki Van Denburgh

Sceloporus becki Van Denburgh, 1905, Proc. Calif. Acad. Sci., (3), **4**: 9, pl. 4.—San Miguel Island, Santa Barbara County, California.

Sceloporus occidentalis becki Grinnell and Camp, 1917, Univ. Calif. Publ. Zool., **17**: 162.

Range.—Islands off the coast of Santa Barbara County, California.

Common name.—Island fence lizard.

Sceloporus occidentalis biseriatus Hallowell

Sceloporus biseriatus Hallowell, 1854, Proc. Acad. Nat. Sci. Phila., **7**: 93.—El Paso Creek, Tejon Valley, California.

Sceloporus occidentalis biseriatus Camp, 1916, Univ. Calif. Publ. Zool., **17**: 65.

Sceloporus undulatus var. bocourtii Boulenger, 1885, Cat. Lizards Brit. Mus., **2**: 229.—Monterey, California.

Range.—Eastern Oregon and southwestern Idaho, through Nevada and western Utah, extending through central California to the coast, thence southward into northwestern Lower California. The Great Basin representative of the Pacific fence lizard.

Common name.—Great Basin fence lizard.

Sceloporus occidentalis taylori Camp

Sceloporus occidentalis taylori Camp, 1916, Univ. Calif. Publ. Zool., **17**: 65. —Half way between Merced Lake and Sunrise Trail, 7,500 feet, Yosemite National Park, California.

Range.—Yosemite National Park, in the Canadian Life Zone.

Common name.—Yosemite fence lizard.

Sceloporus woodi Stejneger

Sceloporus woodi Stejneger, 1918, Proc. Biol. Soc. Wash., **31**: 90.—Auburndale, Polk County, Florida.

Range.—Peninsular Florida.

Common name.—Florida scrub lizard.

Sceloporus graciosus Baird and Girard

Sceloporus graciosus Baird and Girard, 1852, Stansbury's Expl. Surv. Valley of Great Salt Lake, p. 346, pl. 5, figs. 1–3.—Valley of Great Salt Lake.

Range.—The Great Basin and adjacent mountain areas, southwestward into southern California.

Common name.—Sagebrush lizard.

Sceloporus graciosus graciosus Baird and Girard

Sceloporus graciosus graciosus Camp, 1917, Univ. Calif. Publ. Zool., **17**: 67.

Range.—Throughout Nevada and Utah and into adjacent areas of the bordering states, north into southwestern Montana; essentially the entire Great Basin.

Common name.—Sagebrush lizard.

Sceloporus graciosus gracilis Baird and Girard

Sceloporus gracilis Baird and Girard, 1852, Proc. Acad. Nat. Sci. Phila., **6**: 175.—Oregon; restr. to vicinity of Klamath Falls.

Sceloporus graciosus gracilis Van Denburgh, 1922, Occ. Papers Calif. Acad. Sci., **10**: 280.

Range.—Western Washington, most of western Oregon (to the range of *graciosus graciosus*), southward in the Sierras in California to Ventura County.

Common name.—Sierra pine lizard.

Sceloporus graciosus vandenburgianus Cope

Sceloporus vandenburgianus Cope, 1896, Amer. Nat., **30**: 834.—Summit of the Coast Range, San Diego County, California.

Sceloporus graciosus vandenburgianus Camp, 1916, Univ. Calif. Publ. Zool., **17**: 67.

Range.—Coast Range in southern California from Ventura County southward into northern Lower California.

Common name.—Van Denburgh's pine lizard.

Uta Baird and Girard

> Uta Baird and Girard, 1852, Stansbury's Expl. Surv. Valley of Great Salt
> Lake, p. 345.—Type: *stansburiana*.
>
> *Uro-saurus* Hallowell, 1854, Proc. Acad. Nat. Sci. Phila., **7**: 92.—Type:
> *graciosus;* Mittleman, 1942, Bull. Mus. Comp. Zool., **41**: 107.
>
> *Streptosaurus* Mittleman, 1942, Bull. Mus. Comp. Zool., **41**: 111.—Type:
> *mearnsi.*

Uta stansburiana Baird and Girard

> *Uta stansburiana* Baird and Girard, 1852, Stansbury's Expl. Surv. Valley of
> Great Salt Lake, p. 345, pl. 5, figs. 4–6.—Valley of Great Salt Lake.

Range.—The Great Basin and Colorado Desert regions, westward into southern California, southward into northern Lower California.

Common name.—Side-blotched uta.

Uta stansburiana stansburiana Baird and Girard

> *Uta stansburiana stansburiana* Stejneger and Barbour, 1917, Check list, ed. 1,
> p. 51.

Range.—South central Washington through the Great Basin, meeting the range of *Uta stansburiana stejnegeri* in northern New Mexico and Arizona and southern Utah, Nevada, and California.

Common name.—Northern side-blotched uta.

Uta stansburiana hesperis Richardson

> *Uta stansburiana hesperis* Richardson, 1915, Proc. U. S. Nat. Mus., **48**: 415.
> —Arroyo Seco Canyon, near Pasadena, Los Angeles County, California.

Range.—Coastal region of southern California, into northwestern Lower California.

Common name.—California side-blotched uta.

Uta stansburiana stejnegeri Schmidt

> *Uta stansburiana stejnegeri* Schmidt, 1921, Amer. Mus. Nov., **15**: 1.—Mouth
> of Dry Canyon, Alamogordo, Otero County, New Mexico.

Range.—Southern Nevada and southeastern California through Arizona and New Mexico and western Texas; southward in the adjacent Mexican states.

Common name.—Desert side-blotched uta.

Uta microscutata Van Denburgh

> *Uta microscutata* Van Denburgh, 1894, Proc. Calif. Acad. Sci., (2), **4**: 298.—
> San Pedro Martir Mountains, Lower California.

Uta parviscutata Cope, 1900, Ann. Rept. U. S. Nat. Mus., **1898**: 324, fig. 45.—Substitute name.

Range.—Borego Palm Canyon, San Diego County, California, southward through the San Pedro Martir Mountains into central Lower California.

Common name.—Small-scaled uta.

Uta graciosa Hallowell

Uro-saurus graciosus Hallowell, 1854, Proc. Acad. Nat. Sci. Phila., **7**: 92.— "Lower California" (= southern California); restr. to borders of Colorado River at Yuma.

Uta graciosa Baird, 1859, U. S. Mex. Bound. Surv., **2**: pt. 2, p. 7.

Range.—Bank of Colorado River, and adjacent territory in California, Arizona, and extreme southern Nevada, and in adjacent Lower California and Sonora.

Common name.—Long-tailed uta.

Uta ornata Baird and Girard

Uta ornata Baird and Girard, 1852, Proc. Acad. Nat. Sci. Phila., **6**: 126.— Rio San Pedro (= Devils River), Val Verde County, Texas.

Range.—Rocky Mountain region and southern Great Basin.

Common name.—Tree uta.

Uta ornata ornata Baird and Girard

Uta ornata ornata Schmidt, 1921, Amer. Mus. Nov., **22**: 6.

Range.—Central western Texas, and adjacent Coahuila and Nuevo León in Mexico.

Common name.—Texas tree uta.

Uta ornata chiricahuae Mittleman

Uta ornata chiricahuae Mittleman, 1941, Proc. Biol. Soc. Wash., **54**: 165.— Pinery Canyon, 6,000 feet alt., Chiricahua Mountains, Arizona.

Range.—Chiricahua and Dos Cabezos mountains, southeastern Arizona.

Common name.—Chiricahua tree uta.

Uta ornata levis Stejneger

Uta levis Stejneger, 1890, N. Amer. Fauna, **3**: 108.—Tierra Amarilla, Rio Arriba County, New Mexico.

Range.—Rio Arriba and northern Sandoval counties, New Mexico.

Common name.—Smooth tree uta.

Uta ornata linearis Baird

Uta ornata var. *linearis* Baird, 1857, U. S. Mex. Bound. Surv., **2**, pt. 2, p. 7.—Los Nogales, Sonora.
Uta ornata linearis Schmidt, 1921, Amer. Mus. Nov., **22**: 6.

Range.—Western half of New Mexico and most of Arizona, south of 35° N. Lat.; adjacent Sonora and Chihuahua.

Common name.—Lined tree uta.

Uta ornata schmidti Mittleman

Uta ornata schmidti Mittleman, 1940, Herpetologica, **2**: 33, pl. 3, fig. 1.—Fort Davis, Jeff Davis County, Texas.

Range.—Trans-Pecos Texas and adjacent Chihuahua and Coahuila.

Common name.—Big Bend uta.

Uta ornata symmetrica Baird

Uta symmetrica Baird, 1858, Proc. Acad. Nat. Sci. Phila., **10**: 253.—Fort Yuma, Imperial County, California.
Uta ornata symmetrica Schmidt, 1921, Amer. Mus. Nov., **22**: 6.

Range.—Colorado River lowland in California and Arizona and adjacent Lower California and Sonora.

Common name.—Colorado River tree uta.

Uta ornata wrighti Schmidt

Uta wrighti Schmidt, 1921, Amer. Mus. Nov., **22**: 3.—Grand Gulch, 4,000–5,000 feet alt., San Juan County, Utah.

Range.—Northern Arizona, northeastern New Mexico, southern and central Utah, and adjacent southwest corner of Colorado.

Common name.—Northern cliff uta.

Uta mearnsi Stejneger

Uta mearnsi Stejneger, 1894, Proc. U. S. Nat. Mus., **17**: 589.—Summit of the Coast Range, Mexican boundary of San Diego County, California.

Range.—Desert slopes of the Coast Range in San Diego County, California, and adjacent terrain in Lower California.

Common name.—California collared uta.

Phrynosoma Wiegmann

Phrynosoma Wiegmann, 1828, Isis, **21**: 367.—Type: *orbiculare;* Reeve, 1952, Univ. Kansas Sci. Bull., **34**: 817–960, pls. 89–90, text figs. 1–12 (maps).

Phrynosoma coronatum Blainville

Agama (*Phrynosoma*) *coronatum* Blainville, 1835, Nouv. Ann. Mus. Hist.
  Nat. Paris, **4**: 284, pl. 25, fig. 1.—"California"; restr. to La Paz, Lower
  California.
Phrynosoma coronatum Duméril and Bibron, 1837, Erpét. Gén., **4**: 318.

Range.—Southern California and the Lower California peninsula.

Common name.—Crowned horned toad.[12]

Phrynosoma coronatum blainvillei Gray

Phrynosoma blainvillii Gray, 1839, Zool. Beechey's Voy., p. 96, pl. 29, fig. 1.
  —"California"; restr. to San Diego, San Diego County.
Phrynosoma coronatum blainvillei Smith, 1946, Handbook Lizards, p. 293,
  pl. 75, text fig. 86 A–C, map 22.

Range.—Southern coastal California from southwestern San Bernardino County southward into northwestern Lower California.

Common name.—San Diego horned toad.

Phrynosoma coronatum frontale Van Denburgh

Phrynosoma frontalis Van Denburgh, 1894, Proc. Calif. Acad. Sci., (2),
  4: 296.—Bear Valley, San Benito County, California.
Phrynosoma coronatum frontale Linsdale, 1932, Univ. Calif. Publ. Zool.,
  38: 367.

Range.—California west of the Sierra Nevada, from the northern Sacramento Valley to the Los Angeles Basin; isolated additional areas in Lower California west of the Sierra de Juárez and the San Pedro Mártir, and on Cedros Island.

Common name.—California horned toad.

Phrynosoma cornutum Harlan

Agama cornuta Harlan, 1825, Jour. Acad. Nat. Sci. Phila., **4**: 299, pl. 20.—
  Great Plains east of the Rocky Mountains; restr. to Fort Towson, Indian
  Territory [Choctaw County, Oklahoma].
Phrynosoma cornutum Gray, 1831, Syn. Rept., *in* Griffith's Anim. Kingd.,
  9: 45.
Phrynosoma bufonium Wiegmann, 1828, Isis, **21**: 367.—Surinam, *in errore;*
  designated as San Antonio, Texas.
Phrynosoma harlanii Wiegmann, 1834, Herp. Mex., p. 54.—Mexico; restr. to
  San Antonio [Texas].

[12] The misnomer "horned toad" is so genuinely popular and well known as the vernacular name for the lizards of the genus *Phrynosoma* that it seems best to adopt it rather than to attempt to force the use of the book name "horned lizard."

Phrynosoma planiceps Hallowell, 1852, Proc. Acad. Nat. Sci. Phila., **6**: 178.—
Western Texas, near the Rio Grande; restr. to vicinity of El Paso.

Phrynosoma brevicorne Boulenger, 1916, Proc. Zool. Soc. London, **1916:**
537, pl. 1.—Texas; restr. to vicinity of Laredo.

Range.—Kansas, entering western Arkansas and Missouri, southeastern Colorado, southward and southwestward through Oklahoma
and Texas (exclusive of the eastern forested region), and New
Mexico to the southeastern Arizona grasslands; adjacent northern
states of Mexico.

Common name.—Horned toad, Texas horned toad, horned lizard.

Phrynosoma douglassi Bell

Agama douglassii Bell, 1829, Trans. Linn. Soc. London, **16:** 105, pl. 10.—
Banks of the Columbia River.

Phrynosoma douglassi Wagler, 1930, Syst. Amphib., p. 146.

Range.—Interior of the western United States from the Canadian
border southward into Mexico.

Common name.—Short-horned horned toad.

Phrynosoma douglassi douglassi Bell

Phrynosoma douglassii douglassii Cope, 1875, Bull. U. S. Nat. Mus., **1:** 49.

Phrynosoma douglassii var. *exilis* Cope, 1871, Ann. Rept. U. S. Geol. Surv.
Terr., **1871:** 468.—Carrington's Lake, Montana, and Fort Hall, Idaho;
restr. to Fort Hall, Idaho.

Phrynosoma douglassii pygmaea Yarrow, 1882, Proc. U. S. Nat. Mus., **5:** 443.
—Des Chutes River, Oregon.

Range.—South central British Columbia, southward through eastern Washington and Oregon, most of Idaho, and to northern California and Nevada.

Common name.—Pigmy horned toad.

Phrynosoma douglassi brevirostre Girard

Tapaya brevirostre Girard, 1858, U. S. Expl. Exped., Herp., p. 397.—Plains
of Nebraska.

Phrynosoma douglassii brevirostre Smith, 1946, Handbook Lizards, p. 302,
pl. 79.

Range.—Northwestern Kansas, northwestward through northern
Colorado to northeastern Utah; western Nebraska, western South
Dakota, Wyoming, and through Montana, presumably into extreme
southern Alberta and Saskatchewan.

Common name.—Eastern short-horned horned toad.

Phrynosoma douglassi ornatissimum Girard

Tapaya ornatissima Girard, 1858, U. S. Expl. Exped., Herp., p. 396.—Mountainous region of New Mexico.

Phrynosoma douglassii ornatissimum Yarrow, 1875, *in* Wheeler, Expl. Surv. W. 100th Meridian, **5**: 581.

Range.—Southern Colorado through New Mexico, extreme eastern Arizona, and southward through Trans-Pecos Texas into adjacent Mexico.

Common name.—Desert short-horned horned toad.

Phrynosoma douglassi hernandesi Girard

Tapaya hernandesi Girard, 1858, U. S. Expl. Exped., Herp., p. 395.—New Mexico; restr. to vicinity of Las Cruces.

Phrynosoma douglassii hernandesi Cope, 1900, Rept. U. S. Nat. Mus., **1898**: 413, fig. 70.

Range.—Southern Utah, extreme western Colorado, southward through Arizona into adjacent Mexico.

Common name.—Mountain short-horned horned toad.

Phrynosoma douglassi ornatum Girard

Phrynosoma ornatum Girard, 1858, U. S. Expl. Exped., Herp., Atlas, pl. 21, figs. 1–5.—Salt Lake.

Phrynosoma douglassii ornatum Stejneger, 1919, Copeia, **1919**: 3.

Range.—Basin of Great Salt Lake, northeastern Nevada, and southward to Millard County, Utah.

Common name.—Salt Lake horned toad.

Phrynosoma m'calli Hallowell

Anota m'callii Hallowell, 1852, Proc. Acad. Nat. Sci. Phila., **6**: 182.—Colorado Desert, between Vallecita [sic] and Camp Yuma, 160 miles east of San Diego, California.

Phrynosoma maccallii Cope, 1866, Proc. Acad. Nat. Sci. Phila., **18**: 310.

Phrynosoma m'callii Stejneger and Barbour, 1917, Check list, ed. 1, p. 59.

Range.—Colorado Desert, in southeastern California, southwestern Arizona, and adjacent Lower California and Sonora.

Common name.—Flat-tailed horned toad.

Phrynosoma modestum Girard

Phrynosoma modestum Girard, 1852, Stansbury's Expl. Surv. Valley of Great Salt Lake, pp. 361, 365, pl. 6, figs. 4–8.—The Rio Grande, west of San Antonio, Texas; between San Antonio and El Paso.

Range.—Western Texas, most of New Mexico, and extreme southeastern Arizona; southward in Mexico.

Common name.—Bleached horned toad.

Phrynosoma platyrhinos Girard

> *Phrynosoma platyrhinos* Girard, 1852, Stansbury's Expl. Surv. Valley of Great Salt Lake, pp. 361, 363, pl. 7, figs. 1–5.—Great Salt Lake Valley.

Range.—Great Basin and Sonora desert regions.

Common name.—Snub-nosed horned toad.

Phrynosoma platyrhinos platyrhinos Girard

> *Phrynosoma platyrhinos platyrhinos* Klauber, 1939, Bull. Zool. Soc. San Diego, **14:** 94.

Range.—Great Basin and Colorado Desert, from extreme southeastern Washington, through southwestern Idaho, northern Nevada, adjacent California, and western Utah.

Common name.—Great Basin horned toad.

Phrynosoma platyrhinos calidiarum Cope

> *Anota calidiarum* Cope, 1896, Amer. Nat., **30:** 833.—Death Valley, California.
> *Phrynosoma platyrhinos calidiarum* Reeve, 1952, Univ. Kansas Sci. Bull., **34:** 856, fig. 3.

Range.—Deserts of southeastern California and adjacent Nevada and Arizona, to southwestern Utah.

Common name.—Sonoran Desert horned toad.

Phrynosoma solare Gray

> *Phrynosoma solaris* Gray, 1845, Cat. Lizards Brit. Mus., p. 229.—"California," *in errore;* designated type locality: Tucson, Arizona.
> *Phrynosoma solare* Cope, 1900, Ann. Rept. U. S. Nat. Mus., **1898:** 420, fig. 73.
> *Phrynosoma regale* Girard, 1858, U. S. Expl. Exped., Herp., p. 406.—Valleys of the Zuni and Colorado rivers.

Range.—Borders of the Colorado Desert, especially the Phoenix and Tucson areas in Arizona; Lower California (opposite Angel de la Guarda Island) and Sonora.

Common name.—Regal horned toad.

ANGUIDAE

Ophisaurus Daudin

Ophisaurus Daudin, 1803, Bull. Soc. Phil. Paris, **3**: 188.—Type: *ventralis*.

Ophisaurus ventralis Linnaeus

Anguis ventralis Linnaeus, 1766, Syst. Nat., ed. 12, **1**: 391.—Carolina; restr. to Charleston, South Carolina.

Ophisaurus ventralis Daudin, 1803, Hist. Nat. Rept., **7**: 352, pl. 88.

Ophisaurus punctatus Cuvier, 1829, Règne Animal, ed. 2, **2**: 70.—Nomen nudum.

Ophisaurus striatulus Cuvier, 1829, Règne Animal, ed. 2, **2**: 70.—Nomen nudum.

Ophisaurus lineatus Gray, 1838, Ann. Mag. Nat. Hist., (1), **1**: 391.—North America; restr. to Charleston, South Carolina.

Range.—Atlantic and Gulf coastal plains from central Virginia through South Carolina, North Carolina, Georgia, and Florida through eastern Louisiana; extensions along river valleys as far as southeastern Oklahoma, east central Missouri, and the Piedmont of Georgia.

Common name.—Eastern glass snake.

Ophisaurus compressus Cope

Ophisaurus ventralis compressus Cope, 1900, Ann. Rept. U. S. Nat. Mus., **1898**: 501, fig. 90.—South Island, Georgetown County, South Carolina.

Ophisaurus compressus McConkey, 1952, Nat. Hist. Misc., **102**: 1.

Range.—Coastal areas and islands off South Carolina, Georgia, and Florida, and sand pine scrub and adjacent flatwoods areas of peninsular Florida.

Common name.—Coastal glass snake.

Ophisaurus attenuatus Baird

Ophisaurus ventralis attenuatus Baird, 1880, *in* Cope, Bull. U. S. Nat. Mus., **17**: 18.—Texas [by implication].

Range.—Mississippi Basin and Atlantic and Gulf coastal plains. Bounded by Wisconsin, Nebraska, Texas, Virginia, and Florida.

Common name.—Slender glass snake.

Ophisaurus attenuatus attenuatus Baird

Ophisaurus attenuatus attenuatus McConkey, 1952, Nat. Hist. Misc., **102**: 2.

Ophisaurus ventralis attenuatus var. *sulcatus* Cope, 1880, Bull. U. S. Nat. Mus., **17**: 18.—Dallas, Texas.

Range.—Mississippi Basin, north to the Chicago region, west to Nebraska, and south to Louisiana; west through central and southern Texas.

Common name.—Western slender glass snake.

Ophisaurus attenuatus longicaudus McConkey

Ophisaurus attenuatus longicaudus McConkey, 1952, Nat. Hist. Misc., **102**: 1.—12 miles southeast of Newton, Baker County, Georgia.

Range.—South of the Ohio River and east of the Mississippi to the Atlantic and Gulf coasts; northward in the east to Virginia.

Common name.—Eastern slender glass snake.

Gerrhonotus Wiegmann

Gerrhonotus Wiegmann, 1828, Isis, **21**: 379.—Type: *tessellatus* = *liocephalus*.

Gerrhonotus coeruleus Wiegmann

Gerrhonotus coeruleus Wiegmann, 1828, Isis, **21**: 380.—"Brasilia," *in errore;* by subsequent designation, San Francisco, California.

Range.—Southern British Columbia and southwestern Alberta to California and Montana.

Common name.—Northern alligator lizard.

Gerrhonotus coeruleus coeruleus Wiegmann

Gerrhonotus coeruleus coeruleus Fitch, 1934, Copeia, **1934**: 6; idem, 1938, Amer. Midl. Nat., **20**: 413, fig. 5.

Gerrhonotus burnetti Gray, 1839, Syn. Rept., *in* Griffith's Anim. Kingd., **9**: 64.—Type locality unknown.

Elgaria formosa Baird and Girard, 1852, Proc. Acad. Nat. Sci. Phila., **6**: 175. —California.

Range.—Coast of central California, southern Sonoma County to Monterey, in a narrow strip of Transition Life Zone.

Common name.—San Francisco alligator lizard.

Gerrhonotus coeruleus principis Baird and Girard

Elgaria principis Baird and Girard, 1852, Proc. Acad. Nat. Sci. Phila., **6**: 175. —Oregon and Puget Sound; restr. to Puget Sound.

G[errhonotus] c[oeruleus] principis Fitch, 1934, Copeia, **1934**: 6.

Range.—Southern British Columbia, with eastern tip of Vancouver Island, most of Washington, northern Idaho, western Montana, and coastal Oregon.

Common name.—Northern alligator lizard.

Gerrhonotus coeruleus shastensis Fitch

Gerrhonotus coeruleus shastensis Fitch, 1934, Copeia, **1934**: 6.—South side of Burney Creek, 3,000 feet alt., 2 miles southwest of Burney, Shasta County, California.

Range.—Southern Oregon, south through California to the coast and south in the Sierra Nevada to northern Sonoma County.

Common name.—Shasta alligator lizard.

Gerrhonotus coeruleus palmeri Stejneger

Gerrhonotus scincicauda palmeri Stejneger, 1893, N. Amer. Fauna, **7**: 196.— South Fork of King's River, Fresno County, California.

G[*errhonotus*] c[*oeruleus*] *palmeri* Fitch, 1934, Copeia, **1934**: 6; idem, 1938, Amer. Midl. Nat., **20**: 418, fig. 5.

Range.—The Sierra Nevada in California, southward to northern Kern County, mainly in Hudsonian, Canadian, and Transition Life Zones.

Common name.—Sierra alligator lizard.

Gerrhonotus kingi Gray

Elgaria kingii Gray, 1838, Ann. Mag. Nat. Hist., (1), **1**: 390.—No locality, said to be "Mexico"; restr. to Huachuca Mountains, Arizona.

Gerrhonotus kingii O'Shaughnessy, 1873, Ann. Mag. Nat. Hist., (4), **12**: 46; Fitch, 1938, Amer. Midl. Nat., **20**: 402, fig. 3.

Elgaria nobilis Baird and Girard, 1852, Proc. Acad. Nat. Sci. Phila., **6**: 129.— Fort Webster, copper mines of the Gila (Santa Rita del Cobre), New Mexico.

Elgaria marginata Hallowell, 1852, Proc. Acad. Nat. Sci. Phila., **6**: 179.— New Mexico.

Range.—Southeastern Arizona and southwestern New Mexico; adjacent parts of Sonora and Chihuahua.

Common name.—Sonora alligator lizard.

Gerrhonotus multicarinatus Blainville

Cordylus (*Gerrhonotus*) *multi-carinatus* Blainville, 1835, Nouv. Ann. Mus. Hist. Nat. Paris, **4**: 57.—California; restr. to vicinity of Monterey.

Range.—Southern Washington through California, southward into northern Lower California.

Common name.—Red-backed alligator lizard.

Gerrhonotus multicarinatus multicarinatus Blainville

Gerrhonotus multi-carinatus multi-carinatus Fitch, 1934, Copeia, **1934**: 172· idem, 1938, Amer. Midl. Nat., **20**: 390, fig. 1.

Gerrhonotus wiegmanni Gray, 1845, Cat. Lizards Brit. Mus., p. 54.—Northwest coast of Central America, *in errore;* designated type locality, San Francisco, California.

Range.—California, on the west slopes of the northern Sierra Nevada, west of the Sacramento Valley along the coast to Ventura County, and on the islands off Santa Barbara.

Common name.—Red-backed alligator lizard.

Gerrhonotus multicarinatus scincicauda Skilton

Tropidolepis scincicauda Skilton, 1849, Amer. Jour. Sci. Arts, (2), **7:** 202.— The Dalles, Wasco County, Oregon.

Gerrhonotus multi-carinatus scincicauda Fitch, 1934, Copeia, **1934:** 173.

Elgaria grandis Baird and Girard, 1852, Proc. Acad. Nat. Sci. Phila., **6:** 176. —Oregon.

Range.—Interior valleys between the Coast Range and the Cascades in Oregon, and into southern Washington; eastward along the Columbia River into north central Oregon; southward in northwestern California to the coast.

Common name.—Oregon alligator lizard.

Gerrhonotus multicarinatus webbi Baird

Gerrhonotus webbii Baird, 1858, Proc. Acad. Nat. Sci. Phila., **10:** 255.— "From San Diego to El Paso"; restr. to vicinity of San Diego, San Diego County, California.

Gerrhonotus multi-carinatus webbii Fitch, 1934, Copeia, **1934:** 173.

Range.—Sonoran Life Zone of the western Sierra Nevada from Amador County, California, southward through western California into the San Pedro Mártir Mountains of Lower California.

Common name.—San Diego alligator lizard.

Gerrhonotus liocephalus Wiegmann

Gerrhonotus liocephalus Wiegmann, 1828, Isis, **21:** 381.

Range.—Southwestern Texas to southern Mexico.

Common name.—Smooth-headed alligator lizard.

Gerrhonotus liocephalus infernalis Baird

Gerrhonotus infernalis Baird, 1858, Proc. Acad. Nat. Sci. Phila., **10:** 255.

Gerrhonotus liocephalus infernalis Cope, 1900, Ann. Rept. U. S. Nat. Mus., **1898:** 517, fig. 91.

Range.—Central and southwestern Texas; adjacent parts of Coahuila to San Luis Potosí.

Common name.—Texas alligator lizard.

Gerrhonotus levicollis Stejneger

Barissia levicollis Stejneger, 1890, Proc. U. S. Nat. Mus., **13**: 184.—"Mexican Border"; restr. to extreme southwestern New Mexico.

Range.—Northern Mexico in Chihuahua and to the United States boundary.

Common name.—Smooth-necked alligator lizard.

Gerrhonotus levicollis levicollis Stejneger

Gerrhonotus levicollis levicollis Smith, 1946, Handbook Lizards, p. 464, pl. 132, text fig. 133, map 37.

Range.—Mexican boundary in southwestern New Mexico and southeastern Arizona [perhaps not yet taken north of the Mexican boundary].

Common name.—Sierra Madre alligator lizard.

HELODERMATIDAE

Heloderma Wiegmann

Heloderma Wiegmann, 1829, Isis, **22**: 624.—Type: *horridum.*

Heloderma suspectum Cope

Heloderma suspectum Cope, 1869, Proc. Acad. Nat. Sci. Phila., **21**: 5.—Sierra de la Union, Arizona.

Range.—Southwestern Utah and southern Nevada through southern Arizona to southwestern New Mexico and into adjacent Mexico.

Common name.—Gila monster.

ANNIELLIDAE

Anniella Gray

Anniella Gray, 1852, Ann. Mag. Nat. Hist., (2), **10**: 440.—Type: *pulchra.*

Anniella pulchra Gray

Anniella pulchra Gray, 1852, Ann. Mag. Nat. Hist., (2), **10**: 440.—California; restr. to San Diego, San Diego County, California.

Range.—Coastal southwestern California.

Common name.—Footless lizard, anniella.

Anniella pulchra pulchra Gray

Anniella pulchra pulchra Klauber, 1940, Copeia, **1940**: 15.

Range.—Coastal California from Contra Costa County southward to northwestern Lower California, and east of the San Joaquin Valley northward to Fresno and the Sequoia National Park.

Common name.—Silvery footless lizard, silvery anniella.

Anniella pulchra nigra Fischer

Anniella nigra Fischer, 1886, Abh. Naturw. Ver. Hamburg, **9**: 9.—San Diego, California, *in errore;* designated as vicinity of Pacific Grove, Monterey County, California.

Anniella pulchra nigra Klauber, 1940, Copeia, **1940**: 15.

Range.—Monterey Peninsula and vicinity, California.

Common name.—Black footless lizard, black anniella.

XANTUSIDAE

Xantusia Baird

Xantusia Baird, 1858, Proc. Acad. Nat. Sci. Phila., **10**: 255.—Type: *vigilis.*

Xantusia arizonae Klauber

Xantusia arizonae Klauber, 1931, Trans. San Diego Soc. Nat. Hist., **7**: 1, pl. 1.—Yarnell, Yavapai County, Arizona.

Range.—Rocky terrain in Yavapai, Mohave, and Pinal counties, Arizona.

Common name.—Arizona night lizard.

Xantusia henshawi Stejneger

Xantusia henshawi Stejneger, 1893, Proc. U. S. Nat. Mus., **16**: 467.—Witch Creek, San Diego County, California.

Range.—Rocky areas on both sides of the Coast Range from northern Riverside County southward through San Diego County into the San Pedro Mártir in Lower California.

Common name.—Granite night lizard.

Xantusia riversiana Cope

Xantusia riversiana Cope, 1883, Proc. Acad. Nat. Sci. Phila., **36**: 29.—"California"; corrected by the collector of the type to San Nicolas Island, off the California coast.

Xantusia riversiana reticulata Smith, 1946, Jour. Wash. Acad. Sci., **36**: 392. —San Clemente Island.

Range.—San Nicolas, Santa Barbara, and San Clemente Islands, coast of California.

Common name.—Island night lizard.

Xantusia vigilis Baird

Xantusia vigilis Baird, 1858, Proc. Acad. Nat. Sci. Phila., **10**: 255.—Fort Tejon, California.

Range.—The deserts of southern California, southern Nevada, and Washington County, Utah; southeast of the California Coast Range in San Diego County into northern Lower California.

Common name.—Yucca night lizard.

TEIDAE

Cnemidophorus Wagler

Cnemidophorus Wagler, 1830, Syst. Amph., p. 154.—Type: *murinus.*

Cnemidophorus tessellatus Say

Ameiva tessellata Say, 1823, *in* Long's Exped. Rocky Mts., **2**: 50.—Arkansas River, near Castle Rock Creek [now Beaver Creek, eastern Fremont County, Colorado].

Cnemidophorus tessellatus Baird, 1859, Pacif. R. R. Surv., **10**, pt. 4, p. 18 [combination only]; Smith and Burger, 1949, Bull. Chicago Acad. Sci., **8**: 283.

Cnemidophorus grahamii Baird and Girard, 1852, Proc. Acad. Nat. Sci. Phila., **6**: 128.—Between San Antonio and El Paso, Texas.

Range.—Western Texas from the Panhandle to the Trans-Pecos region, and southeastern New Mexico northward to east central Colorado; probably southward in Coahuila.

Common name.—Checkered race runner.

Cnemidophorus tigris Baird and Girard

Cnemidophorus tigris Baird and Girard, 1852, Proc. Acad. Nat. Sci. Phila., **6**: 69.—Valley of Great Salt Lake, Utah.

Range.—Southwestern United States; southward in northern Mexico.

Common name.—Tessellated race runner, whiptail.

Cnemidophorus tigris tigris Baird and Girard

Cnemidophorus tigris tigris Camp, 1916, Univ. Calif. Publ. Zool., **12**: 529.

Cnemidophorus tessellatus tessellatus Stejneger and Barbour, 1943, Check list, ed. 5, p. 106.

Range.—Great Basin north and west of the Colorado plateau, westward to the Sierra Nevada, and northward to southeastern Oregon and southern Idaho.

Common name.—Tessellated race runner.

Cnemidophorus tigris septentrionalis Burger

> *Cnemidophorus tigris septentrionalis* Burger, 1950, Nat. Hist. Misc., **65**: 8.— Una, Garfield County, Colorado.

Range.—Colorado plateau, including the northern half of Arizona, the northwestern quarter of New Mexico, the southeastern half of Utah, and the southern quarter of Colorado.

Common name.—Northern tessellated race runner.

Cnemidophorus tigris mundus Camp

> *Cnemidophorus tigris mundus* Camp, 1916, Univ. Calif. Publ. Zool., **17**: 71. —Fort Miller, Fresno County, California.

Range.—Northern California west of the Sierra Nevada, and south to Point Conception, Santa Barbara County.

Common name.—California tessellated race runner.

Cnemidophorus tigris multiscutatus Cope

> *Cnemidophorus tessellatus multiscutatus* Cope, 1892, Trans. Amer. Phil. Soc., **17**: 38.—Cerros Island, Lower California.
> *Cnemidophorus tigris multiscutatus* Burger, 1950, Nat. Hist. Misc., **65**: 7.

Range.—Los Angeles County, California; southward into Lower California.

Common name.—Coastal tessellated race runner.

Cnemidophorus tigris gracilis Baird and Girard

> *Cnemidophorus gracilis* Baird and Girard, 1852, Proc. Acad. Nat. Sci. Phila., **6**: 128.—Desert of Colorado; restr. to Yuma, Yuma County, Arizona.
> *Cnemidophorus tigris gracilis* Burger, 1950, Nat. Hist. Misc., **65**: 7.
> *Cnemidophorus undulatus* Hallowell, 1854, Proc. Acad. Nat. Sci. Phila., **7**: 94.—Near Fort Yuma, California; restr. to vicinity of Yuma, Arizona, in Imperial County, California.
> *Cnemidophorus melanostethus* Cope, 1863, Proc. Acad. Nat. Sci. Phila., **15**: 104.—Region of the Colorado [River] of California; restr. to vicinity of Yuma, Yuma County, Arizona.

Range.—Colorado Desert, eastward through southern New Mexico, west of the Rio Grande, south into adjacent Mexico.

Common name.—Colorado Desert tessellated race runner.

Cnemidophorus tigris marmoratus Baird and Girard

Cnemidophorus marmoratus Baird and Girard, 1852, Proc. Acad. Nat. Sci. Phila., 6: 128.—Between San Antonio and Paso del Norte [= El Paso], Texas; restr. to El Paso.

Cnemidophorus tigris marmoratus Burger, 1950, Nat. Hist. Misc., 65: 7.

Range.—Southern New Mexico, east of the Rio Grande, and Trans-Pecos, Texas; southward into adjacent Mexico.

Common name.—Big Bend tessellated race runner.

Cnemidophorus sacki Wiegmann

Cnemidophorus sackii Wiegmann, 1834, Herp. Mex., p. 28.—Mexico; restr. to Cuernavaca, Morelos.

Range.—Southwestern United States; southward to southern Mexico.

Common name.—Blue-bellied race runner.

Cnemidophorus sacki gularis Baird and Girard

Cnemidophorus gularis Baird and Girard, 1852, Proc. Acad. Nat. Sci. Phila., 6: 128.—Indianola and Valley of the Rio Grande del Norte; restr. to mouth of Devils River, Val Verde County, Texas.

Cnemidophorus sackii gularis Smith and Taylor, 1950, Bull. U. S. Nat. Mus., 199: 183.

Cnemidophorus guttatus Hallowell (nec Wiegmann), 1854, Proc. Acad. Nat. Sci. Phila., 7: 192.—Texas; restr. to Brownsville.

Cnemidophorus gularis sericeus Cope, 1892, Trans. Amer. Phil. Soc., 17: 48. —San Diego, Duval County, Texas.

Range.—Oklahoma and most of Texas, southward in eastern Mexico.

Common name.—Blue-bellied race runner.

Cnemidophorus sacki semifasciatus Cope

Cnemidophorus gularis semifasciatus Cope, 1892, Trans. Amer. Phil. Soc., 17: 49.—Agua Nueva, Coahuila.

Cnemidophorus sackii semifasciatus Burger, 1950, Nat. Hist. Misc., 65: 4.

Cnemidophorus septemvittatus Cope, 1892, Trans. Amer. Phil. Soc., 17: 40. —El Dorado County, California, in errore; designated as Boquillas, Brewster County, Texas.

Range.—Big Bend region in Trans-Pecos Texas; adjacent Mexico.

Common name.—Big Bend blue-bellied race runner.

Cnemidophorus sacki stictogrammus Burger

Cnemidophorus sackii stictogrammus Burger, 1950, Nat. Hist. Misc., 65: 5. —Yank Springs, 6 miles southeast of Ruby, Santa Cruz County, Arizona.

Range.—Vicinity of El Paso, Texas, through southern New Mexico and southern Arizona, east of the Colorado Desert.

Common name.—New Mexican race runner.

Cnemidophorus sacki innotatus Burger

Cnemidophorus sackii innotatus Burger, 1950, Nat. Hist. Misc., **65**: 4.— Vicinity of Kanab, Kane County, Utah.

Range.—Colorado plateau, southern Utah, northern Arizona, and northern New Mexico.

Common name.—Colorado plateau race runner.

Cnemidophorus perplexus Baird and Girard

Cnemidophorus perplexus Baird and Girard, 1852, Proc. Acad. Nat. Sci. Phila., **6**: 128.—Valley of the Rio San Pedro, tributary of the Rio Grande del Norte, Texas.

Range.—Western Texas; known only from the type locality.

Common name.—Devils River race runner.

Cnemidophorus inornatus Baird

Cnemidophorus inornatus Baird, 1859, Proc. Acad. Nat. Sci. Phila., **10**: 255. —Pesqueria Grande, Nuevo León, Mexico; Burger, 1950, Nat. Hist. Misc., **65**: 2.

Cnemidophorus octolineatus Baird and Girard, 1858, Proc. Acad. Nat. Sci. Phila., **10**: 255.—Pesqueria Grande, Nuevo León.

Cnemidophorus gularis velox Springer, 1928, Copeia, **169**: 102.—Sandy deserts south of the Colorado River, from Lee's Ferry, Arizona, to Pueblo Bonito, New Mexico; restr. to Lee's Ferry, Arizona.

Range.—Western Texas, most of New Mexico, southeastern Arizona; northern Mexico.

Common name.—Dwarf race runner.

Cnemidophorus sexlineatus Linnaeus

Lacerta sexlineata Linnaeus, 1866, Syst. Nat., ed. 12, **1**: 364.—Carolina; restr. to Charleston, South Carolina.

Cnemidophorus sexlineatus Duméril and Bibron, 1839, Erpét. Gén., **5**: 131.

Lacerta fallax Merrem, 1820, Syst. Amph., p. 63.—Carolina; restr. to Charleston, South Carolina.

Range.—United States, east of the Appalachian foothills, from Maryland to Key West; westward in the South to eastern Texas; northward in the interior to Indiana, Illinois and along rivers in southern Wisconsin and Minnesota; and through Oklahoma to South Dakota and southeastern Wyoming.

Common name.—Eastern race runner, six-lined race runner.

Cnemidophorus hyperythrus Cope

> *Cnemidophorus hyperythrus* Cope, 1863, Proc. Acad. Nat. Sci. Phila., **15:** 103.—Cape St. Lucas, Lower California.

Range.—Lower California, northward into southern California.

Common name.—Orange-throated race runner.

Cnemidophorus hyperythrus beldingi Stejneger

> *Verticaria beldingi* Stejneger, 1894, Proc. U. S. Nat. Mus., **17:** 17.—Cerros Island, Lower California [= Cedros Island].
>
> *Cnemidophorus hyperythrus beldingi* Linsdale, 1932, Univ. Calif. Publ. Zool., **38:** 373.

Range.—Southwestern San Bernardino County, California, south through San Diego County to central Lower California.

Common name.—Orange-throated race runner.

SCINCIDAE

Lygosoma Gray

> *Lygosoma* Gray, 1828, Zool. Jour., **3:** 228.—Type: *Lygosoma serpens* Gray = *Lacerta chalcides* Linnaeus.

Subgenus Scincella Mittleman

> *Scincella* Mittleman, 1950, Herpetologica, **6:** 19.—Type: *laterale*.

Lygosoma laterale Say

> *Scincus laterale* Say, 1823, *in* Long's Exped. Rocky Mts., **2:** 324.—Banks of the Mississippi below Cape Girardeau, Missouri.
>
> *Lygosoma lateralis* Duméril and Bibron, 1839, Erpét. Gén., **5:** 719.
>
> *Scincella laterale* Mittleman, 1950, Herpetologica, **6:** 20.
>
> *Scincus unicolor* Harlan, 1825, Jour. Acad. Nat. Sci. Phila., **5:** 156, 221.— Southern states; restr. to Charleston, South Carolina.
>
> *Leiolopisma unicolor* Stejneger and Barbour, 1943, Check list, ed. 5, p. 107.
>
> *Lygosoma (Scincella) laterale* Conant, 1951, The Reptiles of Ohio, p. 208.

Range.—Southeastern United States, southward from southern New Jersey and southeastern Pennsylvania, southern Ohio, Indiana, Illinois, and northern Missouri; westward to eastern Kansas, eastern and central Oklahoma, and Texas.

Common name.—Little brown skink.

Eumeces Wiegmann

Eumeces Wiegmann, 1834, Herp. Mex., p. 36.—Type: *pavimentatus.*

Eumeces fasciatus Linnaeus

Lacerta fasciata Linnaeus, 1758, Syst. Nat., ed. 10, **1**: 209.—Carolina; restr. to Charleston, South Carolina.

Eumeces fasciatus Cope, 1875, Bull. U. S. Nat. Mus., **1**: 45.

Lacerta quinquelineata Linnaeus, 1766, Syst. Nat., ed. 12, **1**: 366.—Carolina; restr. to Charleston, South Carolina.

Plestiodon vittigerum Hallowell, 1856, Proc. Acad. Nat. Sci. Phila., **8**: 310.—Flint, Michigan.

Plistodon striatus Abbott, 1868, Geol. New Jersey, **1868**: 801.

Plistodon lineatus Cope, 1871, Ann. Rept. Peabody Acad. Sci., **2** and **3**: 82 [*lapsus*].

Range.—Eastern United States and southern Ontario, northward to east central New York, upper Michigan, and Massachusetts, westward to central Texas, eastern Oklahoma, and eastern Kansas; northwestward along the Missouri bottom land in Nebraska and South Dakota; absent from Florida.

Common name.—Five-lined skink.

Eumeces laticeps Schneider

Scincus laticeps Schneider, 1801, Hist. Amph., **2**: 189.—Locality unknown; designated type locality, Charleston, South Carolina.

Eumeces laticeps Peters, 1864, Monatsber. Akad. Wiss. Berlin, **1864**: 49.

Lacerta tristata Latreille, 1801, Hist. Nat. Rept., **1**: 248.—Carolina; restr. to Charleston, South Carolina.

Scincus erythrocephalus Gilliams, 1818, Jour. Acad. Nat. Sci. Phila., (1), **1**: 461, pl. 18.—Southern states; restr. to Charleston, South Carolina.

Scincus bicolor Harlan, 1824, Jour. Acad. Nat. Sci. Phila., (1), **4**: 286, pl. 18, fig. 1.—Southern states; restr. to Charleston, South Carolina.

Scincus americanus Harlan, 1835, Med. Phys. Res., p. 138.—Southern states; restr. to Charleston, South Carolina.

Range.—Southeastern United States; southern Pennsylvania and Delaware, through southern Ohio, Indiana, Illinois (northward to Rock Island County), and southeastern Missouri, west to eastern Kansas, eastern Oklahoma, and eastern Texas.

Common name.—Greater five-lined skink.

Eumeces inexpectatus Taylor

Eumeces inexpectatus Taylor, 1932, Univ. Kansas Sci. Bull., **20**: 251, pl. 17, figs. 1–5.—Citrus County, Florida.

Range.—All of peninsular Florida; southeastern Georgia; and scattered records in South Carolina, North Carolina, southeastern Virginia, Alabama, Mississippi, and Louisiana.

Common name.—Florida five-lined skink.

Eumeces brevilineatus Cope

Eumeces brevilineatus Cope, 1880, Bull. U. S. Nat. Mus., **17**: 18, 44, 46.— Helotes, Bexar County, Texas.

Range.—Central and Trans-Pecos Texas; Nuevo León.

Common name.—Short-lined skink.

Eumeces callicephalus Bocourt

Eumeces callicephalus Bocourt, 1879, Miss. Sci. Mex., Rept., Livr. 6, p. 431, pl. 22 D, fig. 2, pl. 22 E, fig. 2.—Guanajuato, Guanajuato.

Range.—Southeastern Arizona; northern Mexico.

Common name.—Mountain skink.

Eumeces tetragrammus Baird

Plestiodon tetragrammus Baird, 1858, Proc. Acad. Nat. Sci. Phila., **10**: 256.— Lower Rio Grande.

Eumeces tetragrammus Cope, 1875, Bull. U. S. Nat. Mus., **1**: 45.

Range.—Southern Texas; through Tamaulipas to northernmost Vera Cruz.

Common name.—Four-lined skink.

Eumeces obsoletus Baird and Girard

Plestiodon obsoletum Baird and Girard, 1852, Proc. Acad. Nat. Sci. Phila., **6**: 129.—Valley of the Rio San Pedro, an affluent of the Rio Grande del Norte.

Eumeces obsoletus Cope, 1875, Bull. U. S. Nat. Mus., **1**: 45.

Lamprosaurus guttulatus Hallowell, 1852, Proc. Acad. Nat. Sci. Phila., **6**: 206.—Fort Fillmore, below Jornada del Muerte, New Mexico.

Range.—Southeastern Utah, Colorado, and southern Nebraska; southward through Kansas, central and western Oklahoma, western Texas (east of the forested region), New Mexico, and eastern Arizona; northern Mexico in Chihuahua, Nuevo León, and Tamaulipas.

Common name.—Great Plains skink.

Eumeces multivirgatus Hallowell

Plestiodon multivirgatum Hallowell, 1857, Proc. Acad. Nat. Sci. Phila., **9**: 215.—Posa Creek, 460 miles west of Fort Riley, Kansas [probably Cow Creek, Larimer County, Colorado, *fide* Taylor].

Eumeces multivirgatus Cope, 1875, Bull. U. S. Nat. Mus., **1**: 45.

Plestiodon leptogrammus Baird, 1858, Proc. Acad. Nat. Sci. Phila., **10**: 256.— Platte River Valley [Nebraska?].

Plestiodon inornatus Baird, 1858, Proc. Acad. Nat. Sci. Phila., **10**: 256.— Sand hills of Platte River, Nebraska.

Eumeces epipleurotis Cope, 1880, Bull. U. S. Nat. Mus., **17**: 40.—Northern boundary of Texas, and Nebraska at Fort Kearney; restr. to northern boundary of Texas.

Range.—Southwestern South Dakota, southeastern Wyoming, western Nebraska, eastern Colorado, and northwestern Kansas; northern Arizona and New Mexico, northward into Costillo and Alamosa counties in Colorado, and southeastward into Trans-Pecos Texas.

Common name.—Many-lined skink.

Eumeces gaigei Taylor

Eumeces gaigei Taylor, 1935, Univ. Kansas Sci. Bull., **22**: 219, fig. 1.—Near Taos, New Mexico.

Range.—Central New Mexico, Guadalupe Mountains in New Mexico and Trans-Pecos Texas, and southwestern New Mexico.

Common name.—Two-lined skink.

Eumeces taylori Smith

Eumeces taylori Smith, 1942, Proc. New England Zool. Club, **21**: 94.—Southern Guadalupe Mountains, 6,000 feet alt., near Frijole, Culberson County, Texas.

Range.—Guadalupe Mountains and upper Pecos Valley, New Mexico, and Trans-Pecos Texas.

Common name.—Pecos skink.

Eumeces anthracinus Baird

Plestiodon anthracinus Baird, 1849, Jour. Acad. Nat. Sci. Phila., (2), **1**, fig. 294.—North Mountain, near Carlisle, Pennsylvania.

Eumeces anthracinus Cope, 1875, Bull. U. S. Nat. Mus., **1**: 45.

Range.—Eastern and central United States to the Gulf Coast.

Common name.—Coal skink, Baird's skink.

Eumeces anthracinus anthracinus Baird

Eumeces anthracinus anthracinus Smith, 1946, Univ. Kansas Publ., Mus. Nat. Hist., **1**: 85.

Range.—Western New York through Pennsylvania, Maryland, West Virginia, and Virginia to the southern Appalachians in westtern North Carolina and adjacent northern Georgia; central Kentucky; Tuscaloosa County, Alabama.

Common name.—Coal skink.

Eumeces anthracinus pluvialis Cope

Eumeces pluvialis Cope, 1880, Bull. U. S. Nat. Mus., **17**: 19.—Near Mobile, Alabama.

Eumeces anthracinus pluvialis Smith, 1946, Univ. Kansas Publ., Mus. Nat. Hist., **1**: 85.

Range.—Southern Missouri, western Arkansas, southeastern Kansas, eastern Oklahoma, eastern Texas, and northwestern Louisiana; western North Carolina, and southwestward through northern Georgia to southeastern Louisiana.

Common name.—Southern coal skink.

Eumeces septentrionalis Baird

Plestiodon septentrionalis Baird, 1858, Proc. Acad. Nat. Sci. Phila., **10**: 256. —Minnesota and Nebraska; restr. to Fort Ripley, Minnesota.

Eumeces septentrionalis Cope, 1875, Bull. U. S. Nat. Mus., **1**: 44.

Range.—Manitoba to Texas.

Common name.—Prairie skink.

Eumeces septentrionalis septentrionalis Baird

Eumeces septentrionalis septentrionalis Taylor, 1935, Kansas Univ. Sci. Bull., **23**: 394, pl. 34, text figs. 66, 67.

Range.—Southern Manitoba, south through eastern North and South Dakota, most of Minnesota, northwestern Wisconsin, western Iowa, extreme northwestern Missouri, and eastern Nebraska and Kansas to northern Oklahoma.

Common name.—Northern prairie skink.

Eumeces septentrionalis obtusirostris Bocourt

Eumeces obtusirostris Bocourt, 1879, Miss. Sci. Mex., Rept., Livr. 6, p. 423, pl. 22 D, fig. 1.—Texas.

Eumeces septentrionalis obtusirostris Taylor, 1935, Kansas Univ. Sci. Bull., **23**: 405, pl. 28, figs. 1, 2, text fig. 67.

Eumeces pachyurus Cope, 1880, Bull. U. S. Nat. Mus., **17**: 19.—Near Dallas, Texas.

Range.—Central Oklahoma south through central Texas, mostly east of the Edwards Plateau.

Common name.—Southern prairie skink.

Eumeces septentrionalis pallidus Smith and Slater

> *Eumeces septentrionalis pallidus* Smith and Slater, 1949, Trans. Kansas Acad. Sci., **52**: 438, figs. 1, 2.—Palo Pinto, Palo Pinto County, Texas.

Range.—Edwards Plateau and adjacent parts of Texas to the Big Bend region, Brewster County, Texas.

Common name.—Edwards Plateau skink.

Eumeces skiltonianus Baird and Girard

> *Plestiodon skiltonianum* Baird and Girard, 1852, Proc. Acad. Nat. Sci. Phila., **6**: 69.—Oregon.
>
> *Eumeces skiltonianus* Cope, 1875, Bull. U. S. Nat. Mus., **1**: 45.
>
> *Eumeces quadrilineatus* Hallowell, 1859, Expl. Surv. R. R. Route Pac., 1853, pt. 4 (Williamson Route), p. 10, pl. 9, fig. 3.—Mojave River, and San Bernardino Valley, California.
>
> *Eumeces hallowelli* Bocourt, 1879, Miss. Sci. Mex., Rept., Livr. 6, p. 435, pl. 22 E, fig. 7.—California.
>
> *Eumeces skiltonianus* var. *amblygrammus* Cope, 1900, Ann. Rept. U. S. Nat. Mus., **1898**: 643.—Fort Humboldt.

Range.—South central British Columbia and Vancouver Island, southward in eastern Washington, Idaho, and western Montana, Oregon, and northern California; southward along the coast of California into northern Lower California; southward in the Great Basin in eastern Nevada and western Utah into northwestern Arizona.

Common name.—Western skink.

Eumeces gilberti Van Denburgh

> *Eumeces gilberti* Van Denburgh, 1896, Proc. Calif. Acad. Sci., (2), **6**: 350.—Yosemite Valley, Mariposa County, California.

Range.—Southwestern United States.

Common name.—Gilbert's skink.

Eumeces gilberti gilberti Van Denburgh

> *Eumeces gilberti gilberti* Taylor, 1935, Kansas Univ. Sci. Bull., **23**: 438, pls. 37, 38, text figs. 71, 72.
>
> *Eumeces skiltonianus* var. *brevipes* Cope, 1900, Ann. Rept. U. S. Nat. Mus., **1898**: 643.—Fresno, Fresno County, California.

Range.—The northern Sierra Nevada and the northwestern plateau region in Arizona, and through southern Nevada to southwestern Utah.

Common name.—Greater western skink.

Eumeces gilberti placerensis Rodgers

Eumeces gilberti placerensis Rodgers, 1944, Copeia, **1944**: 101, figs. 1, 2.

Range.—Foothills of Sierra Nevada, below 2,500 feet alt., in southern Yuba County, and in Nevada, Placer, Sacramento, El Dorado, Amador, and San Joaquin counties, California; on the valley floor east of the San Joaquin River in San Joaquin County.

Common name.—San Joaquin skink.

Eumeces gilberti rubricaudatus Taylor

Eumeces gilberti rubricaudatus Taylor, Kansas Univ. Sci. Bull., **23**: 446, pl. 39, text figs. 72, 73.

Range.—Southern Sierra Nevada, and Coast Range, southward into northern Lower California.

Common name.—Western red-tailed skink.

Eumeces gilberti cancellosus Rodgers and Fitch

Eumeces gilberti cancellosus Rodgers and Fitch, 1947, Univ. Calif. Publ. Zool., **48**: 200, pl. 9.—8 miles west and 1.1 miles south of Altamont, 900 feet alt., Alameda County, California.

Range.—Eastern Contra Costa and Alameda counties, southwestern San Joaquin County, and northwestern Merced County, California.

Common name.—Alameda skink.

Eumeces egregius Baird

Plestiodon egregius Baird, 1858, Proc. Acad. Nat. Sci. Phila., **10**: 256.—Indian Key, Florida.
Eumeces egregius Cope, 1875, Bull. U. S. Nat. Mus., **1**: 45.

Range.—Southern Alabama and Georgia through Florida.

Common name.—Florida red-tailed skink.

Eumeces egregius egregius Baird

Eumeces egregius egregius Taylor, 1935, Kansas Univ. Sci. Bull., **23**: 490, pl. 31, fig. 2, text figs. 83, 84.

Range.—Southern Georgia, southeastern Alabama, and northern and extreme southern Florida.

Common name.—Striped red-tailed skink.

Eumeces egregius onocrepis Cope

> *Plistodon onocrepis* Cope, 1871, Rept. Peabody Acad. Sci. Salem, **1869–1870**: 82.—Dummet's Plantation, 20 miles south of New Smyrna [now Allenhurst], Florida.
> *Eumeces egregius onocrepis* Taylor, 1935, Kansas Univ. Sci. Bull., **23**: 497, pl. 31, fig. 1, text fig. 84.

Range.—Central Florida, Lake County to Dade County.

Common name.—Brown red-tailed skink.

Neoseps Stejneger

> *Neoseps* Stejneger, 1910, Proc. U. S. Nat. Mus., **39**: 33.—Type: *reynoldsi.*

Neoseps reynoldsi Stejneger

> *Neoseps reynoldsi* Stejneger, 1910, Proc. U. S. Nat. Mus., **39**: 34.—Near Spring Lake, Fruitland Park, Lake County, Florida.

Range.—Alachua, Lake, and Polk counties, Florida.

Common name.—Sand skink.

AMPHISBAENIDAE

Rhineura Cope

> *Rhineura* Cope, 1861, Proc. Acad. Nat. Sci. Phila., **13**: 75.—Type: *floridana.*

Rhineura floridana Baird

> *Lepidosternon floridanum* Baird, 1858, Proc. Acad. Nat. Sci. Phila., **10**: 255.—Micanopy, Florida.
> *Rhineura floridana* Cope, 1861, Proc. Acad. Nat. Sci. Phila., **13**: 75.

Range.—Northern and central Florida.

Common name.—Florida worm lizard.

Order SERPENTES

LEPTOTYPHLOPIDAE

Leptotyphlops Fitzinger

> *Leptotyphlops* Fitzinger, 1843, Syst. Rept., p. 24.—Type: *nigricans.*

Leptotyphlops dulcis Baird and Girard

> *Rena dulcis* Baird and Girard, 1853, Cat. N. Amer. Rept., pt. 1, p. 142.—Between San Pedro and Comanche Springs, Texas.
> *Leptotyphlops dulcis* Stejneger, 1891, Proc. U. S. Nat. Mus., **14**: 501.

Range.—Southwestern Kansas, through Oklahoma and Texas to southeastern Arizona and northeastern Mexico.

Common name.—Blind snake.

Leptotyphlops dulcis dulcis Baird and Girard

Leptotyphlops dulcis dulcis Klauber, 1940, Trans. San Diego Soc. Nat. Hist., **9**: 108, map 1.

Range.—Central and southern Texas; northward into southwestern Oklahoma; southward into Tamaulipas and Nuevo León.

Common name.—Texas blind snake.

Leptotyphlops dulcis dissecta Cope

Glauconia dissecta Cope, 1896, Amer. Nat., **30**: 753.—Lake Valley, New Mexico.

Leptotyphlops dulcis dissectus Klauber, 1940, Trans. San Diego Soc. Nat. Hist., **9**: 112, map 1.

Range.—Southeastern Arizona through southern New Mexico and Trans-Pecos Texas to southern Coahuila; a distinctly separate area in southern Kansas and central Oklahoma.

Common name.—New Mexico blind snake.

Leptotyphlops humilis Baird and Girard

Rena humilis Baird and Girard, 1853, Cat. N. Amer. Rept., pt. 1, p. 143.—Valliecitas, California.

Leptotyphlops humilis Ruthven, 1907, Bull. Amer. Mus. Nat. Hist., **23**: 573.

Range.—Southern California, Nevada, and southwestern Utah to southwestern Texas.

Common name.—Dwarf blind snake.

Leptotyphlops humilis humilis Baird and Girard

Leptotyphlops humilis humilis Klauber, 1931, Trans. San Diego Soc. Nat. Hist., **6**: 340.

Range.—The coastal area and Pacific slopes of the Coast Range in southern California; the Mojave Desert, and eastward into southern Nevada; central and southeastern Arizona; southward into Lower California.

Common name.—Western blind snake.

Leptotyphlops humilis cahuilae Klauber

Leptotyphlops humilis cahuilae Klauber, 1931, Trans. San Diego Soc. Nat. Hist., **6**: 339.—Yaqui Well, San Diego County, California.

Range.—Colorado Desert of southeastern California and southwestern Arizona; desert areas in Lower California.

Common name.—Desert blind snake.

Leptotyphlops humilis utahensis Tanner

Leptotyphlops humilis utahensis Tanner, 1938, Proc. Utah Acad. Sci. Arts Letters, **12**: 267.

Range.—Washington County, extreme southwestern Utah.

Common name.—Utah blind snake.

Leptotyphlops humilis segregus Klauber

Leptotyphlops humilis segregus Klauber, 1939, Trans. San Diego Soc. Nat. Hist., **9**: 67.—Chalk Draw, Brewster County, Texas.

Range.—Trans-Pecos Texas and southeastern Arizona; presumably in southern New Mexico; northern Coahuila.

Common name.—Trans-Pecos blind snake.

BOIDAE

Lichanura Cope

Lichanura Cope, 1861, Proc. Acad. Nat. Sci. Phila., **13**: 304.—Type: *trivirgata.*

Lichanura roseofusca Cope

Lichanura roseofusca Cope, 1868, Proc. Acad. Nat. Sci. Phila., **20**: 2.—Northern Lower California.

Range.—Southern California to southwestern Arizona; southward into Lower California.

Common name.—California boa.

Lichanura roseofusca roseofusca Cope

Lichanura roseofusca roseofusca Klauber, 1931, Trans. San Diego Soc. Nat. Hist., **6**: 316.

Range.—Southwestern California and northwestern Lower California west of the Coast Range and the San Pedro Mártir.

Common name.—California boa.

Lichanura roseofusca gracia Klauber

Lichanura roseofusca gracia Klauber, 1931, Trans. San Diego Soc. Nat. Hist., **6**: 307.—Randsburg, Kern County, California.

Range.—Desert regions of southeastern California and southwestern Arizona; adjacent parts of Lower California and Sonora.

Common name.—Desert boa.

Charina Gray

Charina Gray, 1849, Cat. Snakes Brit. Mus., p. 113.—Type: *bottae.*

Charina bottae Blainville

Tortrix bottae Blainville, 1835, Nouv. Ann. Hist. Nat. Paris, **4**: 289, pl. 26, figs. 1, 1B.—California; restr. to Coast Range, opposite Monterey.

Charina bottae Gray, 1849, Cat. Snakes Brit. Mus., p. 113.

Range.—Western North America.

Common name.—Rubber boa.

Charina bottae bottae Blainville

Charina bottae bottae Van Denburgh, 1920, Proc. Calif. Acad. Sci., (4), **10**: 31.

Wenona isabella Baird and Girard, 1852, Proc. Acad. Nat. Sci. Phila., **6**: 176.—Puget Sound, Washington.

Wenona plumbea Baird and Girard, 1852, Proc. Acad. Nat. Sci. Phila., **6**: 176.—Puget Sound, Washington.

Charina brachyops Cope, 1888, Proc. U. S. Nat. Mus., **11**: 88.—Point Reyes, Marin County, California.

Range.—The Coast Range of California, northward from Monterey County into Oregon; the Sierra Nevada from Tulare County northward to Placer County, California, and Douglas County, Nevada; coastal British Columbia and Washington, including Vancouver Island, west of the Cascades.

Common name.—Pacific rubber boa.

Charina bottae umbratica Klauber

Charina bottae umbratica Klauber, 1943, Trans. San Diego Soc. Nat. Hist., **10**: 83.—Fern Valley, near Idyllwild, Riverside County, California.

Range.—Known only from the type locality.

Common name.—Southern California rubber boa.

Charina bottae utahensis Van Denburgh

Charina bottae utahensis Van Denburgh, 1920, Proc. Calif. Acad. Sci., (4), **10**: 31.—Little Cottonwood Canyon, Wasatch Mountains, Wasatch County, Utah.

Range.—Montane and forested areas in north central Utah, central Nevada, western Wyoming, Idaho, western Montana, eastern

Washington and Oregon, and northeastern California; southeastern British Columbia.

Common name.—Rocky Mountain rubber boa.

COLUBRIDAE[13]

Natrix Laurenti

    Natrix Laurenti, 1768, Syn. Rept., p. 73.—Type: *vulgaris = natrix.*

Natrix grahami Baird and Girard

    Regina grahamii Baird and Girard, 1853, Cat. N. Amer. Rept., pt. 1, p. 47.—
        Rio Salado = Salado Creek, Bell County, Texas.
    Natrix grahamii Cope, 1892, Proc. U. S. Nat. Mus., **14:** 668.

Range.—Mississippi Valley and the Chicago region, west through the eastern half of Kansas and south to Louisiana and eastern Texas.

Common name.—Graham's water snake.

Natrix rigida Say

    Coluber rigidus Say, 1825, Jour. Acad. Nat. Sci. Phila., (1), **4:** 239.—The
        southern states; restr. to Charleston, South Carolina.
    Natrix rigida Cope, 1892, Proc. U. S. Nat. Mus., **14:** 668.

Range.—Virginia (New Kent County), and South Carolina, to Louisiana, eastern Texas, and southeastern Oklahoma; exclusive of peninsular Florida.

Common name.—Striped water snake.

Natrix septemvittata Say

    Coluber septemvittatus Say, 1825, Jour. Acad. Nat. Sci. Phila., (1), **4:** 240.—
        Pennsylvania.
    Natrix septemvittata Cope, 1895, Trans. Amer. Phil. Soc., **18:** 216.

Range.—Vicinity of Philadelphia, southward to northern Florida and Alabama, westward to Wisconsin and Illinois.

Common name.—Queen snake, moon snake, queen water snake.

---

    [13] Classification of the genera of colubrid snakes into subfamilies has not been attempted; reference may be made to Dunn, E. R., 1928, A tentative key and arrangement of the American genera of Colubridae, Bull. Antiv. Inst. Amer., **2:** 18–24; Bogert, C. M., 1940, Herpetological results of the Vernay Angola Expedition, Bull. Amer. Mus. Nat. Hist., **77:** 1–107, 1 pl., 18 text figs.; and Schmidt, K. P., 1950, Modes of evolution discernible in the taxonomy of snakes, Evolution, **4:** 79–86, 2 figs. The order of arrangement essentially follows that of Dunn.

Natrix cyclopion Duméril, Bibron, and Duméril

Tropidonotus cyclopion Duméril, Bibron, and Duméril, 1854, Erpét. Gén., **7**: 576.—New Orleans.

Natrix cyclopium Cope, 1892, Proc. U. S. Nat. Mus., **14**: 673.

Range.—South Carolina to Florida, westward through the southern states to eastern Texas, and in the Mississippi Valley to southern Indiana.

Common name.—Green water snake.

Natrix cyclopion cyclopion Duméril, Bibron, and Duméril

Natrix cyclopion cyclopion Goff, 1936, Occ. Papers Mus. Zool. Univ. Mich., **327**: 1.

Range.—Southern Alabama to southeastern Texas and northward in the Mississippi Valley to southern Indiana.

Common name.—Green water snake.

Natrix cyclopion floridana Goff

Natrix cyclopion floridana Goff, 1936, Occ. Papers Mus. Zool. Univ. Mich., **327**: 1.—Leesburg, Florida.

Range.—Florida to coastal South Carolina.

Common name.—Florida green water snake.

Natrix erythrogaster Forster

Coluber erythrogaster Forster, 1771, *in* Bossu, Travels through that part of America formerly called Louisiana, **1**: 364, n.—Presumed to be South Carolina; restricted to "near Parker's Ferry, Edisto River Swamp, Charleston Co., South Carolina."

Range.—Southeastern and central United States.

Common name.—Plain-bellied water snake.

Natrix erythrogaster erythrogaster Forster

Natrix erythrogaster erythrogaster Burt, 1935, Amer. Midl. Nat., **16**: 333; Conant, 1949, Copeia, **1949**: 1, pl. 1, fig. 2.

Range.—From the Pocomoke River, eastern shore of Maryland, southward in the coastal plain and adjacent Piedmont to northern Florida.

Common name.—Red-bellied water snake, eastern copperbelly.

Natrix erythrogaster neglecta Conant

Natrix erythrogaster neglecta Conant, 1949, Copeia, **1949**: 5, pl. 1, fig. 1.—3 miles east of Mount Victory, Hardin County, Ohio.

Range.—South central Michigan and northwestern Ohio, southwestward through Indiana to extreme southeastern Illinois and adjacent Kentucky.

Common name.—Northern copperbelly.

Natrix erythrogaster flavigaster Conant

> *Natrix erythrogaster flavigaster* Conant, 1949, Copeia, **1949**: 2, pl. 1, fig. 3. —Frenier Beach, St. John the Baptist Parish, Louisiana.

Range.—Extreme southeastern Missouri and western Tennessee, southward to the Gulf; eastern Texas and western Alabama.

Common name.—Yellow-bellied water snake.

Natrix erythrogaster transversa Hallowell

> *Tropidonotus transversus* Hallowell, 1852, Proc. Acad. Nat. Sci. Phila., **6**: 177.—Creek boundary [i.e., Creek Nation boundary], banks of the Arkansas and its tributaries.
>
> *Natrix erythrogaster transversa* Taylor, 1929, Univ. Kansas Sci. Bull., **19**: 58.
>
> *Nerodia woodhousii* Baird and Girard, 1853, Cat. N. Amer. Rept., pt. 1, p. 42.—Indianola, between Indianola and San Antonio, Sabinal, and New Braunfels, Texas; restr. to Indianola, Calhoun County, Texas.

Range.—Eastern and southern Kansas, southward through Oklahoma and central Texas, and westward to the Pecos in New Mexico and Texas; adjacent Mexico.

Common name.—Blotched water snake.

Natrix harteri Trapido

> *Natrix harteri* Trapido, 1941, Amer. Midl. Nat., **25**: 673.—Brazos River, north of Palo Pinto, Palo Pinto County, Texas.

Range.—Confined to a short stretch of the Brazos River where there is a gravel and coarse rock shingle, with other localities in Tom Green County, Texas.

Common name.—Brazos water snake.

Natrix kirtlandi Kennicott

> *Regina kirtlandii* Kennicott, 1856, Proc. Acad. Nat. Sci. Phila., **8**: 95.— Northern Illinois.
>
> *Natrix kirtlandii* Cope, 1900, Ann. Rept. U. S. Nat. Mus., **1898**: 995, fig. 266.

Range.—Central middle west (southeastern Wisconsin, northeastern and central Illinois, Indiana, southern Michigan, and northern Kentucky), and through Ohio to western Pennsylvania.

Common name.—Kirtland's water snake.

Natrix rhombifera Hallowell

Tropidonotus rhombifera Hallowell, 1852, Proc. Acad. Nat. Sci. Phila., **6**: 177.—Arkansas River and its tributaries near the northern boundary of the Creek Nation; restr. to Fort Smith, Arkansas.

Natrix rhombifera Cope, 1889, Proc. U. S. Nat. Mus., **11**: 398.

Range.—Southeastern United States southward into Mexico.

Common name.—Diamond-backed water snake.

Natrix rhombifera rhombifera Hallowell

Natrix rhombifera rhombifera Clay, 1938, Ann. Carnegie Mus., **27**: 252.

Nerodia holbrookii Baird and Girard, 1853, Cat. N. Amer. Rept., pt. 1, p. 43. —Prairie Mer Rouge, Morehouse Parish, Louisiana.

Range.—Mississippi Valley, from southern Illinois and Indiana through Kentucky, Tennessee, Mississippi, and Alabama; southern Missouri, Arkansas, Oklahoma, and Texas; along the Gulf Coast to northeastern Mexico; an isolated population in southern Mexico.

Common name.—Diamond-backed water snake.

Natrix sipedon Linnaeus

Coluber sipedon Linnaeus, 1758, Syst. Nat., ed. 10, **1**: 219.—North America; restr. to vicinity of New York City.

Natrix sipedon Kirsch, 1895, Bull. U. S. Fish Comm., **14**: 333.

Range.—Eastern North America.

Common name.—Common water snake.

Natrix sipedon sipedon Linnaeus

Natrix sipedon sipedon Stejneger and Barbour, 1917, Check list, ed. 1, p. 96.

Coluber poecilogaster Wied, 1839, Reise Nord Amer., **1**: 106.—Dutotsburg, near Delaware Water Gap, Pennsylvania.

Range.—Northeastern North America, from southern Maine, Quebec, and Ontario, through Michigan and Wisconsin to Minnesota; westward along rivers through Oklahoma, Kansas, and Nebraska to Colorado; southward to Tennessee and northern North Carolina, farther south in the mountains.

Common name.—Northern water snake, water moccasin.[14]

Natrix sipedon fasciata Linnaeus

Coluber fasciatus Linnaeus, 1766, Syst. Nat., ed. 12, **1**: 378.—Carolina; restr. to Charleston, South Carolina.

[14] The confusing name "water moccasin" is widely applied to this harmless snake in regions where the venomous water moccasin is not found.

Natrix sipedon fasciata Stejneger and Barbour, 1917, Check list, ed. 1, p. 96.

Range.—Atlantic and Gulf coastal plains, westward to Alabama.

Common name.—Banded water snake.

Natrix sipedon engelsi Barbour

Natrix sipedon engelsi Barbour, 1943, Proc. New England Zool. Club, **22:** 1, pl. 1.—Mullet Pond, Shackleford Banks, Carteret County, North Carolina.

Range.—Shackleford Banks, Carteret County, North Carolina.

Common name.—Carteret water snake.

Natrix sipedon insularum Conant and Clay

Natrix sipedon insularum Conant and Clay, 1937, Occ. Papers Mus. Zool. Univ. Mich., **346:** 1.—Pelee Island, Lake Erie (Ontario).

Range.—Pelee and islands to the south, in Lake Erie (Ontario and Ohio).

Common name.—Lake Erie water snake.

Natrix sipedon pleuralis Cope

Natrix fasciata pleuralis Cope, 1892, Proc. U. S. Nat. Mus., **14:** 672.—Summerville, Harnett County, North Carolina.

Natrix sipedon pleuralis Clay, 1938, Copeia, **1938:** 178; Neill, 1947, Herpetologica, **4:** 75.

Range.—Extreme southern Illinois and Indiana, western Kentucky and Tennessee, and southeastern Missouri; through Arkansas to southeastern Oklahoma; northern Mississippi, Alabama, and Georgia to western South Carolina; Pearl River drainage in Louisiana.

Common name.—Midland water snake.

Natrix sipedon confluens Blanchard

Natrix fasciata confluens Blanchard, 1923, Occ. Papers Mus. Zool. Univ. Mich., **140:** 1.—Butler County, Missouri.

Natrix sipedon confluens Stejneger and Barbour, 1933, Check list, ed. 3, p. 117.

Range.—Louisiana, eastern Texas, extreme southeastern Oklahoma, Arkansas, southeastern Missouri, extreme southern Illinois and Indiana, and extreme western Kentucky, Tennessee, and Mississippi.

Common name.—Mississippi River water snake, oblique-banded water snake.

Natrix sipedon pictiventris Cope

Natrix fasciata pictiventris Cope, 1895, Amer. Nat., **29**: 677.–Palatka, Florida.

Natrix sipedon pictiventris Stejneger and Barbour, 1917, Check list, ed. 1, p. 96.

Range.–Bodies of fresh water throughout peninsular Florida.

Common name.–Florida water snake.

Natrix sipedon compressicauda Kennicott

Nerodia compressicauda Kennicott, 1860, Proc. Acad. Nat. Sci. Phila., **12**: 335.–Tampa Bay, Florida.

Natrix compressicauda Cope, 1889, Proc. U. S. Nat. Mus., **11**: 392.

Tropidonotus compsolaema Cope, 1860, Proc. Acad. Nat. Sci. Phila., **12**: 368.–Key West, Florida.

Natrix compressicauda walkerii Yarrow, 1883, Proc. U. S. Nat. Mus., **6**: 154. –Clearwater, Pinellas County, Florida.

Natrix usta Cope, 1889, Proc. U. S. Nat. Mus., **11**: 392.–Charlotte Harbor, Charlotte County, Florida.

Natrix compressicauda bivittata Cope, 1889, Proc. U. S. Nat. Mus., **11**: 392. –Georgiana, Florida.

Natrix compressicauda obscura Lönnberg, 1894, Proc. U. S. Nat. Mus., **17**: 330.–Key West, Florida.

Range.–Southwestern and southern Florida and the Keys, especially in mangrove swamps; north coast of Cuba.

Common name.–Mangrove water snake.

Natrix sipedon taeniata Cope

Natrix compressicauda taeniata Cope, 1895, Amer. Nat., **29**: 676.–Volusia [now National Gardens], Volusia County, Florida.

Natrix sipedon taeniata Carr and Goin, 1942, Proc. New England Zool. Club, **21**: 47, pl. 6.

Range.–East coast of Florida.

Common name.–Atlantic salt marsh snake.

Natrix sipedon clarki Baird and Girard

Regina clarkii Baird and Girard, 1853, Cat. N. Amer. Rept., pt. 1, p. 48.– Indianola, Calhoun County, Texas.

Natrix sipedon clarkii Clay, 1938, Copeia, **1938**: 180.

Tropidonotus medusa Günther, 1858, Cat. Colubr. Snakes Brit. Mus., p. 78. –Texas; restr. to Indianola, Calhoun County.

Range.–Gulf Coast, northwestern Florida to Texas.

Common name.–Gulf salt marsh snake.

Natrix taxispilota Holbrook

> *Tropidonotus taxispilotus* Holbrook, 1842, N. Amer. Herp., ed. 2, **4:** 35, pl. 8.—South Carolina seaboard and the Altamaha River, Georgia.
> *Natrix taxispilota* Cope, 1889, Proc. U. S. Nat. Mus., **11:** 392.

Range.—Atlantic and Gulf coastal plains, from eastern Virginia to Mississippi, and southward to Dade County in Florida.

Common name.—Brown water snake, water pilot.

Seminatrix Cope

> *Seminatrix* Cope, 1895, Amer. Nat., **29:** 678.—Type: *pygaea.*

Seminatrix pygaea Cope

> *Contia pygaea* Cope, 1871, Proc. Acad. Nat. Sci. Phila., **23:** 223.—Volusia [now National Gardens], Volusia County, Florida.
> *Seminatrix pygaea* Cope, 1895, Amer. Nat., **29:** 678.

Range.—South Carolina through peninsular Florida.

Common name.—Black swamp snake.

Seminatrix pygaea pygaea Cope

> *Seminatrix pygaea pygaea* Dowling, 1950, Misc. Publ. Mus. Zool. Univ. Mich., **76:** 7, map 1.

Range.—Northern Florida.

Common name.—Black swamp snake.

Seminatrix pygaea paludis Dowling

> *Seminatrix pygaea paludis* Dowling, 1950, Misc. Publ. Mus. Zool. Univ. Mich., **76:** 12, map 1.—Camp Davis, near Hollyridge, Onslow County, North Carolina.

Range.—Coastal North and South Carolina.

Common name.—Carolina swamp snake.

Seminatrix pygaea cyclas Dowling

> *Seminatrix pygaea cyclas* Dowling, 1950, Misc. Publ. Mus. Zool. Univ. Mich., **76:** 14, map 1.—Indian Prairie, northeast of Lakeport, Glades County, Florida.

Range.—Southern Florida.

Common name.—South Florida swamp snake.

Storeria Baird and Girard

> *Storeria* Baird and Girard, 1853, Cat. N. Amer. Rept., pt. 1, p. 135.—Type: *dekayi.*

Storeria dekayi Holbrook

Tropidonotus dekayi Holbrook, 1842, N. Amer. Herp., ed. 2, **4**: 53, pl. 14.—
Massachusetts and New York; restr. to Cambridge, Massachusetts.
Storeria dekayi Baird and Girard, 1853, Cat. N. Amer. Rept., pt. 1, p. 135.

Range.—Eastern North America.

Common name.—DeKay's snake.

Storeria dekayi dekayi Holbrook

Storeria dekayi dekayi Trapido, 1944, Amer. Midl. Nat., **31**: 47.

Range.—Northeastern North America, from southern Quebec and
Ontario, and western Maine, throughout New England and the Atlantic states to North Carolina; westward to Michigan, Ohio, and
Kentucky, intergrading broadly with *dekayi wrightorum* in the lower peninsula of Michigan, all of Ohio, and North Carolina.

Common name.—DeKay's snake, brown snake.

Storeria dekayi wrightorum Trapido

Storeria dekayi wrightorum Trapido, 1944, Amer. Midl. Nat., **31**: 57, figs.
38–44, map 3.—Reelfoot Lake, Tennessee.

Range.—Southern peninsula of Michigan and western Ohio, southward through Kentucky, Tennessee, South Carolina, Georgia, Alabama, and Mississippi; westward through Illinois, southern Wisconsin, eastern Iowa and all of Missouri and Arkansas into eastern Oklahoma; eastern Louisiana; northwestern Florida.

Common name.—Midland brown snake.

Storeria dekayi texana Trapido

Storeria dekayi texana Trapido, 1944, Amer. Midl. Nat., **31**: 63, figs. 45–50,
map 3.—Edge Falls, 4 miles south of Kendalia, Kendall County, Texas.

Range.—Eastern and central Texas, eastward into southwestern
Louisiana; eastern and central Oklahoma; eastern Kansas; central
Iowa; southern Minnesota; intergrading with *dekayi wrightorum* in
Wisconsin, Iowa, Kansas, Missouri, and Oklahoma.[15]

Common name.—Texas brown snake.

---

[15] "Intergrades" between *S. d. texana* and *S. d. temporalineata* Trapido are
listed by Trapido from Texas and Louisiana, and of *temporalineata* with
wrightorum from Louisiana and Mississippi. This is not geographically intelli-
gible, and further studies of *Storeria dekayi* are obviously required to clarify
the status of the populations in the lower Mississippi Basin.

Storeria dekayi victa Hay

Storeria victa Hay, 1892, Science, **19**: 199.—Bank of Oklawaha River, some distance north of Kissimee, Florida.

Storeria dekayi victa Neill, 1950, Copeia, **1950**: 156.

Range.—Peninsular Florida, northward to southern Georgia.

Common name.—Florida brown snake.

Storeria occipitomaculata Storer

Coluber occipito-maculatus Storer, 1839, Rept. Massachusetts, p. 230.

Storeria occipitomaculata Cope, 1900, Ann. Rept. U. S. Nat. Mus., **1898**: 1003, fig. 269.

Range.—Eastern North America.

Common name.—Red-bellied snake.

Storeria occipitomaculata occipitomaculata Storer

Storeria occipito-maculata occipito-maculata Trapido, 1944, Amer. Midl. Nat., **31**: 20, figs. 11–13 and 20, map 2.

Coluber venustus Hallowell, 1847, Proc. Acad. Nat. Sci. Phila., **3**: 274.—Copper Harbor, Lake Superior, Michigan.

Range.—Eastern North America and eastern Canada, exclusive of southeastern Georgia and peninsular Florida; westward to Manitoba and the Dakotas; northern Ohio, Indiana, and Illinois, southern Iowa, and northern Missouri; otherwise westward into eastern Kansas and Oklahoma, and throughout southern Missouri, Arkansas, and Louisiana.

Common name.—Red-bellied snake.

Storeria occipitomaculata obscura Trapido

Storeria occipito-maculata obscura Trapido, 1944, Amer. Midl. Nat., **31**: 33, figs. 14–20, map 2.—Gainesville, Alachua County, Florida.

Range.—Southeastern Georgia and northern two-thirds of the Florida peninsula.

Common name.—Florida red-bellied snake.

Thamnophis Fitzinger

Thamnophis Fitzinger, 1843, Syst. Rept., p. 26.—Type: *sauritus*.

Thamnophis angustirostris Kennicott[16]

> *Eutaenia angustirostris* Kennicott, 1860, Proc. Acad. Nat. Sci. Phila., **12:** 332.—Parras, Coahuila, Mexico.
>
> *Thamnophis angustirostris* Ruthven, 1908, Bull. U. S. Nat. Mus., **61:** 120.
>
> *Chilopoma rufipunctatum* Cope, 1875, *in* Yarrow, Wheeler's Rept. Geogr. Geol. Expl. Surv. W. 100th Meridian, **5:** 544.—Southern Arizona.
>
> *Atomarchus multimaculatus* Cope, 1883, Amer. Nat., **17:** 1300.—San Francisco River, New Mexico.

Range.—Southeastern Arizona and southwestern New Mexico, southward into Chihuahua, Coahuila, and Durango.

Common name.—Narrow-headed garter snake.

Thamnophis eques Reuss

[Two subspecies, of which one is confined to Mexico.]

> *Coluber eques* Reuss, 1834, Abh. Senck. Mus., **1:** 152, pl. 8, fig. 2.—Mexico; restr. to El Limon Totalco, Vera Cruz.
>
> *Thamnophis eques* Ruthven, 1908, Bull. U. S. Nat. Mus., **61:** 158.

Range.—Western Texas to southern Arizona, southward throughout the Mexican plateau.

Common name.—Mexican garter snake.

Thamnophis eques megalops Kennicott

> *Eutaenia megalops* Kennicott, 1860, Proc. Acad. Nat. Sci. Phila., **12:** 330.— Tucson, Arizona, or Santa Magdalena, Sonora; restr. to Tucson.
>
> *Thamnophis eques megalops* Smith, 1951, Copeia, **1951:** 139.
>
> *Thamnophis stejnegeri* McLain, 1899, Contr. Neotr. Herp., p. 4, pl.—Salamanca, Guanajuato.

Range.—Southern Arizona, New Mexico, and western Texas; southward on the Mexican plateau.

Common name.—Arizona garter snake.

Thamnophis cyrtopsis Kennicott

[New comb.]

> *Eutaenia cyrtopsis* Kennicott, 1860, Proc. Acad. Nat. Sci. Phila., **12:** 333.— Rinconada, Coahuila.

Range.—Southern Utah and Colorado to Central America.

Common name.—Black-necked garter snake.

---

[16] The supposition that the type of *angustirostris* is a hybrid between the population of garter snakes in southeast Arizona and the Mexican *melanogaster* (Smith, H. M., 142, Zoologica, **27:** 97) does not invalidate the use of *angustirostris* in its current check-list sense, since the action of earlier authors allocates the name.

Thamnophis cyrtopsis cyrtopsis Kennicott

> *Thamnophis cyrtopsis cyrtopsis* Cope, 1892, Proc. U. S. Nat. Mus., **14**: 656.
> *Eutaenia cyrtopsis ocellata* Cope, 1880, Bull. U. S. Nat. Mus., **17**: 22.—
> Helotes, Bexar County, Texas.
> *Eutaenia aurata* Cope, 1892, Proc. U. S. Nat. Mus., **14**: 659.—Lake Valley,
> New Mexico.

Range.—Utah, Arizona, southern Colorado, Texas, and New Mexico; southward into Mexico.

Common name.—Black-necked garter snake.

Thamnophis marcianus Baird and Girard

> *Eutaenia marciana* Baird and Girard, 1853, Cat. N. Amer. Rept., pt. 1, p. 36.
> —Red River, Arkansas, determined as vicinity of Slough Creek, east of
> Hollister, Tillman County, Oklahoma.
> *Thamnophis marcianus* Ruthven, 1908, Bull. U. S. Nat. Mus., **61**: 849, pl.
> 93.

Range.—Kansas, Oklahoma, and Texas, westward to southeastern California; northeastern Mexico.

Common name.—Marcy's garter snake, checkered garter snake.

Thamnophis marcianus marcianus Baird and Girard

> *Thamnophis marcianus marcianus* Mittleman, 1949, Bull. Chicago Acad. Sci.,
> **8**: 244, fig. 1.

Range.—Central and southern Texas.

Common name.—Marcy's garter snake, checkered garter snake.

Thamnophis marcianus nigrolateris Brown

> *Eutaenia nigrolateris* Brown, 1889, Proc. Acad. Nat. Sci. Phila., **41**: 421.—
> Tucson, Arizona.
> *Thamnophis marcianus nigrolateris* Mittleman, 1949, Bull. Chicago Acad.
> Sci., **8**: 246, fig. 1.

Range.—Western Great Plains from southwestern Nebraska to Texas, and through New Mexico and Arizona to the Colorado River.

Common name.—Western checkered garter snake.

Thamnophis ordinoides Baird and Girard

> *Tropidonotus ordinoides* Baird and Girard, 1852, Proc. Acad. Nat. Sci. Phila.,
> **6**: 176.—Puget Sound.
> *Thamnophis ordinoides* Ruthven, 1908, Bull. U. S. Nat. Mus., **61**: 147; Fox,
> 1948, Copeia, **1948**: 115.
> *Thamnophis ordinoides ordinoides* Ruthven, 1908, Bull. U. S. Nat. Mus.,
> **61**: 147.

Eutainia leptocephala Baird and Girard, 1853, Cat. N. Amer. Rept., pt. 1, p. 29.—Puget Sound.

Eutainia cooperi Kennicott, 1860, *in* Cooper, Expl. Surv. R. R. Miss. Pacific, **12**, Book 2, pt. 3, no. 4, p. 296.—Cathlapootle Valley and Willopah Valley, Oregon Territory.

Thamnophis leptocephala olympia Meek, 1899, Field Col. Mus. Zool., **1**: 235.—Port Angeles, Clallam County, Washington.

Thamnophis rubristriata Meek, 1899, Field Col. Mus., Zool., **1**: 235.—Port Angeles, Clallam County, Washington.

Range.—Southern Vancouver Island and mainland of southwestern British Columbia; southward through Washington and Oregon west of the Cascade Mountains; and western Del Norte County, California.

Common name.—Red-striped garter snake.

Thamnophis elegans Baird and Girard

Eutainia elegans Baird and Girard, 1853, Cat. N. Amer. Rept., pt. 1, p. 31.—El Dorado County, California.

Thamnophis elegans Johnson, 1947, Herpetologica, **3**: 159.

Range.—Western North America.

Common name.—Western garter snake.

Thamnophis elegans elegans Baird and Girard

Tropidonotus tri-vittatus Hallowell, 1853, Proc. Acad. Nat. Sci. Phila., **6**: 237.—Cosumnes River, California.

Range.—Southern Oregon, between Coast Range and Cascades from southern end of the Willamette Valley southward; northern California, southward on the coast to Napa County; southward east of the Sacramento Valley in the Sierra Nevada (in California and Nevada) to Fresno County, with an isolated population in the San Bernardino Mountains.

Common name.—Mountain garter snake.

Thamnophis elegans terrestris Fox

Thamnophis elegans terrestris Fox, 1951, Univ. Calif. Publ. Zool., **50**: 499, fig. 3.—Strawberry Canyon, Berkeley, Alameda County, California.

Range.—A narrow strip along the California coast from Santa Barbara County northward around the east side of San Francisco Bay, and northward to the Oregon border.

Common name.—Coast garter snake.

Thamnophis elegans vagrans Baird and Girard

Eutaenia vagrans Baird and Girard, 1853, Cat. N. Amer. Rept., pt. 1, pl. 35.—"California," *in errore;* restr. to southwestern Utah.

Thamnophis elegans vagrans Fitch, 1948, Copeia, **1948:** 125.

Eutaenia vagrans plutonia Yarrow, 1883, Proc. U. S. Nat. Mus., **6:** 152.—Arizona; restr. to northwestern Arizona.

Eutaenia henshawi Yarrow, 1883, Proc. U. S. Nat. Mus., **6:** 152.—Fort Walla Walla, Washington.

Eutaenia elegans lineolata Cope, 1892, Proc. U. S. Nat. Mus., **14:** 655.—California, Nevada, Oregon, and Washington; restr. to Lake Tahoe, Nevada.

Range.—Great Basin and Rocky Mountain regions in North America from Banff and Rocky Mountain Park, Alberta, southward to the Black Hills and to extreme western Oklahoma; in Montana, Wyoming, montane Colorado, and most of New Mexico; throughout Idaho, Nevada, and Utah; in Washington and Oregon only west of the Cascades; entering central California from the Great Basin, westward to the Sierra Nevada in Tulare County, northwestern Arizona.

Common name.—Wandering garter snake.

Thamnophis elegans nigrescens Johnson

Thamnophis elegans nigrescens Johnson, 1947, Herpetologica, **3:** 161.—Tacoma, Washington.

Range.—Vancouver Island, Puget Sound area in Washington and British Columbia.

Common name.—Puget Sound garter snake.

Thamnophis elegans biscutatus Cope

Eutaenia biscutata Cope, 1883, Proc. Acad. Nat. Sci. Phila., **35:** 21.—Shores of Klamath Lake, Oregon.

Thamnophis elegans biscutatus Fitch, 1948, Copeia, **1948:** 125.

Eutaenia elegans brunnea Cope, 1892, Proc. U. S. Nat. Mus., **14:** 654.—Fort Bidwell, California.

Range.—Klamath Lakes Basin, upper Klamath River, and Warner Lakes Basin, south central Oregon and northern California.

Common name.—Klamath garter snake.

Thamnophis elegans hydrophila Fitch

Thamnophis ordinoides hydrophila Fitch, 1936, Amer. Midl. Nat., **17:** 648.—Trail Creek, 6 miles from its mouth, Jackson County, Oregon.

Thamnophis elegans hydrophila Fitch, 1948, Copeia, **1948:** 125.

Range.—Southwestern Oregon and northwestern California.

Common name.—Oregon gray garter snake.

Thamnophis elegans couchi Kennicott

Eutaenia couchii Kennicott, 1859, U. S. Pac. R. R. Surv., **10**: 10.—Pitt River, California; restr. to near mouth of Hat Creek.

Thamnophis elegans couchii Fitch, 1948, Copeia, **1948**: 126.

Range.—Sierra Nevada of California, eastward into adjoining west central Nevada.

Common name.—Sierra Nevada garter snake.

Thamnophis elegans gigas Fitch

Thamnophis ordinoides gigas Fitch, 1940, Univ. Calif. Publ. Zool., **44**: 69, pl. 3, fig. 3, pl. 5, fig. 7, and pl. 7, fig. 7; text fig. 11.—Gadwell, Merced County, California.

Thamnophis elegans gigas Fitch, 1948, Copeia, **1948**: 126.

Range.—Lower altitudes of the interior valley of California from Sacramento and Antioch south to Buena Vista Lake.

Common name.—Giant garter snake.

Thamnophis elegans aquaticus Fox

Thamnophis elegans aquaticus Fox, 1951, Univ. Calif. Publ. Zool., **50**: 493, fig. 2.—Dillon Beach, Marin County, California.

Range.—San Francisco Bay, northward in northwestern California to meet the range of *elegans hydrophila.*

Common name.—California garter snake.

Thamnophis elegans atratus Kennicott

Eutainia atrata Kennicott, 1860, *in* Cooper, Expl. Surv. R. R. Miss. Pacific, **12**, Book 2, pt. 3, no. 4, p. 296.—San Francisco, California.

Thamnophis elegans atratus Fitch, 1948, Copeia, **1948**: 126; Fox, 1951, Univ. Calif. Publ. Zool., **50**: 489, fig. 1.

Eutaenia infernalis vidua Cope, 1892, Proc. U. S. Nat. Mus., **14**: 658.—San Francisco, California.

Range.—Coastal counties of California, from San Francisco Bay southward to Santa Barbara County.

Common name.—Coastal mountain garter snake.

Thamnophis elegans hammondi Kennicott

Eutainia hammondii Kennicott, 1860, Proc. Acad. Nat. Sci. Phila., **12**: 322.—San Diego and Fort Tejon, California; restr. to San Diego.

Thamnophis elegans hammondii Fitch, 1948, Copeia, **1948**: 126.

Range.—Coastal slopes west of Coast Range divide in California, southward from Monterey Bay, and into northwestern Lower California.

Common name.—Two-striped garter snake.

Thamnophis radix Baird and Girard

Eutainia radix Baird and Girard, Cat. N. Amer. Rept., pt. 1, p. 34.—Racine, Wisconsin. Probably *in errore;* restr. to vicinity of Chicago, Illinois.
Thamnophis radix Jordan, 1899, Man. Vert. Anim. U. S., ed. 8, p. 193.

Range.—The Great Plains, eastward through Illinois, with isolated populations in Ohio, in the "Prairie Peninsula."

Common name.—Great Plains garter snake.

Thamnophis radix radix Baird and Girard

Thamnophis radix radix Blanchard, Papers Mich. Acad. Sci., **4,** pt. 2, p. 18.
Tropidonotus kennicotti Jan, 1863, Elenco Sist. Ofidi, p. 70.—North America; restr. to Racine, Wisconsin (Smith and Brown, 1946).

Range.—Eastern Iowa and Missouri, Illinois, southwestern Wisconsin, and an isolated population in north central Ohio.

Common name.—Eastern plains garter snake.

Thamnophis radix haydeni Kennicott

Eutaenia haydenii Kennicott, 1860, Expl. Surv. R. R. Miss. Pacific, **12,** Book 2, pt. 3, no. 4, p. 298, pl. 14.—Fort Pierre, Nebraska (= Stanley County, South Dakota).
Eutaenia radix twiningi Coues and Yarrow, 1878, Bull. U. S. Geol. Surv. Terr., **4:** 279.—Two forks of Milk River, upper Missouri.

Range.—The Great Plains, eastward into Iowa, southward to the Texas Panhandle.

Common name.—Western plains garter snake.

Thamnophis butleri Cope

Eutaenia butleri Cope, 1889, Proc. U. S. Nat. Mus., **11:** 399.—Richmond, Indiana.
Thamnophis butleri Stejneger, 1895, Proc. U. S. Nat. Mus., **17:** 593.
Eutaenia radix melanotaenia Cope, 1888, Proc. U. S. Nat. Mus., **11:** 400.—Franklin County, Indiana.

Range.—The "Prairie Peninsula" in Indiana, Ohio, and southern Michigan; an isolated population in southeastern Wisconsin.

Common name.—Butler's garter snake.

Thamnophis brachystoma Cope

Eutaenia brachystoma Cope, 1892, Amer. Nat., **26**: 964.—Franklin, Venango County, Pennsylvania.

Thamnophis brachystoma Smith, 1945, Proc. Biol. Soc. Wash., **58**: 149; Richmond, 1952, Ann. Carnegie Mus., **32**: 315, fig. 1 (map).

Range.—Southwestern New York and northwestern Pennsylvania.

Common name.—Short-headed garter snake.

Thamnophis sauritus Linnaeus

Coluber saurita Linnaeus, 1766, Syst. Nat., ed. 12, **1**: 385.—Carolina; restr. to Charleston, South Carolina.

Thamnophis saurita Stejneger, 1893, N. Amer. Fauna, **7**: 210.

Range.—Eastern and central North America.

Common name.—Ribbon snake.

Thamnophis sauritus sauritus Linnaeus

Thamnophis sauritus sauritus Blanchard, 1924, Papers Mich. Acad. Sci., **4**: 18.

Range.—Michigan and Ontario to Maine, southward to Mississippi, Alabama, and Georgia.

Common name.—Eastern ribbon snake.

Thamnophis sauritus proximus Say

Coluber proximus Say, 1823, *in* Long's Exped. Rocky Mts., **1**: 187.—Stone quarry on west side of Missouri River, 3 miles above the mouth of Boyer's River, Pottawattamie County, Iowa.

Thamnophis sauritus proximus Ruthven, 1908, Bull. U. S. Nat. Mus., **61**: 98.

Eutainia faireyi Baird and Girard, 1853, Cat. N. Amer. Rept., pt. 1, p. 25.— Prairie Mer Rouge, Morehouse Parish, Louisiana.

Range.—Nebraska, throughout the plains states, northern Iowa, southern Wisconsin, and Illinois, southward to Louisiana and Texas; southward in eastern Mexico to Central America.

Common name.—Western ribbon snake.

Thamnophis sauritus sackeni Kennicott

Eutaenia sackenii Kennicott, 1859, Proc. Acad. Nat. Sci. Phila., **11**: 98.— Florida; restr. to Gainesville, Florida.

Thamnophis sauritus sackenii Ruthven, 1908, Bull. U. S. Nat. Mus., **61**: 107.

Prymnomiodon chalceus Cope, 1860, Proc. Acad. Nat. Sci. Phila., **12**: 558. —Siam, *in errore;* restr. to Gainesville, Florida.

Range.—Florida, westward in the Gulf coastal plain through Alabama to Mississippi.

Common name.—Florida ribbon snake.

Thamnophis sirtalis Linnaeus

Coluber sirtalis Linnaeus, 1758, Syst. Nat., ed. 10, **1**: 222 [exclusive of type
specimen].—Canada; restr. to vicinity of Quebec; Klauber, 1948, Copeia,
1948: 8; Schmidt and Conant, 1950, Copeia, **1950**: 58; 1951, Bull.
Zool. Nomenclature, **2**: 67.[17]
Thamnophis sirtalis Garman, 1892, Bull. Essex Inst., **24**: 104.

Range.—North America, from southern Canada southward.

Common name.—Common garter snake.

Thamnophis sirtalis sirtalis Linnaeus

Thamnophis sirtalis sirtalis Stejneger and Barbour, 1923, Check list, ed. 1,
p. 103.
Coluber ordinatus Linnaeus, 1766, Syst. Nat., ed. 12, **1**: 379.—Carolina;
restr. to Charleston, South Carolina.
Tropidonotus taenia Schoepff, 1788, Reise Ver. Staaten, **1**: 496.—New York?;
restr. to vicinity of New York City.
Coluber ibibe Daudin, 1803, Hist. Nat. Rept., **7**: 181.—Carolina; restr. to
Charleston, South Carolina.
Tropidonotus bipunctatus Schlegel, 1837, Essai Physion. Serp., p. 320.—
Nashville, Tennessee.
Tropidonotus jauresii Duméril, Bibron, and Duméril, 1854, Erpét. Gén.,
7: 606.—No locality; designated as Charleston, South Carolina.
Eutaenia sirtalis obscura Cope, 1875, *in* Wheeler, Expl. Surv. W. 100th
Mer., **5**: 546.—Westport, New York; Lac qui Parle, Minnesota; and Fort
Benton, Montana; restr. to Lac qui Parle, Minnesota.
Eutaenia sirtalis graminea Cope, 1889, Proc. U. S. Nat. Mus., **11**: 399.—
Brookville, Franklin County, Indiana.
Eutaenia sirtalis semifasciata Cope, 1892, Proc. U. S. Nat. Mus., **14**: 662.—
Aux Plaines, Illinois [= Des Plaines, Illinois].
Thamnophis sirtalis pallidula Allen, 1899, Proc. Boston Soc. Nat. Hist.,
29: 64.—Intervale, New Hampshire.
Tropidonotus obalskii Mocquard, 1903, Bull. Mus. Hist. Nat. Paris, **9**: 211.—
Black Lake, Canada.

Range.—Eastern North America, from southern Canada westward
to the tier of states beyond the Mississippi, and into eastern Texas,
Oklahoma, and southeastern Kansas.

Common name.—Eastern garter snake.

[17] The transfer of this name to the ribbon snake, shown by Klauber to be
technically correct, has been avoided by fiat decision, as provided for in the
International Rules of Zoological Nomenclature.

Thamnophis sirtalis parietalis Say

Coluber parietalis Say, 1823, in Long's Exped. Rocky Mts., 1: 186.—Stone quarry on west side of Missouri River, 3 miles above the mouth of Boyer's River, Pottawattamie County, Iowa.

Thamnophis sirtalis var. parietalis Jordan, 1899, Man. Vert. Anim. U. S., ed. 8, p. 193.

Eutaenia ornata Baird and Girard, 1859, U. S. Mex. Bound. Surv., 2: 16, pl. 9.—Indianola, San Antonio, and lower Rio Grande, Texas; restr. to El Paso, Texas (Smith and Brown, 1946).

Range.—Great Plains, in the second tier of states west of the Mississippi, westward to Utah and Nevada, and from Manitoba and Alberta southward to Texas.

Common name.—Red-sided garter snake.

Thamnophis sirtalis concinnus Hallowell

Tropidonotus concinnus Hallowell, 1852, Proc. Acad. Nat. Sci. Phila., 6: 182. —Oregon; restr. to Fort Vancouver, Oregon Territory (= Vancouver, Washington).

Thamnophis sirtalis concinnus Ruthven, 1908, Bull. U. S. Nat. Mus., 61: 173.

Range.—Southern British Columbia and Vancouver Island; Washington and Oregon west of the Cascade Mountains.

Common name.—Pacific red-sided garter snake.

Thamnophis sirtalis infernalis Blainville

Coluber infernalis Blainville, 1835, Nouv. Ann. Mus. Hist. Nat. Paris, 4: 291, pl. 26, fig. 3.—California; restr. to vicinity of San Francisco.

Thamnophis sirtalis infernalis Van Denburgh and Slevin, 1918, Proc. Calif. Acad. Sci., (4), 8: 198.

Range.—Southwestern Oregon, western Nevada, and California except for the northwestern coastal area.

Common name.—California red-sided garter snake.

Thamnophis sirtalis pickeringi Baird and Girard

Eutainia pickeringii Baird and Girard, 1853, Cat. N. Amer. Rept., pt. 1, p. 27.—Puget Sound, Washington; restr. to Tacoma.

Thamnophis sirtalis pickeringii Johnson, 1942, Copeia, 1942: 17.

Range.—Confined to Puget Sound region, mainly in Pierce and Thurston counties, Washington.

Common name.—Puget Sound red-sided garter snake.

Thamnophis sirtalis trilineata Cope
[New comb.]

Eutainia sirtalis trilineata Cope, 1892, Proc. U. S. Nat. Mus., **14**: 665.—Port Townsend, Oregon [now Washington].

Range.—Puget Sound region and Vancouver Island.

Common name.—Vancouver garter snake.

Thamnophis sirtalis tetrataenia Cope

Eutaenia sirtalis tetrataenia Cope, in Yarrow, 1875, in Wheeler, Expl. Surv. W. 100th Mer., Zool., **5**: 546.—Banks of Pitt River, California, *in errore;* designated as San Francisco peninsula.

Thamnophis sirtalis tetrataenia Johnson, 1942, Copeia, **1942**: 17 (cited for combination only); Fox, 1951, Copeia, **1951**: 260.

Range.—San Francisco peninsula, southward to Crystal Lake and on the coast to Point Año Nuevo, San Mateo County, California.

Common name.—San Francisco garter snake.

Thamnophis sirtalis fitchi Fox

Thamnophis sirtalis fitchi Fox, 1951, Copeia, **1951**: 264.—Greylodge Refuge, 9 miles west of Gridley, Butte County, California.

Range.—The great valleys of California between the Coast Range and the Sierras, extending into western Nevada; reaching the coast in northwestern California and southwestern Oregon; eastern Oregon and Washington into Idaho and British Columbia.

Common name.—Fitch's garter snake.

Tropidoclonion Cope

Tropidoclonion Cope, 1860, Proc. Acad. Nat. Sci. Phila., **12**: 76.—Type: lineatum.

Tropidoclonion lineatum Hallowell

Microps lineatum Hallowell, 1856, Proc. Acad. Nat. Sci. Phila., **8**: 241.—Kansas; restr. to vicinity of Kansas City.

Tropidoclonion lineatum Cope, 1860, Proc. Acad. Nat. Sci. Phila., **12**: 76.

Range.—Central Illinois through Missouri and Iowa to southeastern South Dakota, and southward through eastern Nebraska, Kansas, Oklahoma, Texas, and Arkansas.

Common name.—Lined snake.

Haldea Baird and Girard

Haldea Baird and Girard, 1853, Cat. N. Amer. Rept., pt. 1, p. 122.—Type: striatula.

Potamophis Fitzinger, 1843, Syst. Rept., p. 25.—Type: *striatulus*. (Preoccupied by *Potamophis* Cantor, 1836.)

Virginia Baird and Girard, 1853, Cat. N. Amer. Rept., pt. 1, p. 127.—Type: *valeriae*.

Conocephalus Bibron, 1853, Prodrome des Ophidiens, p. 46.—Type: *striatulus*.

Amphiardis Cope, 1889, Proc. U. S. Nat. Mus., **11**: 391.—Type: *inornatus*.

Haldea striatula Linnaeus

Coluber striatula Linnaeus, 1866, Syst. Nat., ed. 12, **1**: 375.—Carolina; restr. to Charleston, South Carolina.

Haldea striatula Cope, 1900, Ann. Rept. U. S. Nat. Mus., **1898**: 1009, fig. 272.

Virginia inornata Garman, 1883, Mem. Mus. Comp. Zool., **8**, pt. 3, p. 391.—Dallas, Texas.

Range.—Atlantic and Gulf states from Virginia to northern Florida, westward to central Texas; through eastern Oklahoma to southeastern Kansas, and eastward in Missouri, Arkansas, Tennessee, and Kentucky.

Common name.—Southern ground snake.

Haldea valeriae Baird and Girard

Virginia valeriae Baird and Girard, 1853, Cat. N. Amer. Rept., pt. 1, p. 127.—Kent County, Maryland.

Range.—Eastern and central United States.

Common name.—Valery's ground snake.

Haldea valeriae valeriae Baird and Girard

Haldea valeriae valeriae Stejneger and Barbour, 1943, Check list, ed. 5, p. 165.

Carphophis harperti Duméril, Bibron, and Duméril, 1854, Erpét. Gén., **7**: 135.—Savannah, South Carolina [= Savannah, Georgia].

Range.—New Jersey, Pennsylvania, and southern Ohio, southward through eastern Kentucky, Tennessee, the Virginias, and North Carolina.

Common name.—Eastern ground snake.

Haldea valeriae elegans Kennicott

Virginia elegans Kennicott, 1859, Proc. Acad. Nat. Sci. Phila., **11**: 99.—Southern Illinois.

Haldea valeriae elegans Stejneger and Barbour, 1943, Check list, ed. 5, p. 165.

Range.—Southern Indiana, Illinois, and Iowa, western Kentucky, and Tennessee; southwestern Alabama, Mississippi, Missouri, Arkansas, eastern Oklahoma, Louisiana, and eastern and central Texas.

Common name.—Western ground snake.

Liodytes Cope

Liodytes Cope, 1885, Proc. Amer. Phil. Soc., **22**: 194.—Type: *alleni.*

Liodytes alleni Garman

Helicops alleni Garman, 1874, Proc. Boston Soc. Nat. Hist., **17**: 92.—
Hawkinsville, Florida, correctly 2 miles south of Crow's Bluff, Lake County (Robert E. Hellman, personal communication).
Liodytes alleni Cope, 1888, Proc. U. S. Nat. Mus., **11**: 393; Auffenburg, 1950, Herpetologica, **6**: 13, fig. 3 (map).

Range.—Peninsular Florida, and extreme southern Georgia.

Common name.—Allen's mud snake.

Liodytes alleni alleni Garman

Liodytes alleni alleni Auffenburg, 1950, Herpetologica, **6**: 14, figs. 1, 3.

Range.—Southern Georgia through northern two-thirds of peninsular Florida, Lake Okeechobee.

Common name.—Allen's mud snake.

Liodytes alleni lineapiatus Auffenburg

Liodytes alleni lineapiatus Auffenburg, 1950, Herpetologica, **6**: 13, figs. 1–3.
—15 miles southwest of Miami, Dade County, Florida.

Range.—Southern part of the Florida peninsula, south of Lake Okeechobee.

Common name.—South Florida mud snake.

Heterodon Latreille

Heterodon Latreille, 1802, Hist. Nat. Rept., **4**: 32.—Type: *platirhinos =*
platyrhinos.

Heterodon platyrhinos Latreille

Heterodon platyrhinos Latreille, 1802, Hist. Nat. Rept., **4**: 32.—Vicinity of Philadelphia.

Range.—Eastern and southern United States.

Common name.—Hog-nosed snake.

Heterodon platyrhinos platyrhinos Latreille

Heterodon platyrhinos platyrhinos Klauber, 1948, Copeia, **1948**: 8.

Coluber heterodon Daudin, 1803, Hist. Nat. Rept., **7**: 153, pl. 60, fig. 28.—Vicinity of Philadelphia.

Coluber cacodaemon Shaw, 1802, Gen. Zool., **3**: 377, pl. 102.—Carolina; restr. to Charleston, South Carolina.

Scytale niger Daudin, 1803, Hist. Nat. Rept., **5**: 342.—[By implication, Carolina; restr. to Charleston, South Carolina.]

Coluber thraso Harlan, 1835, Med. Phys. Res., p. 120.—Broad River, affluent of the Delaware, Pennsylvania.

Heterodon annulatus Troost, 1836, Ann. Lyc. Nat. Hist. New York, **3**: 188. —Perry County, Tennessee.

Heterodon tigrinus Troost, 1836, Ann. Lyc. Nat. Hist. New York, **3**: 189.—Nashville, Davidson County, and Maury County, Tennessee; restr. to Nashville.

Heterodon atmodes Baird and Girard, 1853, Cat. N. Amer. Rept., pt. 1, p. 57.—Georgia, and Charleston, South Carolina; restr. to Charleston, South Carolina.

Range.—Eastern United States, southward from New Hampshire to central Florida; westward through Ontario to Minnesota; and present in all of the first tier of states west of the Mississippi.

Common name.—Eastern hog-nosed snake, puffing adder, spreading adder, blow snake.

Heterodon platyrhinos browni Stejneger

Heterodon browni Stejneger, 1903, Proc. Biol. Soc. Wash., **16**: 123.—Lemon City, Dade County, Florida [now a part of Miami].

Range.—Eastern Dade County, Florida.

Common name.—South Florida hog-nosed snake.

Heterodon nasicus Baird and Girard

Heterodon nasicus Baird and Girard, 1852, Stansbury's Expl. Surv. Valley of Great Salt Lake, p. 352.—Texas; restr. to Amarillo by R. A. Edgren (p.c.).

Range.—Great Plains.

Common name.—Western hog-nosed snake.

Heterodon nasicus nasicus Baird and Girard

Heterodon nasicus nasicus Cope, 1900, Ann. Rept. U. S. Nat. Mus., **1898**: 774, fig. 168.

Heterodon cognatus Baird and Girard, 1853, Cat. N. Amer. Rept., pt. 1, p. 54.—Indianola and New Braunfels, Texas.

Range.—Second tier of states west of the Mississippi to the Rocky Mountains, with an isolated colony in the sand region near Havana,

Illinois; southward to New Mexico, and adjacent northeastern Mexico.

Common name.—Western hog-nosed snake.

Heterodon nasicus kennerlyi Kennicott

Heterodon kennerlyi Kennicott, 1860, Proc. Acad. Nat. Sci. Phila., **12:** 336.—Rio Grande and Sonora; restr. to mouth of the Pecos River.

Heterodon nasicus kennerlyi Cope, 1900, Ann. Rept. U. S. Nat. Mus., **1898:** 773.

Range.—Trans-Pecos Texas and southern New Mexico; southward into Mexico.

Common name.—Southwestern hog-nosed snake.

Heterodon simus Linnaeus

Coluber simus Linnaeus, 1766, Syst. Nat., ed. 12, **1:** 375.—Carolina; restr. to Charleston, South Carolina.

Heterodon simus Holbrook, 1842, N. Amer. Herp., ed. 2, **4:** 57, pl. 15.

Heterodon catesbyi Günther, 1858, Cat. Col. Snakes Brit. Mus., p. 83.—"North America and Texas"; restr. to Charleston, South Carolina.

Range.—North Carolina to central Florida, northward to southern Indiana.

Common name.—Southern hog-nosed snake.

Rhadinea Cope

Rhadinea Cope, 1863, Proc. Acad. Nat. Sci. Phila., **15:** 101.—Type: *vermiculaticeps* (of Costa Rica).

Rhadinea flavilata Cope

Dromicus flavilatus Cope, 1871, Proc. Acad. Nat. Sci. Phila., **23:** 222.—Fort Macon, North Carolina.

Rhadinea flavilata Cope, 1894, Proc. Acad. Nat. Sci. Phila., **46:** 429.

Leimadophis flavilatus Stejneger and Barbour, 1917, Check list, ed. 1, p. 86.

Range.—Eastern North Carolina and on the Atlantic and Gulf coastal plains to eastern Texas.

Common name.—Yellow-lipped snake.

Diadophis Baird and Girard

Diadophis Baird and Girard, 1853, Cat. N. Amer. Rept., pt. 1, p. 112.—Type: *punctatus.*

Diadophis amabilis Baird and Girard

Diadophis amabilis Baird and Girard, Cat. N. Amer. Rept., pt. 1, p. 113.—San Jose, California.

Range.—Western United States.

Common name.—Western ring-necked snake.

Diadophis amabilis amabilis Baird and Girard

Diadophis amabilis amabilis Blanchard, 1923, Occ. Papers Mus. Zool. Univ. Mich., **142**: 3.

Range.—Vicinity of San Francisco and San Joaquin and Sacramento valleys.

Common name.—Pacific ring-necked snake.

Diadophis amabilis modestus Bocourt

Diadophis punctatus var. *modestus* Bocourt, 1886, Miss. Sci. Mex., **3**, pt. 10, p. 623.—California; restr. to San Bernardino Mountains.
Diadophis amabilis modestus Blanchard, Occ. Papers Mus. Zool. Univ. Mich., **142**: 8.

Range.—San Bernardino Mountains, Los Angeles County, and Santa Catalina Island, California.

Common name.—San Bernardino ring-necked snake.

Diadophis amabilis occidentalis Blanchard

Diadophis amabilis occidentalis Blanchard, Occ. Papers Mus. Zool. Univ. Mich., **142**: 6.—Bridgeville, Humboldt County, California.

Range.—Sonoma County, California, northward to Washington.

Common name.—Northwestern ring-necked snake.

Diadophis amabilis pulchellus Baird and Girard

Diadophis pulchellus Baird and Girard, 1853, Cat. N. Amer. Rept., pt. 1, p. 115.—El Dorado County, California.
Diadophis amabilis pulchellus Blanchard, 1923, Occ. Papers Mus. Zool. Univ. Mich., **142**: 8.

Range.—Western slopes of the Sierra Nevada.

Common name.—Coral-bellied ring-necked snake.

Diadophis amabilis similis Blanchard

Diadophis amabilis similis Blanchard, 1923, Occ. Papers Mus. Zool. Univ. Mich., **142**: 4.—San Diego, California.

Range.—Southwestern San Bernardino County, southward through San Diego County to northern Lower California.

Common name.—San Diegan ring-necked snake.

Diadophis amabilis vandenburghi Blanchard

> *Diadophis amabilis vandenburghi* Blanchard, 1923, Occ. Papers Mus. Zool. Univ. Mich., **142:** 5.—Carmel, Monterey County, California.

Range.—Ventura County to Santa Cruz County, California.

Common name.—Monterey ring-necked snake.

Diadophis regalis Baird and Girard

> *Diadophis regalis* Baird and Girard, 1853, Cat. N. Amer. Rept., pt. 1, p. 115. —Sonora, Mexico.

Range.—Utah and Colorado, southward to Sonora and Trans-Pecos Texas.

Common name.—Regal ring-necked snake.

Diadophis regalis regalis Baird and Girard

> *Diadophis regalis regalis* Blanchard, 1923, Occ. Papers Mus. Zool. Univ. Mich., **142:** 1 [cited for combination only]; Schmidt and Smith, 1944, Field Mus. Nat. Hist., Zool. Ser., **29:** 89.
>
> *Diadophis punctatus laetus* Jan, 1863, Arch. Zool. Anat. Fisiol., **2:** 262.
>
> *Diadophis regalis arizonae* Blanchard, 1923, Occ. Papers Mus. Zool. Univ. Mich., **142:** 2.—Sabino Canyon, Santa Catalina Mountains, Pima County, Arizona.

Range.—Isolated mountains of Arizona and Sonora, in the desert region, northward to Utah and Colorado.

Common name.—Regal ring-necked snake.

Diadophis regalis blanchardi Schmidt and Smith[18]

> *Diadophis regalis blanchardi* Schmidt and Smith, 1944, Field Mus. Nat. Hist., Zool. Ser., **29:** 89.—Basin, Chisos Mountains, Brewster County, Texas.

Range.—Southeast Arizona grassland region and isolated mountain regions east to Trans-Pecos Texas; southward into adjacent Sonora and Chihuahua.

Common name.—Big Bend regal ring-necked snake.

[18] I have maintained this arrangement against the opinion of Smith and Taylor, 1945, Bull. U. S. Nat. Mus., **187:** 48, with whom I agree that the problem of subdivision of *regalis* is by no means satisfactorily solved.

Diadophis punctatus Linnaeus

Coluber punctatus Linnaeus, 1766, Syst. Nat., ed. 12, 1: 376.—Carolina; restr. to Charleston, South Carolina.

Diadophis punctatus Baird and Girard, 1853, Cat. N. Amer. Rept., pt. 1, p. 112.

Range.—Eastern North America.

Common name.—Ring-necked snake.

Diadophis punctatus punctatus Linnaeus

Diadophis punctatus punctatus Barbour, 1919, Proc. New England Zool. Club, 7: 7.

Ablabes occipitalis Günther, 1858, Cat. Col. Snakes Brit. Mus., p. 29.— Mexico, in errore; designated type locality: Charleston, S.C.

Diadophis punctatus var. pallidus Cope, 1860, Proc. Acad. Nat. Sci. Phila., 12: 250.—California, in errore; designated as Charleston, South Carolina.

Diadophis dysopes Cope, 1860, Proc. Acad. Nat. Sci. Phila., 11: 251.—Type locality unknown; designated as vicinity of Philadelphia.

Range.—Atlantic states from Maryland south into Florida.

Common name.—Southeastern ring-necked snake.

Diadophis punctatus edwardsi Merrem

Coluber torquatus Shaw (nec Lacépède), 1802, Gen. Zool., 3: 553.—Pennsylvania.

Coluber edwardsii Merrem, 1820, Tent. Syst. Amphib., p. 136.—Pennsylvania; restr. to vicinity of Philadelphia.

Diadophis punctatus edwardsii Barbour, 1919, Proc. New England Zool. Club, 7: 9.

Range.—Northeastern North America, from Nova Scotia, New Brunswick, and Quebec, to New York, Pennsylvania, and New Jersey, westward through Michigan, Wisconsin, and Minnesota; southward in the Appalachian Mountains to North Carolina.

Common name.—Eastern ring-necked snake, northeastern ring-necked snake.

Diadophis punctatus docilis Baird and Girard

Diadophis docilis Baird and Girard, Cat. N. Amer. Rept., pt. 1, p. 114.— Between Rio San Pedro (Devils River) and Comanche Spring, Texas; restr. to Devils River.

Diadophis punctatus docilis Jan, 1863, Arch. Zool. Anat. Fisiol., 2: 262; Blanchard, 1942, Bull. Chicago Acad. Sci., 7: 66, map 4.

Range.—Western Texas, southern Staked Plains to Devils River.

Common name.—Texas ring-necked snake.

Diadophis punctatus stictogenys Cope

Diadophis punctatus var. *stictogenys* Cope, 1860, Proc. Acad. Nat. Sci. Phila., **12**: 250.—Unknown; designated as southern Illinois.
Diadophis texensis Kennicott, 1860, Proc. Acad. Nat. Sci. Phila., **12**: 328.— East of Galveston, head of Trinity River, and Llano Estacado, Texas, and Monticello, Mississippi; restr. to Texas east of Galveston.

Range.—Southern Illinois, through the states on both sides of the Mississippi to Alabama and eastern Texas.

Common name.—Mississippi ring-necked snake.

Diadophis punctatus arnyi Kennicott

Diadophis arnyi Kennicott, 1858, Proc. Acad. Nat. Sci. Phila., **10**: 99.— Hyatt, Anderson County, Kansas.
Diadophis punctatus arnyi Stejneger and Barbour, 1923, Check list, ed. 2, p. 83.

Range.—Prairie and Great Plains region, southwestern Wisconsin, Iowa, and eastern Nebraska, southward through Missouri, Kansas, and southeastern Colorado, Arkansas, and Oklahoma into central Texas.

Common name.—Prairie ring-necked snake.

Carphophis Gervais

Carphophis Gervais, 1843, D'Orbigny's Dict. Univ. Hist. Nat., **3**: 191.— Type: *amoenus.*

Carphophis amoenus Say

Coluber amoenus Say, 1825, Jour. Acad. Nat. Sci. Phila., (1), **4**: 237.— Pennsylvania; restr. to vicinity of Philadelphia.
Carphophis amoena Gervais, 1843, D'Orbigny's Dict. Univ. Hist. Nat., **3**: 191.

Range.—Eastern and central United States.

Common name.—Worm snake.

Carphophis amoenus amoenus Say

Carphophis amoena amoena Blanchard, 1924, Papers Mich. Acad. Sci., **4**: 527.

Range.—Connecticut to New York and Pennsylvania, southward through the Atlantic states to central Florida, east of the Appalachians.

Common name.—Eastern worm snake.

Carphophis amoenus helenae Kennicott

Celuta helenae Kennicott, 1859, Proc. Acad. Nat. Sci. Phila., **11**: 100.—
Monticello, Lawrence County, Mississippi.
Carphophis amoena helenae Blanchard, 1924, Papers Mich. Acad. Sci.,
4: 527.

Range.—West Virginia, Ohio, and central Illinois, southward through Kentucky and Tennessee to Alabama and Mississippi.

Common name.—Mid-west worm snake.

Carphophis amoenus vermis Kennicott

Celuta vermis Kennicott, 1859, Proc. Acad. Nat. Sci. Phila., **11**: 99.
Carphophis amoena vermis Blanchard, 1924, Papers Mich. Acad. Sci.,
4: 527.

Range.—Iowa and southeastern Nebraska, eastern Kansas and Oklahoma, southward west of the Mississippi to the Gulf.

Common name.—Western worm snake.

Abastor Gray

Abastor Gray, 1849, Cat. Col. Snakes Brit. Mus., p. 78.—Type: *erythro-grammus.*

Abastor erythrogrammus Latreille

Coluber erythrogrammus Latreille, 1802, Hist. Nat. Rept., **4**: 141.—"L'Amé-rique septentrionale"; restr. to Alachua County, Florida.

Range.—Charles County, Maryland, through the lower Atlantic coastal plain to central Florida and Alabama.

Common name.—Rainbow snake.

Farancia Gray

Farancia Gray, 1832, Zool. Misc., p. 78.—Type: *drummondi* = *abacura.*

Farancia abacura Holbrook

Coluber abacurus Holbrook, 1836, N. Amer. Herp., ed. 1, **1**: 119, pl. 23.—
South Carolina; restr. to Charleston, South Carolina.
Farancia abacura Baird and Girard, 1853, Cat. N. Amer. Rept., pt. 1, p. 123.

Range.—Southeastern United States.

Common name.—Mud snake, stingin' snake, horn snake.

Farancia abacura abacura Holbrook

Farancia abacura abacura Smith, 1938, Copeia, **1938**: 112, pl. 1, figs. 1, 2,
text figs. 1, 2.

Farancia drummondi Gray, 1842, Zool. Misc., p. 68.—California, *in errore;* designated as Charleston, South Carolina.

Range.—Southeastern United States, from Virginia through Georgia and Florida to eastern Alabama.

Common name.—Eastern mud snake.

Farancia abacura reinwardti Schlegel

Farancia reinwardtii Schlegel, 1837, Essai Physion. Serp., **1**: 173.—Louisiana; restr. to vicinity of New Orleans.

Farancia abacura reinwardtii Smith, 1938, Copeia, **1938**: 116, pl. 1, fig. 3, text figs. 1, 2.

Farancia fasciata Gray, 1849, Cat. Snakes Brit. Mus., p. 74.—New Orleans, Louisiana.

Range.—Lower Mississippi Basin from southern Indiana and Illinois, eastward into Alabama, westward into extreme southeastern Oklahoma, eastern Texas, and along the Gulf to Corpus Christi.

Common name.—Western mud snake.

Coniophanes Hallowell

Coniophanes Hallowell, 1860, *in* Cope, Proc. Acad. Nat. Sci. Phila., **12**: 248. —Type: *fissidens* of southern Mexico.

Coniophanes imperialis Baird

Taeniophis imperialis Baird, 1859, U. S. Mex. Bound. Surv., **2**, pt. 2, Rept., p. 23, pl. 19, fig. 1.—Brownsville, Texas.

Coniophanes imperialis Cope, 1861, Proc. Acad. Nat. Sci. Phila., **13**: 74.

Range.—Southern Texas to northern Central America.

Common name.—Dust snake.

Coniophanes imperialis imperialis Baird

Coniophanes imperialis imperialis Bailey, 1937, Occ. Papers Mus. Zool. Univ. Mich., **362**: 6.

Range.—Extreme southern Texas; south to Vera Cruz, Mexico.

Common name.—Black-striped dust snake.

Coluber Linnaeus

Coluber Linnaeus, 1758, Syst. Nat., ed. 10, **1**: 216.—Type: *constrictor.*

Coluber constrictor Linnaeus

Coluber constrictor (part) Linnaeus, 1758, Syst. Nat., ed. 10, **1**: 216.—Canada.

Range.—North America.

Common name.—Racer.

Coluber constrictor constrictor Linnaeus

> *Coluber constrictor constrictor* Stejneger and Barbour, 1917, Check list, ed. 1, p. 79.

Range.—Eastern North America from southern Maine southward to northern Florida and westward, mainly south of the Ohio River, to the Mississippi.

Common name.—Blacksnake, black racer.

Coluber constrictor priapus Dunn and Wood

> *Coluber constrictor priapus* Dunn and Wood, 1939, Notulae Naturae, **5**: 4.— West Palm Beach, Florida.

Range.—Peninsular Florida.

Common name.—Florida racer.

Coluber constrictor flaviventris Say

> *Coluber flaviventris* Say, 1823, *in* Long's Exped. Rocky Mts., **1**: 185.—Stone quarry on west side of Missouri River, 3 miles above Boyer's River, Pottawattamie County, Iowa.
>
> *Coluber constrictor flaviventris* Garman, 1883, Mem. Mus. Comp. Zool., **8**, no. 3, p. 147.

Range.—Prairie and Great Plains between the Mississippi and Rocky Mountains, northward into North Dakota and Montana, southward to the Gulf of Mexico.

Common name.—Yellow-bellied racer.

Coluber constrictor foxi Baird and Girard

> *Bascanion foxii* Baird and Girard, 1853, Cat. N. Amer. Rept., pt. 1, p. 96.— Grosse Isle, Michigan, and Pittsburgh, Pennsylvania; restr. to Grosse Isle, Michigan.

Range.—The Prairie Peninsula, from the Mississippi River in Illinois and Wisconsin, eastward through Indiana, southern Michigan and Ohio.

Common name.—Blue racer.

Coluber constrictor anthicus Cope

> *Bascanion anthicum* Cope, 1862, Proc. Acad. Nat. Sci. Phila., **14**: 338.— Unknown, possibly "Siam"; designated as Natchitoches, Natchitoches Parish, Louisiana.
>
> *Coluber constrictor anthicus* Dunn and Wood, 1939, Notulae Naturae, **5**: 1.

Range.—Northeastern Louisiana, in Natchitoches, Beauregard, and Allen parishes, and in adjacent Texas and Arkansas.

Common name.—Buttermilk snake.

Coluber constrictor stejnegerianus Cope

Zamenis stejnegerianus Cope, 1895, Amer. Nat., **29:** 676.—Brownsville, Texas.

Coluber constrictor stejnegerianus Mulaik and Mulaik, 1942, Copeia, **1942:** 13.

Range.—Southern Texas southward from San Patricio County; adjacent Mexico and along the Rio Grande to northern Coahuila.

Common name.—Rio Grande racer.

Coluber constrictor mormon Baird and Girard

Coluber mormon Baird and Girard, 1852, Stansbury's Expl. Surv. Valley of Great Salt Lake, App. C, Rept., p. 351.—Valley of the Great Salt Lake.

Coluber constrictor mormon Van Denburgh and Slevin, 1921, Proc. Calif. Acad. Sci., (4), **11:** 28.

Bascanion vetustus Baird and Girard, 1853, Cat. N. Amer. Rept., pt. 1, p. 97.—San Jose, California, Puget Sound, and Oregon; restr. to San Jose, California.

Range.—Southern British Columbia, through the Great Basin to southern Arizona, and throughout Washington, Oregon, and California.

Common name.—Western racer.

Masticophis Baird and Girard

Masticophis Baird and Girard, 1853, Cat. N. Amer. Rept., pt. 1, p. 98.— Type: *ornatus.*

Masticophis flagellum Shaw

Coluber flagellum Shaw, 1802, Gen. Zool., **3:** 475.—Carolina and Virginia; restr. to Charleston, South Carolina.

Range.—Southern United States and Mexico.

Common name.—Whip snake, coachwhip snake.

Masticophis flagellum flagellum Shaw

Masticophis flagellum flagellum Ortenburger, 1923, Occ. Papers Mus. Zool. Univ. Mich., **139:** 2.

Herpetodryas psammophis Schlegel, 1837, Essai Physion. Serp., **2:** 195.— New Orleans and New York; restr. to New Orleans.

Coluber flagelliformis Holbrook, 1842, N. Amer. Herp., ed. 1, **1:** 107, pl. 19. —Abbeville County, South Carolina.

Range.—Southeastern United States from North Carolina to peninsular Florida and westward along the Gulf Coast to Louisiana; an apparently isolated population ranging from southern Illinois and Missouri through northwestern Arkansas and eastern Oklahoma into western Louisiana and eastern Texas.

Common name.—Coachwhip, whip snake.

Masticophis flagellum testaceus Say

Coluber testaceus Say, 1823, *in* Long's Exped. Rocky Mts., **2**: 48.—[Head waters of Arkansas River] near the Rocky Mountains.

Coluber flagellum testaceus Klauber, 1942, Copeia, **1942**: 93.

Psammophis flavigularis Hallowell, 1852, Proc. Acad. Nat. Sci. Phila., **6**: 178. —Cross Timbers, Indian Territory.

Range.—Great Plains, from western Kansas and eastern Colorado southward through western Oklahoma and central Texas to the Gulf Coast; westward to the Rocky Mountains in New Mexico; northeastern Mexico.

Common name.—Western coachwhip.

Masticophis flagellum piceus Cope

Bascanion piceum Cope, 1892, Proc. U. S. Nat. Mus., **14**: 625.—Camp Grant, Arizona.

Masticophis flagellum piceus Tanner, 1927, Copeia, **163**: 57.

Bascanion flagellum frenatum Stejneger, 1893, N. Amer. Fauna, **7**: 208.— Mountain Springs, Colorado Desert, San Diego County, California.

Range.—The Colorado Desert in southwestern Arizona and southeastern California, and adjacent Lower California.

Common name.—Colorado Desert whip snake, black whip snake (for the two color phases).

Masticophis flagellum lineatulus Smith

Masticophis flagellum lineatulus Smith, 1941, Jour. Wash. Acad. Sci., **31**: 374.—11 miles south of San Buenaventura, Chihuahua.

Range.—Extreme southern New Mexico, southward in adjacent Mexico to San Luis Potosí.

Common name.—Lined whip snake.

Masticophis lateralis Hallowell

Leptophis lateralis Hallowell, 1853, Proc. Acad. Nat. Sci. Phila., **6**: 237.— California; restr. to San Diego.

Masticophis lateralis Ortenburger, 1923, Occ. Papers Mus. Zool. Univ. Mich., **139**: 2.

Range.—Southwestern California and northwestern Lower California.

Common name.—California striped whip snake.

Masticophis bilineatus Jan

Masticophis bilineatus Jan, 1863, Elenco sist. ofidi, p. 65.—?Western Mexico; designated as Casas Grandes, Chihuahua.

Bascanion semilineatum Cope, 1892, Proc. U. S. Nat. Mus., **14**: 626.—Camp Grant and Colorado River, Arizona; restr. to Camp Grant [Graham County].

Range.—Southeastern Arizona and southwestern New Mexico; southward in Mexico to Oaxaca.

Common name.—Sonora whip snake.

Masticophis taeniatus Hallowell

Leptophis taeniata Hallowell, 1852, Proc. Acad. Nat. Sci. Phila., **6**: 181.—New Mexico west of the Rio Grande.

Range.—Southwestern United States, from the Great Basin to central Texas and southward into Mexico.

Common name.—Striped whip snake.

Masticophis taeniatus taeniatus Hallowell

Masticophis taeniatus taeniatus Ortenburger, 1923, Occ. Papers Mus. Zool. Univ. Mich., **139**: 2.

Range.—Great Basin and bordering areas from Idaho through eastern Oregon, Utah, and Nevada, eastern California, Arizona, and southwestern New Mexico.

Common name.—Striped whip snake.

Masticophis taeniatus ornatus Baird and Girard

Masticophis ornatus Baird and Girard, Cat. N. Amer. Rept., pt. 1, p. 102.—Between Indianola and El Paso, Texas.

Masticophis taeniatus ornatus Schmidt and Smith, 1944, Field Mus. Nat. Hist., Zool. Ser., **29**: 90.

Coluber taeniatus girardi Stejneger and Barbour, 1917, Check list, ed. 1, p. 80.—Substitute name for *ornatus* Baird and Girard.

Range.—Central and western Texas on the Edwards Plateau; southward in Mexico to Zacatecas.

Common name.—Central Texas whip snake.

Masticophis taeniatus ruthveni Ortenburger

Masticophis ruthveni Ortenburger, 1923, Occ. Papers Mus. Zool. Univ. Mich., **139:** 3, pls. 1–3.—Brownsville, Texas.

Masticophis taeniatus ruthveni Gloyd and Conant, 1934, Occ. Papers Mus. Zool. Univ. Mich., **287:** 16.

Range.—Extreme southern Texas; adjacent Tamaulipas and Nuevo León to San Luis Potosí.

Common name.—Ruthven's whip snake.

Masticophis taeniatus schotti Baird and Girard

Masticophis schotti Baird and Girard, 1853, Cat. N. Amer. Rept., pt. 1, p. 160.—Eagle Pass, Texas.

Masticophis taeniatus schotti Gloyd and Conant, 1934, Occ. Papers Mus. Zool. Univ. Mich., **287:** 5, pls. 2, 3, map 1.

Range.—Southern Texas from Comal and Bexar counties to the Brownsville region; southwestward into Mexico; this is the mesquite and desert grass savanna area of the higher portion of the Gulf coastal plain in Texas.

Common name.—Schott's whip snake.

Opheodrys Fitzinger

Opheodrys Fitzinger, 1843, Syst. Rept., p. 26.—Type: *aestivus.*

Opheodrys aestivus Linnaeus

Coluber aestivus Linnaeus, 1766, Syst. Nat., ed. 12, **1:** 387.—Carolina; restr. to Charleston, South Carolina.

Opheodrys aestivus Cope, 1860, Proc. Acad. Nat. Sci. Phila., **12:** 560.

Leptophis majalis Baird and Girard, 1853, Cat. N. Amer. Rept., pt. 1, p. 107. —Indianola and New Braunfels, Texas, and Red River, Arkansas; restr. to New Braunfels, Comal County, Texas.

Range.—Atlantic states from Connecticut to Florida, westward to eastern Texas (and along the Gulf Coast to Tamaulipas), and northward through Oklahoma to southeastern Kansas, Missouri, and extreme southern Iowa; southern Illinois, Indiana and Ohio.

Common name.—Rough green snake.

Opheodrys vernalis Harlan

Coluber vernalis Harlan, 1827, Jour. Acad. Nat. Sci. Phila., (1), **5:** 361.— Pennsylvania and New Jersey; restr. to vicinity of Philadelphia.

Opheodrys vernalis Schmidt and Necker, 1935, Herpetologica, **1:** 64.

Range.—Northern United States, east of the Rocky Mountains.

Common name.—Smooth green snake.

Opheodrys vernalis vernalis Harlan

Opheodrys vernalis vernalis Grobman, Misc. Publ. Univ. Mich. Mus. Zool.,
  50: 38, figs. 1, 2, map 1.

Range.—Glaciated and mountainous areas of northeastern North America east of the prairie-forest border, southward to Madison County, North Carolina.

Common name.—Eastern smooth green snake.

Opheodrys vernalis blanchardi Grobman

Opheodrys vernalis blanchardi Grobman, 1941, Misc. Publ. Univ. Mich. Mus. Zool., 50: 38, figs. 1, 2, map 1.—Spanish Peaks, Colorado.

Range.—Northern Great Plains and prairie region, westward to the Black Hills, and in the Rocky Mountains in Colorado and New Mexico.

Common name.—Western smooth green snake.

Drymobius Fitzinger

Drymobius Fitzinger, 1843, Syst. Rept., p. 26.—Type: margaritiferus.

Drymobius margaritiferus Schlegel

Herpetodryas margaritiferus Schlegel, 1837, Essai Physion. Serp., 2: 184.—New Orleans, in errore; designated as Brownsville, Texas.
Drymobius margaritiferus Cope, 1860, Proc. Acad. Nat. Sci. Phila., 12: 561.

Range.—Extreme southern Texas to Guatemala and northward on the west coast of Mexico to Sonora.

Common name.—Speckled ground snake.

Drymobius margaritiferus margaritiferus Schlegel

Drymobius margaritiferus margaritiferus Smith, 1942, Proc. U. S. Nat. Mus., 92: 383.

Range.—The Brownsville region of Texas; southward to northern Vera Cruz.

Common name.—Speckled ground snake.

Drymarchon Fitzinger

Drymarchon Fitzinger, Syst. Rept., p. 26.—Type: corais.

Drymarchon corais Daudin

Coluber corais Boie, 1827, Isis, 20: 537.—America; restr. to Belem, Pará, Brazil.
Drymarchon corais Amaral, 1929, Mem. Inst. Butantan, 4: 84.

Range.—Southeastern United States, westward into Texas, and throughout Mexico, Central America, and northern South America.

Common name.—Indigo snake.

Drymarchon corais couperi Holbrook

Coluber couperi Holbrook, 1842, N. Amer. Herp., ed. 2, **3**: 75, pl. 16.— Dry pine hills south of Alatamaha, Georgia [= Altamaha River]; restr. to Wayne County, Georgia.

Drymarchon corais couperi Strecker, 1915, Baylor Bull., **18**, no. 4, p. 32.

Range.—South Carolina to Florida and west to Louisiana, in the Atlantic and Gulf coastal plains.

Common name.—Indigo snake.

Drymarchon corais erebennus Cope

Spilotes erebennus Cope, 1860, Proc. Acad. Nat. Sci. Phila., **12**: 342.— Eagle Pass, Texas.

Drymarchon corais erebennus Smith, 1941, Jour. Wash. Acad. Sci., **31**: 478.

Range.—Central southern Texas; southward into adjacent Mexico.

Common name.—Texas indigo snake.

Salvadora Baird and Girard

Salvadora Baird and Girard, 1853, Cat. N. Amer. Rept., pt. 1, p. 104.—Type: *grahamiae.*

Salvadora grahamiae Baird and Girard

Salvadora grahamiae Baird and Girard, 1853, Cat. N. Amer. Rept., pt. 1, p. 104.—Sonora [= Southern Arizona; restr. to Huachuca Mountains, Cochise County, Arizona].

Range.—Southeastern Arizona, southwestern New Mexico, and Trans-Pecos Texas in mountains above the desert zone.

Common name.—Mountain patch-nosed snake.

Salvadora hexalepis Cope

Phimothyra hexalepis Cope, 1866, Proc. Acad. Nat. Sci. Phila., **18**: 304.— Fort Whipple, Arizona.

Salvadora hexalepis Stejneger, 1902, Proc. U. S. Nat. Mus., **25**: 154.

Range.—Southwestern North America.

Common name.—Western patch-nosed snake.

Salvadora hexalepis hexalepis Cope

Salvadora hexalepis hexalepis Schmidt, 1940, Field Mus. Nat. Hist., Zool. Ser., **24**: 146.

Range.—Southwestern Utah through Nevada and western Arizona to California; adjacent Sonora and Lower California.

Common name.—Desert patch-nosed snake.

Salvadora hexalepis deserticola Schmidt

Salvadora hexalepis deserticola Schmidt, 1940, Field Mus. Nat. Hist., Zool. Ser., **24**: 146, fig. 14.—Government Spring, near Chisos Mountains, Brewster County, Texas.

Range.—Desert zone from Trans-Pecos Texas through southern New Mexico and Arizona; adjacent Coahuila and Chihuahua.

Common name.—Big Bend patch-nosed snake.

Salvadora hexalepis virgultea Bogert

Salvadora hexalepis virgultea Bogert, 1935, Bull. S. Calif. Acad. Sci., **34**: 89.—Deerhorn Flat, San Diego County, California.

Range.—Southwestern California and northwestern Lower California, west of the Coast Range and san Pedro Mártir Mountains.

Common name.—Pacific patch-nosed snake.

Salvadora lineata Schmidt

Salvadora lineata Schmidt, 1940, Field Mus. Nat. Hist., Zool. Ser., **24**: 148, fig. 15.—Kingsville, Kleberg County, Texas.

Range.—Central and southern Texas, and adjacent Mexico.

Common name.—Texas patch-nosed snake.

Phyllorhynchus Stejneger

Phyllorhynchus Stejneger, 1899, Proc. U. S. Nat. Mus., **13**: 151.—Type: *browni.*

Phyllorhynchus browni Stejneger

Phyllorhynchus browni Stejneger, 1899, Proc. U. S. Nat. Mus., **13**: 152.—Tucson, Arizona.

Range.—South central Arizona.

Common name.—Brown's leaf-nosed snake.

Phyllorhynchus browni browni Stejneger

Phyllorhynchus browni browni Klauber, 1940, Trans. San Diego Soc. Nat. Hist., **9**: 204, pl. 8, fig. 3.

Range.—Pinal and Pima counties, Arizona.

Common name.—Pima leaf-nosed snake.

Phyllorhynchus browni lucidus Klauber

Phyllorhynchus browni lucidus Klauber, 1940, Trans. San Diego Soc. Nat. Hist., **9**: 202, pl. 8, fig. 2.—Encanto Valley, 7 miles west of Cave Creek, Maricopa County, Arizona.

Range.—Maricopa County, Arizona.

Common name.—Maricopa leaf-nosed snake.

Phyllorhynchus decurtatus Cope

Phimothyra decurtata Cope, 1868, Proc. Acad. Nat. Sci. Phila., **20**: 310.—Upper part of Lower California.

Range.—Colorado Desert region, southward in Sonora and Lower California.

Common name.—Sonora leaf-nosed snake.

Phyllorhynchus decurtatus nubilus Klauber

Phyllorhynchus decurtatus nubilus Klauber, 1940, Trans. San Diego Soc. Nat. Hist., **9**: 197, pl. 8, fig. 1, map.—Xavier, Pima County, Arizona.

Range.—Tucson region, Pima County, Arizona and adjacent Pinal County.

Common name.—Cloudy leaf-nosed snake.

Phyllorhynchus decurtatus perkinsi Klauber

Phyllorhynchus decurtatus perkinsi Klauber, 1935, Bull. Zool. Soc. San Diego, **12**: 11.—Dry Lake, San Diego County, California.

Range.—Colorado Desert, in southeastern California, southwestern Arizona, and extreme southern Nevada.

Common name.—Desert leaf-nosed snake.

Elaphe Fitzinger

Elaphe Fitzinger, *in* Wagler, 1833, Descr. Icon. Amph., pt. 3, pl. 27 (text). —Type: *parreysii = quatuorlineata.*

Elaphe guttata Linnaeus

Coluber guttatus Linnaeus, 1766, Syst. Nat., ed. 12, **1**: 385.—Carolina; restr. to Charleston, South Carolina.

Elaphis guttatus Duméril, Bibron, and Duméril, 1854, Erpét. Gén., **7**: 273.

Range.—Southern New Jersey to the tip of the Florida peninsula, westward to northeastern Mexico, and northward in the interior to Kentucky and Missouri, in the west to western Colorado and Great Salt Lake.

Common name.—Corn snake, rat snake.

Elaphe guttata guttata Linnaeus

Elaphe guttata guttata [by inference] Neill, 1949, Herpetologica, **5,** 2nd
Suppl., p. 10.

Coluber carolinianus Shaw, 1802, Gen. Zool., **3:** 460, pl. 119.—Carolina;
restr. to Charleston, South Carolina.

Coluber maculatus Latreille, 1802, Hist. Nat. Rept., **4:** 73.—Louisiana; restr.
to vicinity of New Orleans.

Coluber pantherinus Merrem, 1820, Tent. Syst. Amph., p. 102.—Type locality unknown; designated as Charleston, South Carolina.

Coluber floridanus Harlan, 1827, Jour. Acad. Nat. Sci. Phila., (1), **5:** 360.—
East Florida.

Coluber guttatus sellatus Cope, 1888, Proc. U. S. Nat. Mus., **11:** 387.—
Arlington, Palatka, and Cape Sable, Florida; restr. to Palatka, Putnam
County.

Range.—New Jersey to Florida in the Atlantic coastal plain, mountains of Virginia and Tennessee, westward to Louisiana, and northward in the Mississippi Valley to Kentucky and Missouri.

Common name.—Corn snake.

Elaphe guttata rosacea Cope

Coluber rosaceus Cope, 1888, Proc. U. S. Nat. Mus., **11:** 388, pl. 36, fig. 3.—
Key West, Florida.

Elaphe guttata rosacea [by inference] Neill, 1949, Herpetologica, **5,** 2nd
Suppl., p. 10.

Range.—Lower Florida Keys and extreme southern Florida.

Common name.—Rosy corn snake.

Elaphe guttata emoryi Baird and Girard

Scotophis emoryi Baird and Girard, 1853, Cat. N. Amer. Rept., pt. 1, p. 157.
—Howard Springs, Ellis County, Oklahoma.

Elaphe emoryi emoryi Dowling, 1951, Copeia, **1951:** 43.

Elaphe guttata emoryi Dowling, 1952, Occ. Papers Mus. Zool. Univ. Mich.,
541: 2.

Coluber rhinomegas Cope, 1860, Proc. Acad. Nat. Sci. Phila., **12:** 255.—
Kansas and Missouri (nomen nudum).

Elaphe laeta intermontanus Woodbury and Woodbury, 1942, Proc. Biol.
Soc. Wash., **55:** 140.—Parriott Ranch, near Moab, Grand County, Utah.

Range.—Colorado and Nebraska southward through the Great
Plains states to Texas and eastward into Missouri, with records from
western Illinois; Colorado plateaus in Utah and Colorado, west of
the Rockies, into central Mexico.

Common name.—Great Plains rat snake.

Elaphe vulpina Baird and Girard

Scotophis vulpinus Baird and Girard, 1853, Cat. N. Amer. Rept., pt. 1, p. 75.—Racine, Wisconsin.

Elaphe vulpinus Ruthven, 1909, Eleventh Rept. Mich. Acad. Sci., p. 116.

Range.—Eastern Nebraska to southern Ontario and western Ohio, and northern Wisconsin and Michigan southward to the Wabash River.

Common name.—Fox snake, spotted adder.

Elaphe vulpina vulpina Baird and Girard

Elaphe vulpina vulpina Conant, 1940, Herpetologica, **2**: 10, pl. 1, fig. 3, text fig. 1, map 1.

Elaphe rubriceps Duméril, Bibron, and Duméril, 1854, Erpét. Gén., **7**: 270.—North America; restr. to vicinity of Chicago.

Range.—Upper Peninsula of Michigan through Wisconsin, southeastern Minnesota and northern Illinois; northwestern Indiana southward to the Wabash River; westward through Iowa to eastern Nebraska and South Dakota.

Common name.—Spotted adder (Illinois), pine snake (Wisconsin), fox snake.

Elaphe vulpina gloydi Conant

Elaphe vulpina gloydi Conant, 1940, Herpetologica, **2**: 2, pl. 1, figs. 1, 2, text fig. 1, map 1.—Little Cedar Point, Jerusalem Township, Lucas County, Ohio.

Range.—Eastern Michigan and adjacent Ohio at the western end of Lake Erie, southern Ontario.

Common name.—Eastern fox snake, timber snake.

Elaphe obsoleta Say

Coluber obsoletus Say, 1823, *in* Long's Exped. Rocky Mts., **1**: 140.—Isle au Vache to Council Bluffs on the Missouri River; restr. to Council Bluffs, Iowa.

Elaphis obsoletus Garman, 1883, Mem. Mus. Comp. Zool., **8**, no. 3, p. 54.

Range.—Eastern North America, westward to central Texas and eastern Texas.

Common name.—Chicken snake, rat snake.

Elaphe obsoleta obsoleta Say

Elaphe obsoleta obsoleta Stejneger and Barbour, 1917, Check list, ed. 1, p. 83.

Scotophis alleghaniensis Holbrook, 1836, N. Amer. Herp., ed. 1, **1**: 111, pl. 20.—Summit of the Blue Ridge in Virginia.

Scotophis confinis Baird and Girard, 1853, Cat. N. Amer. Rept., pt. 1, p. 76. —Anderson, South Carolina.

Elaphis holbrookii Duméril, Bibron, and Duméril, 1854, Erpét. Gén., **7**: 272. —New York and Charleston; restr. to vicinity of New York City.

Range.—Eastern North America, from southern New England (Rutland County, Vermont) to northern Georgia, westward through New York and Ontario to southeastern Minnesota, eastern Kansas and Oklahoma, and northeastern Texas; absent in the Mississippi embayment area.

Common name.—Black chicken snake, pilot black snake.

Elaphe obsoleta quadrivittata Holbrook

Coluber quadrivittatus Holbrook, 1836, N. Amer. Herp., ed. 1, **1**: 113, pl. 21.—"North Carolina to Florida and westward as far as the Mississippi"; restr. to Charleston, South Carolina.

Elaphis quadri-vittatus Duméril, Bibron, and Duméril, 1854, Erpét. Gén., **7**: 265.

Elaphe obsoleta quadrivittata Neill, 1949, Herpetologica, **5**, 2nd Suppl., p. 4.

Elaphe quadrivittata deckerti Brady, 1932, Proc. Biol. Soc. Wash., **45**: 5.— Lower Matecumbe Key, Florida.

Elaphe williamsi Barbour and Carr, 1940, Occ. Papers Boston Soc. Nat. Hist., **8**: 340.—Near Lebanon, Levy County, Florida.

Elaphe quadrivittata parallela Barbour and Engels, 1942, Proc. New England Zool. Club, **22**: 104, pl. 17.—Sam Windsor's Lump, 3 miles from Beaufort Inlet on the Shackleford Banks, Carteret County, North Carolina.

Elaphe obsoleta rossalleni Neill, 1949, Herpetologica, **5**, 2nd Suppl., p. 1, fig. 1.—22 miles northwest of Fort Lauderdale, Broward County, Florida.

Range.—Vicinity of Point Lookout, North Carolina, southward along the coast through all of peninsular Florida.

Common name.—Four-lined chicken snake.

Elaphe obsoleta spiloides Duméril, Bibron, and Duméril

Elaphis spiloides Duméril, Bibron, and Duméril, 1854, Erpét. Gén., **7**: 269.— New Orleans, Louisiana.

Elaphe obsoleta spiloides Dowling, 1952, Occ. Papers Mus. Zool. Univ. Mich., **541**: 5.

Range.—From Tallahassee, Florida, and Macon, Georgia, to western Tennessee and eastern Arkansas, including the greater part of Alabama and Mississippi, and eastern Louisiana.

Common name.—Blotched chicken snake.[19]

[19] This is the form referred to under the name *Elaphe obsoleta confinis* in editions 1 to 5 of the Check list.

Elaphe obsoleta lindheimeri Baird and Girard

Scotophis lindheimeri Baird and Girard, 1853, Cat. N. Amer. Rept., pt. 1, p. 74.—New Braunfels, Texas.

Elaphis obsoletus var. lindheimerii Garman, 1883, Mem. Mus. Comp. Zool., 8, pt. 3, p. 54.

Scotophis laetus Baird and Girard, 1853, Cat. N. Amer. Rept., pt. 1, p. 77.— Red River, Arkansas; restr. to south central Oklahoma.

Range.—Louisiana, westward to Corpus Christi and San Antonio.

Common name.—Texas chicken snake.

Elaphe obsoleta bairdi Yarrow

Coluber bairdi Yarrow, 1880, Bull. U. S. Nat. Mus., 17: 41.—Fort Davis, Jeff Davis County, Texas.

Elaphe bairdi Stejneger and Barbour, 1917, Check list, ed. 1, p. 82.

Elaphe obsoleta bairdi Dowling, 1952, Occ. Papers Mus. Zool. Univ. Mich., 541: 7.

Range.—Mountain ranges of Trans-Pecos Texas; Kerr County, Texas; northern Coahuila.

Common name.—Baird's rat snake.

Elaphe triaspis Cope

Coluber triaspis Cope, 1866, Proc. Acad. Nat. Sci. Phila., 18: 128.—Belize.

Elaphe triaspis Amaral, 1929, Mem. Inst. Butantan, 4: 159.

Range.—Southern Arizona to Costa Rica.

Common name.—Mexican rat snake.

Elaphe triaspis intermedia Boettger

Pityophis intermedia Boettger, 1883, Ber. Offenbach. Ver. Naturk., 22/23: 148.—"Guyana," in errore; corrected to Mexico.

Elaphe triaspis intermedia Dowling, 1952, Occ. Papers Mus. Zool. Univ. Mich., 541: 8.

Coluber chlorosoma Günther, 1894, Biol. Centr.-Amer., Rept., p. 115, pl. 41. —Atoyac and Amulo in Guerrero and San Ramón in Jalisco, Mexico; restr. to Atoyac, Guerrero.

Elaphe chlorosoma Stone, 1911, Proc. Acad. Nat. Sci. Phila., 63: 231, p. 82.

Range.—Southeastern Arizona (Santa Rita Mountains); southward in western Mexico.

Common name.—Green rat snake.

Elaphe subocularis Brown

Coluber subocularis Brown, 1901, Proc. Acad. Nat. Sci. Phila., 53: 492, pl. 29.—Davis Mountains, Jeff Davis County, Texas.

Elaphe subocularis Stejneger and Barbour, 1917, Check list, ed. 1, p. 84.

Elaphe sclerotica Smith, 1941, Copeia, **1941**: 135.—Substitute name.

Range.—Trans-Pecos Texas and southern New Mexico, southward in adjacent Coahuila.

Common name.—Trans-Pecos rat snake.

Arizona Kennicott

Arizona Kennicott, *in* Baird, 1859, U. S. Mex. Bound. Surv., **2,** pt. 2, Rept., p. 18.—Type: *elegans.*

Arizona elegans Kennicott

Arizona elegans Kennicott, 1859, *in* Baird, U. S. Mex. Bound. Surv., **2,** pt. 2, Rept., p. 18.—Rio Grande, Texas, and between Arkansas and Cimarron, Oklahoma; restr. to Lower Rio Grande.

Range.—Southwestern United States and northern Mexico.

Common name.—Glossy snake.

Arizona elegans elegans Kennicott

Arizona elegans elegans Blanchard, 1924, Occ. Papers Mus. Zool. Univ. Mich., **150:** 3; Klauber, 1946, Trans. San Diego Soc. Nat. Hist., **10:** 320, pl. 7, fig. 1, text fig. 1, map.

Range.—Texas, west of Long. 98° W., excluding the Panhandle and El Paso County; tentatively, adjacent Coahuila.

Common name.—Texas glossy snake.

Arizona elegans blanchardi Klauber

Arizona elegans blanchardi Klauber, 1946, Trans. San Diego Soc. Nat. Hist., **10:** 328, fig. 1, map.—Cheyenne County, Kansas, 13 miles southeast of Benkelman, Dundy County, Nebraska.

Range.—Eastern Colorado and southwestern Nebraska through western Kansas and Oklahoma, and through the Panhandle of Texas to northeastern New Mexico.

Common name.—Kansas glossy snake.

Arizona elegans philipi Klauber

Arizona elegans philipi Klauber, 1946, Trans. San Diego Soc. Nat. Hist., **10:** 333, fig. 1, map 1.—10 miles east of Winslow, Navajo County, Arizona.

Range.—Central New Mexico, westward into central and southeastern Arizona, El Paso County, Texas, and adjacent Chihuahua.

Common name.—Painted Desert glossy snake.

Arizona elegans noctivaga Klauber

Arizona elegans noctivaga Klauber, 1946, Trans. San Diego Soc. Nat. Hist., **10**: 343, fig. 1, map.—8 miles northwest of Owlshead, Pinal County, Arizona.

Range.—Southwestern Arizona.

Common name.—Arizona glossy snake.

Arizona elegans eburnata Klauber

Arizona elegans eburnata Klauber, 1946, Trans. San Diego Soc. Nat. Hist., **10**: 350, pl. 8, fig. 1, text fig. 1, map.—Benson's Dry Lake, eastern San Diego County, California.

Range.—Desert areas of extreme southwestern Utah, southern Nevada, and southeastern desert areas of California, excluding the western Mojave; adjacent Yuma County, Arizona; adjacent Lower California and Sonora.

Common name.—Desert glossy snake.

Arizona elegans candida Klauber

Arizona elegans candida Klauber, 1946, Trans. San Diego Soc. Nat. Hist., **10**: 364, pl. 8, fig. 2, text fig. 1, map.—Kramer Hills, 6 miles south of Kramer Junction on U. S. Highway 395, San Bernardino County, California.

Range.—Western Mojave Desert.

Common name.—Western Mojave glossy snake.

Arizona elegans occidentalis Blanchard

Arizona elegans occidentalis Blanchard, 1924, Occ. Papers Mus. Zool. Univ. Mich., **150**: 1.—La Jolla, San Diego County, California; Klauber, 1946, Trans. San Diego Soc. Nat. Hist., **10**: 372, pl. 7, fig. 2, text fig. 1, map.

Range.—San Joaquin Valley in California and coastal and cismontane southwestern California from Los Angeles County southward; adjacent Lower California.

Common name.—California glossy snake.

Pituophis Holbrook

Pituophis Holbrook, 1842, N. Amer. Herp., ed. 2, **4**: 7.—Type: *melanoleucus.*

Pituophis melanoleucus Daudin

Coluber melanoleucus Daudin, 1803, Hist. Nat. Rept., **6**: 409.—South Carolina and Florida; restr. to Charleston, South Carolina.

Pituophis melanoleucus Holbrook, 1842, N. Amer. Herp., ed. 2, **4**: 7, pl. 1.

Range.—Eastern United States.

Common name.—Pine snake.

Pituophis melanoleucus melanoleucus Daudin

> *Pituophis melanoleucus melanoleucus* Barbour, 1921, Proc. New England
> Zool. Club, **7**: 117; Stull, 1940, Bull. U. S. Nat. Mus., **175**: 52, figs.
> 27–32.

Range.—South Carolina to Rockland County, New York, and westward to eastern Tennessee.

Common name.—Northern pine snake.

Pituophis melanoleucus lodingi Blanchard

> *Pituophis lodingi* Blanchard, 1924, Papers Mich. Acad. Sci., **4**: 531.—Grand
> Bay, Mobile County, Alabama.
> *Pituophis melanoleucus lodingi* Stull, 1940, Bull. U. S. Nat. Mus., **175**: 79.

Range.—Mobile County, Alabama, and Harrison County, Mississippi.

Common name.—Black pine snake.

Pituophis melanoleucus mugitus Barbour

> *Pituophis melanoleucus mugitus* Barbour, 1921, Proc. New England Zool.
> Club, **7**: 117.—Ten miles north of West Palm Beach, Florida.

Range.—West Palm Beach to Jacksonville, and Pensacola, Florida.

Common name.—Florida pine snake.

Pituophis melanoleucus ruthveni Stull

> *Pituophis melanoleucus ruthveni* Stull, 1929, Occ. Papers Mus. Zool. Univ.
> Mich., **205**: 1.—Longleaf, Rapides Parish, Louisiana.

Range.—Louisiana and eastern Texas.

Common name.—Louisiana pine snake.

Pituophis catenifer Blainville[20]

> *Coluber catenifer* Blainville, 1835, Nouv. Ann. Mus. Hist. Nat. Paris,
> **4**: 290, pl. 26, fig. 2.—California; restr. to vicinity of San Francisco.
> *Pituophis catenifer* Baird and Girard, 1853, Cat. N. Amer. Rept., pt. 1,
> p. 95.

Range.—Western North America, from Wisconsin and Indiana westward to the Pacific coast.

Common name.—Bull snake, gopher snake.

[20] Note Smith and Kennedy (1951, Herpetologica, **7**: 93, fig. 1), who propose that *catenifer* and *melanoleucus* be combined.

Pituophis catenifer catenifer Blainville

Pituophis catenifer catenifer Stejneger and Barbour, 1923, Check list, ed. 2, p. 94; Klauber, 1947, Bull. San Diego Zool. Soc., **22**: 12, figs. 1, 3.

Pityophis heermanni Hallowell, 1853, Proc. Acad. Nat. Sci. Phila., **6**: 236.— Mines on the Cosumnes River, California.

Pituophis wilkesii Baird and Girard, 1853, Cat. N. Amer. Rept., pt. 1, p. 71.— Puget Sound and Oregon Territory; restr. to Puget Sound, Washington.

Range.—British Columbia, Washington, and Oregon, west of the Cascades, and California west of the Sierra Nevada, southward to the northern boundary of Santa Barbara County.

Common name.—Pacific gopher snake.

Pituophis catenifer deserticola Stejneger

Pituophis catenifer deserticola Stejneger, 1893, N. Amer. Fauna, **7**: 206.— Great Basin and southwestern deserts; restr. to Beaverdam Mountain, Washington County, Utah; Klauber, 1947, Bull. San Diego Zool. Soc., **22**: 27, figs. 1, 5.

Pituophis catenifer stejnegeri Van Denburgh, 1920, Proc. Calif. Acad. Sci., (4), **10**: 21.—Fort Douglas, Salt Lake County, Utah.

Range.—Kamloops-Okanagan area in British Columbia southward and eastward through the Great Basin to the northern edge of the Colorado Desert and northern Arizona.

Common name.—Great Basin gopher snake.

Pituophis catenifer sayi Schlegel

Coluber sayi Schlegel, 1837, Essai Physion. Serp., **2**: 157.—Missouri; restr. to vicinity of St. Louis.

[Pituophis catenifer] sayi Klauber, 1947, Bull. San Diego Zool. Soc., **22**: 7, fig. 1.

Churchillia bellona Baird and Girard, 1852, Stansbury's Expl. Surv. Valley of Great Salt Lake, p. 350.—Rio Grande, vicinity of Presidio del Norte.

Pituophis mcclellanii Baird and Girard, 1853, Cat. N. Amer. Rept., pt. 1, p. 68.—Red River, Arkansas.

Range.—Southern Alberta and Saskatchewan, southward through the Great Plains and Prairie states, east of the Rockies, into northeastern Mexico; eastward through southern North Dakota into southwestern Minnesota and southwestern Wisconsin, parts of Illinois, and adjacent Indiana; throughout Missouri, except extreme southeastern area; northwestern Arkansas.

Common name.—Bull snake.

Pituophis catenifer affinis Hallowell

Pityophis affinis Hallowell, 1852, Proc. Acad. Nat. Sci. Phila., **6**: 181.—New Mexico; restr. to Zuni River, New Mexico.

Pituophis catenifer affinis Smith and Mittleman, 1943, Trans. Kansas Acad. Sci., **46**: 248.

Pituophis catenifer rutilus Van Denburgh, 1920, Proc. Calif. Acad. Sci., (4), **10**: 24.—Tucson, Pima County, Arizona.

Range.—Most of Arizona, western New Mexico, extreme western Trans-Pecos Texas, and extreme southeastern California; adjacent northeastern Lower California, Sonora, and Chihuahua.

Common name.—Sonoran gopher snake.

Pituophis catenifer annectens Baird and Girard

Pituophis annectens Baird and Girard, 1853, Cat. N. Amer. Rept., pt. 1, p. 72.—San Diego, California.

Pituophis catenifer annectens Van Denburgh and Slevin, 1919, Proc. Calif. Acad. Sci., (4), **19**: 206.

Range.—Southwestern California, from northern Santa Barbara County southward to the border, west of the Coast Range, and into northwestern Lower California.

Common name.—San Diego gopher snake.

Pituophis catenifer pumilus Klauber

Pituophis catenifer pumilus Klauber, 1946, Trans. San Diego Soc. Nat. Hist., **11**: 41, pl. 3.—Santa Cruz Island, Santa Barbara County, California.

Range.—Confined to Santa Cruz Island (Santa Barbara group), Santa Barbara County, California.

Common name.—Santa Cruz Island gopher snake.

Lampropeltis Fitzinger

Lampropeltis Fitzinger, 1843, Syst. Rept., p. 25.—Type: *getulus* Schlegel (*nec* Linnaeus) = *holbrooki*.

Lampropeltis alterna Brown

Ophibolus alternus Brown, 1902, Proc. Acad. Nat. Sci. Phila., **53**: 612, pl. 34.—Davis Mountains, Jeff Davis County, Texas.

Lampropeltis alterna Stejneger and Barbour, 1917, Check list, ed. 1, pl. 87.

Range.—Mountains of Trans-Pecos Texas; adjacent Coahuila.

Common name.—Davis Mountain king snake.

Lampropeltis blairi Flury

Lampropeltis blairi Flury, 1950, Copeia, **1950**: 215.—8.8 miles west of Dryden, Terrell County, Texas.

Range.—Terrell and Val Verde counties, Texas.

Common name.—Blair's coral king snake.

Lampropeltis calligaster Harlan

Coluber calligaster Harlan, 1827, Jour. Acad. Nat. Sci. Phila., **5**: 359.— Missouri; restr. to vicinity of St. Louis.

Lampropeltis calligaster Cope, 1860, Proc. Acad. Nat. Sci. Phila., **12**: 255.

Range.—Southeastern and central United States.

Common name.—Yellow-bellied king snake.

Lampropeltis calligaster calligaster Harlan

Lampropeltis calligaster calligaster Cook, 1945, Copeia, **1945**: 48.

Ophibolus evansii Kennicott, 1859, Proc. Acad. Nat. Sci. Phila., **11**: 99.

Coronella tigrina Jan, 1863, Arch. Zool. Anat. Phys., **2**: 244.

Range.—Middle western states from southern Wisconsin through Iowa and Missouri to eastern Kansas and most of Oklahoma; Arkansas and Louisiana; eastward into Illinois, Indiana, Tennessee, and northern Mississippi.

Common name.—Yellow-bellied king snake.

Lampropeltis calligaster rhombomaculata Holbrook

Coluber rhombomaculatus Holbrook, 1840, N. Amer. Herp., ed. 1, **4**: 103, pl. 20.—Georgia and Alabama; restr. to vicinity of Atlanta, Georgia.

Lampropeltis calligaster rhombomaculata Cook, 1945, Copeia, **1945**: 48.

Range.—Maryland, Virginia, and eastern Tennessee, south to central Florida, and westward through Alabama and Mississippi.

Common name.—Mole snake.

Lampropeltis getulus Linnaeus

Coluber getulus Linnaeus, 1766, Syst. Nat., ed. 12, **1**: 382.—Carolina; restr. to Charleston, South Carolina.

Lampropeltis getulus Cope, 1860, Proc. Acad. Nat. Sci. Phila., **12**: 255.

Range.—Southern United States; southward into northern Mexico.

Common name.—King snake.

Lampropeltis getulus getulus Linnaeus

Lampropeltis getulus getulus Blanchard, 1919, Occ. Papers Mus. Zool. Univ. Mich., **70**: 1.

Lampropeltis getulus sticticeps Barbour and Engels, 1942, Proc. New England Zool. Club, **20**: 101, pl. 16.—Knoll midway between Ocracoke Inlet and Hatteras Inlet, Ocracoke Island, Hyde County, North Carolina.

Range.—Southern New Jersey to northern Florida and westward to southeastern Alabama.

Common name.—Eastern king snake.

Lampropeltis getulus floridana Blanchard

Lampropeltis getulus floridanus Blanchard, 1919, Occ. Papers Mus. Zool. Univ. Mich., **70**: 1, pl. 1.—Orange Hammock, De Soto County, Florida.

Range.—Central Florida.

Common name.—Florida king snake.

Lampropeltis getulus goini Neill and Allen

Lampropeltis getulus goini Neill and Allen, 1949, Herpetologica, **5**: 101, figs. 1–8.—Chipola River valley at Wewahitchka, Gulf County, Florida.

Range.—The Apalachicola and Chipola River drainages, Florida Panhandle.

Common name.—Florida Panhandle king snake.

Lampropeltis getulus brooksi Barbour

Lampropeltis getulus brooksi Barbour, 1919, Proc. New England Zool. Club, **7**: 1, pl. 1.—Royal Palm Hammock, Dade County, Florida.

Range.—Southeastern Florida.

Common name.—Brooks' king snake.

Lampropeltis getulus niger Yarrow

Ophibolus getulus niger Yarrow, 1882, Proc. U. S. Nat. Mus., **5**: 438.—Wheatland, Indiana.

Lampropeltis getulus niger Blanchard, 1921, Bull. U. S. Nat. Mus., **114**: 43, fig. 33.

Range.—Northern Alabama through Tennessee and Kentucky to southern Indiana and southern Ohio.

Common name.—Black king snake.

Lampropeltis getulus holbrooki Stejneger

Coronella sayi Holbrook, 1842, N. Amer. Herp., ed. 2, **3**: 99, pl. 22.

Lampropeltis holbrooki Stejneger, 1902, Proc. U. S. Nat. Mus., **25**: 152.—Substitute name.

Lampropeltis getulus holbrooki Hurter and Strecker, 1909, Trans. Acad. Sci. St. Louis, **18**: 26.

Range.—Southern Nebraska and Iowa and southwestern Illinois, through Kansas and Missouri, Arkansas, and most of Oklahoma; eastern Texas, Louisiana, Mississippi, and western Alabama; intergradient with *splendida* in southwestern Oklahoma.

Common name.—Speckled king snake.

Lampropeltis getulus splendida Baird and Girard

Ophibolus splendidus Baird and Girard, 1853, Cat. N. Amer. Rept., pt. 1, p. 83.—Sonora.

Lampropeltis getulus splendida Blanchard, 1920, Occ. Papers Mus. Zool. Univ. Mich., **87:** 2.

Range.—Central and western Texas through southern New Mexico and southeastern Arizona; adjacent parts of Mexico.

Common name.—Sonoran king snake.

Lampropeltis getulus yumensis Blanchard

Lampropeltis getulus yumensis Blanchard, 1919, Occ. Papers Mus. Zool. Univ. Mich., **70:** 6, pl. 1, fig. 2.—27 miles west of Indian Oasis, Pima County, Arizona.

Range.—Southwestern Arizona and adjacent Colorado River lowland in California; bordering area of Mexico.

Common name.—Yuma king snake.

Lampropeltis getulus californiae Blainville

Coluber (Ophis) californiae Blainville, 1835, Nouv. Ann. Mus. Hist. Nat. Paris, **4:** 292, pl. 27, fig. 1.—California; restr. to vicinity of Fresno, California.

Lampropeltis getulus californiae Klauber, 1936, Herpetologica, **1:** 26.

Ophibolus boylii Baird and Girard, Cat. N. Amer. Rept., pt. 1, p. 82.—El Dorado County, California.

Coronella balteata Hallowell, 1853, Proc. Acad. Nat. Sci. Phila., **6:** 236.—California; restr. to Fresno, California.

Ophibolus getulus eiseni Yarrow, 1882, Proc. U. S. Nat. Mus., **5:** 439.—Fresno, California.

Range.—Southern Oregon, through California and southern Nevada, southwestern Utah and western Arizona; adjacent northern Lower California.

Common name.—California king snake.

Lampropeltis doliata Linnaeus

Coluber doliatus Linnaeus, 1766, Syst. Nat., ed. 12, **1:** 379.—Carolina; restr. to vicinity of Charleston, South Carolina.

Lampropeltis doliata Klauber, 1948, Copeia, **1948:** 11.

Range.—North America, east of the Rocky Mountains, southward through Central America.

Common name.—Milk snake.

Lampropeltis doliata doliata Linnaeus

> *Lampropeltis doliatus doliatus* Hay, 1902, Proc. Biol. Soc. Wash., **15**: 138 (cited for combination only) [cf. *L. d. doliata* Klauber, 1948, Copeia, **1948**: 11].
>
> *Coluber elapsoides* Holbrook, 1838, N. Amer. Herp., ed. 1, **2**: 123, pl. 28.— South Carolina and Georgia; restr. to vicinity of Charleston, South Carolina.
>
> *Lampropeltis triangulum elapsoides* Stejneger and Barbour, 1943, Check list, ed. 5, p. 150.

Range.—Eastern Kentucky and Tennessee, and North Carolina to Florida; Gulf states as far west as southeastern Louisiana.

Common name.—Scarlet king snake.

Lampropeltis doliata temporalis Cope

> *Ophibolus doliatus temporalis* Cope, 1893, Amer. Nat., **27**: 1068, pl. 25, fig. 4.—Delaware.
>
> *Lampropeltis doliata temporalis* Klauber, 1948, Copeia, **1948**: 11.
>
> *Lampropeltis elapsoides virginiana* Blanchard, 1920, Occ. Papers Mus. Zool. Univ. Mich., **81**: 2.—Raleigh, North Carolina.

Range.—Southern New Jersey, Delaware, and Maryland through Virginia to North Carolina.

Common name.—Coastal Plain milk snake.

Lampropeltis doliata triangulum Lacépède

> *Coluber triangulum* Lacépède, 1788, Hist. Nat. Quadr. Ovip. Serp., **2**, table méthodique, p. 86.—America; restr. to vicinity of New York City, in New York State.
>
> *Lampropeltis doliata triangulum* Klauber, 1948, Copeia, **1948**: 11.
>
> *Coluber eximuis* Harlan, 1827, Jour. Acad. Nat. Sci. Phila., **5**: 360.—Pennsylvania; restr. to vicinity of Philadelphia.
>
> *Ophibolus clericus* Baird and Girard, 1853, Cat. N. Amer. Rept., pt. 1, p. 88.—Clarke County, Virginia.
>
> *Ophibolus doliatus collaris* Cope, 1888, Proc. U. S. Nat. Mus., **11**: 383.— Elmira, Stark County, Illinois.

Range.—Southern Maine through New England, New York, and northern New Jersey, southward in the Appalachians into North Carolina and Tennessee; westward through Quebec, Ontario, Michigan, and Wisconsin to eastern Minnesota; southward through northern Illinois, Indiana, and Ohio.

Common name.—Milk snake, eastern milk snake.

Lampropeltis doliata syspila Cope

Ophibolus doliatus syspilus Cope, 1888, Proc. U. S. Nat. Mus., **11**: 384.— Richland County, Illinois.
Lampropeltis doliatus syspila Klauber, 1948, Copeia, **1948**: 11.

Range.—Iowa through Missouri and northern Arkansas; eastern Kansas and Oklahoma; eastward through southern Illinois and Indiana; central Tennessee.

Common name.—Red milk snake.

Lampropeltis doliata amaura Cope

Lampropeltis amaura Cope, 1860, Proc. Acad. Nat. Sci. Phila., **12**: 258.— "Unknown"; designated as vicinity of New Orleans, Louisiana.
Lampropeltis doliatus parallelus Cope, 1888, Proc. U. S. Nat. Mus., **11**: 383.—Unknown; designated as New Orleans, Louisiana.

Range.—Lower Mississippi Valley, eastward to Meridian, Mississippi, and westward into eastern Texas as far as Dallas; through Arkansas to extreme southeastern Oklahoma.

Common name.—Louisiana milk snake.

Lampropeltis doliata gentilis Baird and Girard

Ophibolus gentilis Baird and Girard, 1853, Cat. N. Amer. Rept., pt. 1, p. 90.—North Fork, Red River, near Sweetwater Creek, Wheeler County, Texas.
Lampropeltis doliatus gentilis Klauber, 1948, Copeia, **1948**: 11.
Lampropeltis multistriata Kennicott, 1860, Proc. Acad. Nat. Sci. Phila., **12**: 328.—Fort Lookout, South Dakota.
Lampropeltis pyromelana caelenops Stejneger, 1903, Proc. U. S. Nat. Mus., **25**: 153.—Mesilla Valley, Dona Ana Co., New Mexico.

Range.—Second tier of states west of the Mississippi; Montana, Colorado, and Utah; New Mexico and Arizona.

Common name.—Western milk snake.

Lampropeltis doliata annulata Kennicott

Lampropeltis annulata Kennicott, 1860, Proc. Acad. Nat. Sci. Phila., **12**: 329.—Matamoros, Tamaulipas.
Lampropeltis doliata annulata Klauber, 1948, Copeia, **1948**: 11.
Coronella doliata var. *conjuncta* Jan, 1861, Icon. Gen. Ophid., Livr. 14, pl. 4, fig. c.—Brazil, *in errore;* designated as Matamoros, Tamaulipas.

Ophibolus doliatus occipitalis Cope, 1888, Proc. U. S. Nat. Mus., **11**: 382.—
Type loc. not designated; here designated as Matamoros, Tamaulipas.

Range.—Extreme southern Texas, northward to Kerr County;
northeastern Mexico.

Common name.—Mexican milk snake.

Lampropeltis zonata Blainville

Coluber (*Zacholus*) *zonatus* Blainville, 1835, Ann. Mus. Hist. Nat. Paris,
(3), **4**: 293.—California; restr. to northern California.
Lampropeltis zonata Van Denburgh, 1897, Occ. Papers Calif. Acad. Sci.,
5: 167.

Range.—California and Arizona, into northern Mexico.

Common name.—Coral king snake.

Lampropeltis zonata zonata Blainville

Lampropeltis zonata zonata Klauber, 1943, Trans. San Diego Soc. Nat.
Hist., **10**: 76 [cited for combination only].
Coronella multifasciata Bocourt, 1886, Miss. Sci. Mex., pt. 3, p. 616, pl. 40,
fig. 2.—California.

Range.—Southwestern Oregon, southward in California, west of
the Central Valley, to northern Lower California.

Common name.—Coast Range coral king snake.

Lampropeltis zonata multicincta Yarrow

Ophibolus getulus multicinctus Yarrow, 1882, Proc. U. S. Nat. Mus., **5**: 440.
—Fresno, California; corrected to Sierra Nevada east of Fresno.
Lampropeltis zonata multicincta Klauber, 1943, Trans. San Diego Soc. Nat.
Hist., **10**: 76.

Range.—The Sierra Nevada of California from Kern County northward to Shasta County.

Common name.—Sierra coral king snake.

Lampropeltis pyromelana Cope

Ophibolus pyromelanus Cope, 1866, Proc. Acad. Nat. Sci. Phila., **18**: 305.—
Fort Whipple, Arizona.
Lampropeltis pyromelana Stejneger and Barbour, 1923, Check list, ed. 2,
p. 100.

Range.—Arizona, exclusive of the southwestern desert regions, extreme southwestern New Mexico, and central Nevada; adjacent
Sonora and Chihuahua.

Common name.—Arizona coral king snake.

Stilosoma Brown

Stilosoma Brown, 1890, Proc. Acad. Nat. Sci. Phila., **42**: 199.—Type: *extenuatum.*

Stilosoma extenuatum Brown

Stilosoma extenuatum Brown, 1890, Proc. Acad. Nat. Sci. Phila., **42**: 199.—Lake Kerr, Marion Co., Florida.

Range.—Central portion of the Florida Peninsula.

Common name.—Short-tailed snake.

Cemophora Cope

Cemophora Cope, 1860, Proc. Acad. Nat. Sci. Phila., **12**: 244.—Type: *coccinea.*

Cemophora coccinea Blumenbach

Coluber coccineus Blumenbach, 1788, Voigt's Mag. Neu. Phys. Naturg., **5**, pt. 1, p. 11, pl. 1.—Florida.
Cemophora coccinea Cope, 1860, Proc. Acad. Nat. Sci. Phila., **12**: 244.

Range.—Southern New Jersey, southward through the Atlantic and Gulf states, westward to Louisiana and Oklahoma.

Common name.—Scarlet snake.

Rhinocheilus Baird and Girard

Rhinocheilus Baird and Girard, 1853, Cat. N. Amer. Rept., pt. 1, p. 120.—Type: *lecontei.*

Rhinocheilus lecontei Baird and Girard

Rhinocheilus lecontei Baird and Girard, 1853, Cat. N. Amer. Rept., pt. 1, p. 120.—San Diego, California.

Range.—Southwestern United States and northern Mexico.

Common name.—Long-nosed snake.

Rhinocheilus lecontei lecontei Baird and Girard

Rhinocheilus lecontei lecontei Klauber, 1941, Trans. San Diego Soc. Nat. Hist., **9**: 296.

Range.—California from Mendocino and Lassen counties southward; southwestern Idaho, Nevada, southwestern Utah, and southern and western Arizona; northern Lower California.

Common name.—Western long-nosed snake.

Rhinocheilus lecontei clarus Klauber

> Rhinocheilus lecontei clarus Klauber, 1941, Trans. San Diego Soc. Nat. Hist.,
> **9**: 308, pl. 13, figs. 1, 2, map.

Range.—The Borego and Coachella valleys, with scattered occurrences in the Colorado, Mojave, and Yuma deserts in southern California, southwestern Arizona, extreme southern Nevada, and northward in Utah to Tooele County.

Common name.—Desert long-nosed snake.

Rhinocheilus lecontei tessellatus Garman

> Rhinocheilus lecontei var. *tessellatus* Garman, 1883, Mem. Mus. Comp. Zool.,
> **8**, no. 3, p. 74.—Monclova, Coahuila.
> Rhinocheilus lecontei tessellatus Klauber, 1941, Trans. San Diego Soc. Nat.
> Hist., **9**: 302, pl. 12, fig. 2, pl. 13, fig. 3, map.

Range.—Central and southern New Mexico, southwestern Kansas, eastern Colorado, western Oklahoma, and Texas; adjacent Coahuila and Nuevo León.

Common name.—Texas long-nosed snake.

Contia Baird and Girard

> Contia Baird and Girard, 1853, Cat. N. Amer. Rept., pt. 1, p. 110.—Type:
> *mitis = tenuis.*
> Lodia Baird and Girard, 1853, Cat. N. Amer. Rept., pt. 1, p. 116.—Type:
> *tenuis.*

Contia tenuis Baird and Girard

> Calamaria tenuis Baird and Girard, 1852, Proc. Acad. Nat. Sci. Phila.,
> **6**: 176.—Puget Sound, Washington.
> Contia tenuis Stejneger and Barbour, 1917, Check list, ed. 1, p. 91.
> Contia mitis Baird and Girard, 1853, Cat. N. Amer. Rept., pt. 1, p. 111.—
> San Jose, California, and Oregon; restr. to San Jose, California.
> Ablabes purpureocauda Günther, 1858, Cat. Col. Snakes Brit. Mus., p. 245.

Range.—Puget Sound to south central California.

Common name.—Sharp-tailed snake.

Sonora Baird and Girard

> Sonora Baird and Girard, 1853, Cat. N. Amer. Rept., pt. 1, p. 117.—Type:
> *semiannulata.*

Sonora episcopa Kennicott

> Lamprosoma episcopum Kennicott, 1859, U. S. Mex. Bound. Surv., **2**, pt. 2,
> p. 22, pl. 8, fig. 2.—Eagle Pass, Maverick County, Texas.
> Sonora episcopa Stickel, 1938, Copeia, **1938**: 184.

Sonora episcopa episcopa Kennicott

Sonora episcopa episcopa Stickel, 1943, Proc. Biol. Soc. Wash., **56**: 121.
Contia episcopa torquata Cope, 1880, Bull. U. S. Nat. Mus., **17**: 21.—Northwestern Texas.
Contia nuchalis Schenkel, 1901, Verh. Nat. Ges. Basel, **8**: 162.—Fort Worth, Texas.

Range.—Eastern Colorado, Kansas, and western Missouri, through eastern New Mexico, Oklahoma, and central Texas.

Common name.—Great Plains ground snake.

Sonora episcopa taylori Boulenger

Contia taylori Boulenger, 1894, Cat. Snakes Brit. Mus., **2**: 265, pl. 12, fig. 3.
—Duval County, Texas, and Nuevo León; restr. to Duval County, Texas.

Range.—South Texas and southward into Nuevo León, Mexico.

Common name.—South Texas ground snake.

Sonora semiannulata Baird and Girard

Sonora semiannulata Baird and Girard, 1853, Cat. N. Amer. Rept., pt. 1, p. 117.—Sonora; restr. to Santa Rita Mountains, Arizona (cf. Stickel, 1943, Proc. Biol. Soc. Wash., **56**: 119).

Range.—Western United States.

Common name.—Ground snake.

Sonora semiannulata semiannulata Baird and Girard

Sonora semiannulata semiannulata Stickel, 1938, Copeia, **1938**: 185.

Range.—Region of Santa Rita Mountains, Pima and Santa Cruz counties, Arizona.

Common name.—Santa Rita ground snake.

Sonora semiannulata isozona Cope

Contia isozona Cope, 1866, Proc. Acad. Nat. Sci. Phila., **18**: 304.—Utah, and Forts Whipple and Mohave, Arizona; restr. to Fort Whipple, Yavapai County, Arizona.
Sonora semiannulata isozona Stickel, 1943, Proc. Biol. Soc. Wash., **56**: 120.
Sonora miniata miniata Stickel, 1938, Copeia, **1938**: 187.—2 miles northwest of Mesa, Maricopa County, Arizona.

Range.—Southern Idaho, southward through Utah and Nevada to Arizona and to the Panamint Mountains of California; southward in Lower California.

Common name.—Great Basin ground snake.

Sonora semiannulata linearis Stickel

Sonora miniata linearis Stickel, 1938, Copeia, **1938:** 189.—Seeley, Imperial County, California.

Sonora semiannulata linearis Stickel, 1943, Proc. Biol. Soc. Wash., **56:** 121.

Range.—Southeastern California.

Common name.—Vermilion-lined ground snake.

Sonora semiannulata blanchardi Stickel

Sonora semiannulata blanchardi Stickel, 1938, Copeia, **1938:** 185.—Northeastern slopes of Chisos Mountains, Brewster County, Texas.

Range.—Trans-Pecos Texas and southern New Mexico; adjacent Chihuahua.

Common name.—Trans-Pecos ground snake.

Sonora semiannulata gloydi Stickel

Sonora semiannulata gloydi Stickel, 1938, Copeia, **1938:** 186.—Bright Angel Trail, Lower Sonoran level, Grand Canyon National Park, Arizona.

Range.—Lower Sonoran levels of the Grand Canyon.

Common name.—Grand Canyon ground snake.

Chionactis Cope

Chionactis Cope, 1860, Proc. Acad. Nat. Sci. Phila., **12:** 241.—Type: *occipitale.*

Sonora (part) Stejneger and Barbour, 1943, Check list, ed. 5, p. 154.

Chionactis occipitalis Hallowell

Rhinostoma occipitale Hallowell, 1854, Proc. Acad. Nat. Sci. Phila., **7:** 95.—Mojave Desert.

Chionactis occipitalis Cope, 1860, Proc. Acad. Nat. Sci. Phila., **12:** 241; Klauber, 1951, Trans. San Diego Soc. Nat. Hist., **11:** 151, pls. 9, 10, map.

Range.—Southwestern Arizona and southeastern California, with adjacent Nevada and Sonora.

Common name.—Shovel-nosed snake.

Chionactis occipitalis occipitalis Hallowell

Chionactis occipitalis occipitalis Cope, 1875, Bull. U. S. Nat. Mus., **1:** 35.

Range.—The Mojave Desert region in southwestern Inyo County, eastern Kern County, northeastern Los Angeles County, parts of San Bernardino and Riverside counties, and northeastern Imperial

County, California; southern Clark County, Nevada; and southwestern Mohave County, Arizona.

Common name.—Mojave shovel-nosed snake.

Chionactis occipitalis annulata Baird

Lamprosoma annulatum Baird, 1850, U. S. Mex. Bound. Surv., **2**, pt. 2, p. 22, pl. 21.—Colorado Desert.
Chionactis occipitalis annulatus Cope, 1875, Bull. U. S. Nat. Mus., **1**: 36.

Range.—Desert foothills and desert areas of San Diego County, Imperial County (except northeast of Chocolate Mountains), California; Yuma County, western and southern Maricopa County, and northwestern Pima County, Arizona; and southward into Sonora.

Common name.—Colorado Desert shovel-nosed snake.

Chionactis occipitalis klauberi Stickel

Sonora occipitalis klauberi Stickel, 1941, Bull. Chicago Acad. Sci., **6**: 138.— Tucson, Pima County, Arizona.
Chionactis occipitalis klauberi Stickel, 1943, Proc. Biol. Soc. Wash., **56**: 124.

Range.—Pima and Pinal counties, Arizona.

Common name.—Tucson shovel-nosed snake.

Chionactis occipitalis talpina Klauber

Chionactis occipitalis talpina Klauber, 1951, Trans. San Diego Soc. Nat. Hist., **11**: 172, pl. 10, fig. 1, map.—50 miles south of Goldfield, on the highway to Beatty, Nye County, Nevada.

Range.—Nye and Esmeralda counties, Nevada.

Common name.—Nevada shovel-nosed snake.

Chionactis palarostris Klauber

Sonora palarostris Klauber, 1937, Trans. San Diego Soc. Nat. Hist., **8**: 363. —5 miles south of Magdalena, Sonora.

Range.—Sonora and western Pima County, Arizona.

Common name.—Sonora shovel-nosed snake.

Chionactis palarostris organica Klauber

Chionactis palarostris organica Klauber, 1951, Trans. San Diego Soc. Nat. Hist., **11**: 178, pl. 10, fig. 2, map.—Sonoyta-Ajo Road, 9 miles north of the U. S.–Mexican border, in the Organ Pipe Cactus National Monument, Pima County, Arizona.

Range.—Known only from western Pima County, Arizona.

Common name.—Organ Pipe shovel-nosed snake.

Ficimia Gray

> *Ficimia* Gray, 1849, Cat. Snakes Brit. Mus., p. 80.—Type: *olivacea.*

Ficimia cana Cope

> *Gyalopium canum* Cope, 1860, Proc. Acad. Nat. Sci. Phila., **12**: 243.—Fort Buchanan, Arizona.
>
> *Ficimia cana* Garman, 1883, Mem. Mus. Comp. Zool., **8,** pt. 3, p. 83.

Range.—Western Texas (from Tom Green and King counties) to Arizona.

Common name.—Western hook-nosed snake.

Ficimia olivacea Gray

> *Ficimia olivacea* Gray, 1849, Cat. Snakes Brit. Mus., p. 80.—Mexico; restr. to "central Vera Cruz."

Range.—Southern Texas to Central America.

Common name.—Hook-nosed snake.

Ficimia olivacea streckeri Taylor

> *Ficimia streckeri* Taylor, 1931, Copeia, **1931**: 5.—Three miles east of Rio Grande City, Texas.
>
> *Ficimia olivacea streckeri* Smith, 1944, Field Mus. Nat. Hist., Zool. Ser., **29**: 139.

Range.—Extreme southern Texas; southward in Mexico to Vera Cruz.

Common name.—Strecker's hook-nosed snake.

Chilomeniscus Cope

> *Chilomeniscus* Cope, 1860, Proc. Acad. Nat. Sci. Phila., **12**: 339.—Type: *stramineus.*

Chilomeniscus cinctus Cope

> *Chilomeniscus cinctus* Cope, 1861, Proc. Acad. Nat. Sci. Phila., **13**: 303.— Guaymas, Sonora.

Range.—Central and southwestern Arizona; adjacent Sonora and Lower California.

Common name.—Banded sand snake.

Hypsiglena Cope

> *Hypsiglena* Cope, 1860, Proc. Acad. Nat. Sci. Phila., **12**: 246.—Type: *ochro-rhynchus.*

Hypsiglena torquata Günther

Leptodeira torquata Günther, 1860, Ann. Mag. Nat. Hist., (3), **5:** 170, pl. 10, fig. A.—Laguna Island, Nicaragua.

Range.—Southwestern United States to Central America and northern South America.

Common name.—Night snake.

Hypsiglena torquata ochrorhyncha Cope

Hypsiglena ochrorhyncha Cope, 1860, Proc. Acad. Nat. Sci. Phila., **12:** 246. —Cape St. Lucas, Lower California.

Hypsiglena torquata ochrorhyncha Bogert and Oliver, 1945, Bull. Amer. Mus. Nat. Hist., **83:** 380.

Range.—Arizona and Trans-Pecos Texas; tip of Lower California.

Common name.—Spotted night snake.

Hypsiglena torquata nuchalata Tanner

Hypsiglena nuchalatus Tanner, 1943, Great Basin Naturalist, **4:** 53, pl. 3, fig. 2, map.—Lemon Cove, Tulare County, California.

Range.—Central valley of California, from Tehama County at the north to Tulare County at the south, and in the Coast Range south of San Francisco.

Common name.—Sierra Nevada night snake.

Hypsiglena torquata klauberi Tanner
[New comb.]

Hypsiglena o. klauberi Tanner, 1945, Great Basin Naturalist, **5:** 71, pl. 1, map.—South Coronado Island, Lower California.

Range.—Southwestern California, from Los Angeles County southward; adjacent Lower California.

Common name.—San Diego night snake.

Hypsiglena torquata deserticola Tanner
[New comb.]

Hypsiglena o. deserticola Tanner, 1945, Great Basin Naturalist, **5:** 59, pl. 1, pl. 3, fig. 3, map.—Between 3 and 4 miles northwest of Chimney Rock Pass, west side of Cedar Valley, Utah County, Utah.

Range.—Great Basin, from western Washington and Oregon and southern Idaho southward through Nevada and Utah into Arizona and California.

Common name.—Desert night snake.

Hypsiglena torquata loreala Tanner
[New comb.]

> *Hypsiglena o. lorealus* Tanner, 1945, Great Basin Naturalist, **5**: 63, pl. 2, figs. 1, 8.—Castle Dale, Emery County, Utah.

Range.—Eastern Utah and extreme southwestern Colorado.

Common name.—Mesa Verde night snake.

Hypsiglena torquata texana Stejneger
[New comb.]

> *Hypsiglena texana* Stejneger, 1893, N. Amer. Fauna, **7**: 205.—Between Laredo and Camargo, Texas.

Range.—Southern Kansas, the western third of Oklahoma, and through Texas to New Mexico; adjacent northeastern Mexico.

Common name.—Texas night snake.

Leptodeira Fitzinger

> *Leptodeira* Fitzinger, 1843, Syst. Rept., p. 27.—Type: *annulata*.

Leptodeira annulata Linnaeus

> *Coluber annulatus* Linnaeus, 1858, Syst. Nat., ed. 10, **1**: 224.—"America"; restr. to Belém, Pará, Brazil.
> *Leptodeira annulata* Günther, 1858, Cat. Col. Snakes Brit. Mus., p. 166.

Range.—Southern Texas to South America.

Common name.—Cat-eyed snake.

Leptodeira annulata septentrionalis Kennicott

> *Dipsas septentrionalis* Kennicott, 1859, *in* Baird, Rep. U. S. Mex. Bound. Surv., **2**, pt. 2, Rept., p. 16, pl. 8, fig. 1.—Matamoros, Tamaulipas, and Brownsville, Texas; restr. to Brownsville, Texas.

Range.—Extreme southern Texas; in eastern Mexico to northern Vera Cruz.

Common name.—Texas cat-eyed snake.

Trimorphodon Cope

> *Trimorphodon* Cope, 1861, Proc. Acad. Nat. Sci. Phila., **13**: 297.—Type: *lyrophanes*.

Trimorphodon lambda Cope

> *Trimorphodon lambda* Cope, 1886, Proc. Amer. Phil. Soc., **23**: 286.—Guaymas, Sonora.
> [*Trimorphodon lyrophanes lambda*] Klauber, 1940, Trans. San Diego Soc. Nat. Hist., **9**: 186.

Range.—Eastern California, southern Nevada, and southwestern Utah; through Arizona to Cochise County; southward in Sonora.

Common name.—Sonora lyre snake.

Trimorphodon vandenburghi Klauber

Trimorphodon vandenburghi Klauber, 1924, Bull. San Diego Zool. Soc., **1**: 17, fig. 3.—Wildwood Ranch (1,520 feet alt.), 5 miles southwest of Ramona, San Diego County, California.

Range.—Coastal and desert southern California, from Los Angeles County and the Argus Mountains, Inyo County, southward to the Mexican border.

Common name.—California lyre snake.

Trimorphodon vilkinsoni Cope

Trimorphodon vilkinsonii Cope, 1886, Proc. Amer. Phil. Soc., **23**: 285.—Chihuahua; restr. to vicinity of city of Chihuahua.

Range.—Trans-Pecos Texas in the vicinity of El Paso; adjacent Chihuahua.

Common name.—Texas lyre snake.

Oxybelis Wagler

Oxybelis Wagler, 1830, Syst. Amph., p. 183.—Type: *aeneus.*

Oxybelis aeneus Wagler

Dryinus aeneus Wagler, 1824, *in* Spix, Serp. Bras., p. 12, pl. 3.—Forest near the river Solimoens, near Ega.
Oxybelis aeneus Duméril, Bibron, and Duméril, 1854, Erpét. Gén., **7**: 819.

Range.—Tropical South America; northward through Central America and Mexico to southern Arizona.

Common name.—Vine snake.

Oxybelis aeneus auratus Bell

Dryinus auratus Bell, 1825, Zool. Jour., **2**: 324, pl. 12.—Mexico; restr. to Sonora.
Oxybelis aeneus auratus Bogert and Oliver, 1945, Bull. Amer. Mus. Nat. Hist., **83**: 381.
Oxybelis microphthalmus Barbour and Amaral, 1926, Proc. New England Zool. Club, **9**: 80.—Calabasas Canyon, Santa Cruz County, California.

Range.—Southern Arizona; southward in Mexico.

Common name.—Mexican vine snake.

Tantilla Baird and Girard

Tantilla Baird and Girard, 1853, Cat. N. Amer. Rept., pt. 1, p. 131.—Type: *coronata.*

Tantilla atriceps Günther

Homalocranium atriceps Günther, 1895, Biol. Centr.-Amer., Rept., p. 146, pl. 52, fig. B.—Nuevo León, Mexico.
Tantilla atriceps Blanchard, 1938, Field Mus. Nat. Hist., Zool. Ser., **20**: 372.

Range.—Oklahoma, Texas, and Arizona; northern Mexico.

Common name.—Mexican black-headed snake.

Tantilla coronata Baird and Girard

Tantilla coronata Baird and Girard, 1853, Cat. N. Amer. Rept., pt. 1, p. 131. —Kemper County, Mississippi.

Range.—Southeastern United States.

Common name.—Crowned snake.

Tantilla coronata coronata Baird and Girard

Tantilla coronata coronata Blanchard, 1938, Field Mus. Nat. Hist., Zool. Ser., **20**: 369.

Range.—Southeastern United States, from Virginia and Kentucky southward; west to Louisiana, with the exception of peninsular Florida.

Common name.—Crowned snake.

Tantilla coronata wagneri Jan

Homalocranium wagneri Jan, 1862, Arch. Zool. Modena, **2**: 51.—Florida.
Tantilla coronata wagneri Blanchard, 1938, Field Mus. Nat. Hist., Zool. Ser., **20**: 369.

Range.—Peninsular Florida.

Common name.—Florida crowned snake.

Tantilla eiseni Stejneger

Tantilla eiseni Stejneger, 1896, Proc. U. S. Nat. Mus., **18**: 117.—Fresno, California.

Range.—Southern California.

Common name.—California black-headed snake.

Tantilla eiseni eiseni Stejneger

Tantilla eiseni [*eiseni*] Klauber, 1943, Trans. San Diego Soc. Nat. Hist., **10**: 72.

Range.—Southern California, except the southeastern desert region.

Common name.—California black-headed snake.

Tantilla eiseni transmontana Klauber

Tantilla eiseni transmontana Klauber, 1943, Trans. San Diego Soc. Nat. Hist., **10**: 71.—One mile east of Yaqui Well, San Diego County, California.

Range.—San Diego County, California, east of the Coast Range; Palm Springs, Riverside County.

Common name.—Desert black-headed snake.

Tantilla gracilis Baird and Girard

Tantilla gracilis Baird and Girard, 1853, Cat. N. Amer. Rept., pt. 1, p. 132.—Indianola, Calhoun County, Texas.

Range.—Central Missouri and eastern Kansas, through Oklahoma and Arkansas to eastern Texas.

Common name.—Slender flat-headed snake.

Tantilla gracilis gracilis Baird and Girard

Tantilla gracilis gracilis Burt, 1934, Amer. Midl. Nat., **16**: 336.

Range.—Southern Oklahoma, adjacent Arkansas, and into central Texas.

Common name.—Slender flat-headed snake.

Tantilla gracilis hallowelli Cope

Tantilla hallowelli Cope, 1860, Proc. Acad. Nat. Sci. Phila., **12**: 77.—Kansas; restr. to vicinity of Manhattan.
Tantilla gracilis hallowelli Smith, 1950, Univ. Kansas Publ., Mus. Nat. Hist. Misc. Publ., **2**: 257.

Range.—Eastern Kansas into Oklahoma and presumably Nebraska, eastward to western Illinois.

Common name.—Northern flat-headed snake.

Tantilla nigriceps Kennicott

Tantilla nigriceps Kennicott, 1860, Proc. Acad. Nat. Sci. Phila., **12**: 328.—Fort Bliss, El Paso County, Texas.

Range.—The Great Plains region.

Common name.—Great Plains black-headed snake.

Tantilla nigriceps nigriceps Kennicott

Tantilla nigriceps nigriceps Smith, 1941, Copeia, **1941**: 112.

Range.—Southwestern Nebraska through most of Kansas, western Oklahoma, and southeastern Colorado, to western Texas, New Mexico, and central Arizona.

Common name.—Great Plains black-headed snake.

Tantilla nigriceps fumiceps Cope

Scolecophis fumiceps Cope, 1860, Proc. Acad. Nat. Sci. Phila., **12**: 371.—No type locality stated; designated as vicinity of San Antonio, Texas.
Tantilla nigriceps fumiceps Smith, 1941, Copeia, **1941**: 112.
Tantilla kirnia Blanchard, 1938, Field Mus. Nat. Hist., Zool. Ser., **20**: 373.— Pleasanton, Atascosa County, Texas.

Range.—Southwestern Oklahoma, southward through central Texas to the Brownsville area.

Common name.—Texas black-headed snake.

Tantilla utahensis Blanchard

Tantilla utahensis Blanchard, 1938, Field Mus. Nat. Hist., Zool. Ser., **20**: 372.—St. George, Washington County, Utah.

Range.—Southwestern Utah and westward in the Sierra Nevada of California.

Common name.—Utah black-headed snake.

Tantilla wilcoxi Stejneger

Tantilla wilcoxi Stejneger, 1902, Proc. U. S. Nat. Mus., **25**: 156.—Fort Huachuca, Arizona.

Range.—Southeastern Arizona.

Common name.—Huachuca black-headed snake.

ELAPIDAE

Micruroides Schmidt

Micruroides Schmidt, 1928, Bull. Antiv. Inst. Amer., **2**: 63.—Type: *euryxanthus*.

Micruroides euryxanthus Kennicott

Elaps euryxanthus Kennicott, 1860, Proc. Acad. Nat. Sci. Phila., **12**: 337.— Sonora; restr. to Guaymas.

Range.—Southern Arizona and New Mexico to Sonora.

Common name.—Arizona coral snake.

Micrurus Wagler

Micrurus Wagler, *in* Spix, 1824, Serp. Bras., p. 48.—Type: *spixii.*

Micrurus fulvius Linnaeus

Coluber fulvius Linnaeus, 1766, Syst. Nat., ed. 12, **1**: 381.—Carolina; restr. to vicinity of Charleston, South Carolina.

Micrurus fulvius Stejneger and Barbour, 1917, Check list, ed. 1, p. 106.

Range.—Southeastern United States, westward to southern Texas and adjacent Tamaulipas.

Common name.—Coral snake.

Micrurus fulvius fulvius Linnaeus

Micrurus fulvius fulvius Schmidt, 1928, Bull. Antiv. Inst. Amer., **2**: 64.

Range.—From North Carolina southward through the Atlantic and Gulf coastal plains to Mississippi; Kentucky and Tennessee.

Common name.—Coral snake, harlequin snake.

Micrurus fulvius tenere Baird and Girard

Elaps tenere Baird and Girard, 1853, Cat. N. Amer. Rept., pt. 1, pp. 22, 156.—San Pedro of the Rio Grande and New Braunfels, Texas; restr. to New Braunfels.

Micrurus fulvius tenere Schmidt, 1936, Field Mus. Nat. Hist., Zool. Ser., **20**: 40.

Elaps tristis Baird and Girard, 1853, Cat. N. Amer. Rept., pt. 1, p. 23.— Kemper County, Mississippi, and Rio Grande, west of San Antonio; restr. to Rio Grande, west of San Antonio.

Range.—West of the Mississippi River in Louisiana, Arkansas, and Texas; northern Tamaulipas.

Common name.—Texas coral snake.

Micrurus fulvius barbouri Schmidt

Micrurus fulvius barbouri Schmidt, 1928, Bull. Antiv. Inst. Amer., **2**: 64.— Royal Palm Hammock, Dade County, Florida.

Range.—Extreme southern Florida.

Common name.—South Florida coral snake.

CROTALIDAE

Ancistrodon Beauvois

Agkishodon [typogr. error] Beauvois, 1799, Trans. Amer. Phil. Soc., **4**: 381. —Type: *mokasen* = *contortrix.*

Ancistrodon [emendation] Baird, 1854, Serp. New York, p. 13; Smith, 1943, Fauna of British India, Serpents, p. 494.

Agkistrodon [emendation] Stejneger and Barbour, 1917, Check list, ed. 1, p. 106.

Ancistrodon contortrix Linnaeus

Boa contortrix Linnaeus, 1766, Syst. Nat., ed. 12, **1**: 373.—Carolina; restr. to Charleston, South Carolina.

Ancistrodon contortrix Baird, 1854, Serp. New York, p. 13.

Range.—Eastern and southeastern United States.

Common name.—Copperhead.

Ancistrodon contortrix contortrix Linnaeus

Ancistrodon contortrix contortrix Klauber, 1948, Copeia, **1948**: 8.

Agkistrodon mokeson austrinus Gloyd and Conant, 1943, Bull. Chicago Acad. Sci., **7**: 153, figs. 2, 8.—Gentilly, Orleans Parish, Louisiana.

Range.—Atlantic and Gulf coastal plains, from Maryland to eastern Texas and southeastern Oklahoma; absent in peninsular Florida; northward in the Mississippi Basin to western Tennessee, Arkansas, Missouri, and southern Illinois.

Common name.—Southern copperhead.

Ancistrodon contortrix mokeson Daudin

Cenchris mokeson Daudin, 1803, Hist. Nat. Rept., **5**: 358.—Vicinity of Philadelphia.

Ancistrodon contortrix mokeson Klauber, 1948, Copeia, **1948**: 8.

Scytalus cupreus Rafinesque, 1818, Amer. Jour. Sci., **1**: 84.—Fishkill, Putnam County, New York.

Acontias atro-fuscus Troost, 1836, Ann. Lyc. Nat. Hist. New York, **3**: 181.—Maury County, Tennessee.

Range.—Massachusetts and Connecticut, extreme southeastern New York, northern New Jersey, Pennsylvania, Maryland, Delaware, Virginia, and North Carolina; westward through southern Ohio, Indiana, and Illinois; Kentucky and Tennessee; extreme southeastern Iowa, Missouri, southeastern Nebraska, eastern Kansas, northeastern Oklahoma, and northwestern Arkansas.

Common name.—Northern copperhead.

Ancistrodon contortrix laticinctus Gloyd and Conant

Agkistrodon mokasen laticinctus Gloyd and Conant, 1934, Occ. Papers Mus. Zool. Univ. Mich., **283**: 2, pl. 1.—26 miles northwest of San Antonio, Bexar County, Texas.

Ancistrodon contortrix laticinctus Klauber, 1948, Copeia, **1948**: 8.

Range.—Central and north central Texas, northward through central Oklahoma to Cowley County, Kansas.

Common name.—Broad-banded copperhead.

Ancistrodon contortrix pictigaster Gloyd and Conant

Agkistrodon mokeson pictigaster Gloyd and Conant, 1943, Bull. Chicago Acad. Sci., **7**: 156, fig. 10.—Maple Canyon, Chisos Mountains, Brewster County, Texas.

Range.—Trans-Pecos Texas, in moist valleys.

Common name.—Trans-Pecos copperhead.

Ancistrodon piscivorus Lacépède

Crotalus piscivorus Lacépède, 1789, Hist. Nat. Serp., **2**, table méthodique, p. 130.

Ancistrodon piscivorus Cope, 1859, Proc. Acad. Nat. Sci. Phila., **11**: 336.

Range.—Southeastern United States.

Common name.—Water moccasin, cottonmouth.

Ancistrodon piscivorus piscivorus Lacépède

Ancistrodon piscivorus piscivorus Cope, 1875, Bull. U. S. Nat. Mus., **1**: 34.

Coluber aquaticus Shaw, 1802, Gen. Zool., **3**: 425, pl. 3.—Carolina; restr. to vicinity of Charleston, South Carolina.

Range.—Lower Atlantic coastal plain from southeastern Virginia southward, throughout Florida, and to southeastern Alabama.

Common name.—Eastern cottonmouth, eastern water moccasin.

Ancistrodon piscivorus leucostoma Troost

Acontias leucostoma Troost, 1836, Ann. Lyc. Nat. Hist. New York, **3**: 176, pl. 5, figs. 1–4.—Western Tennessee; restr. to 10 miles northeast of Bolivar, Hardeman County, Tennessee.

Agkistrodon piscivorus leucostoma Gloyd and Conant, 1943, Bull. Chicago Acad. Sci., **7**: 164, map 2.

Toxicophis pugnax Baird and Girard, 1853, Cat. N. Amer. Rept., pt. 1, pp. 20, 156.

Range.—Southwestern Alabama, the lower Mississippi Basin, including Louisiana, Mississippi, Arkansas, western Tennessee, and Kentucky, southern Missouri and southern Illinois (northernmost record in Monroe County), westward to eastern Oklahoma, and in Texas to the lower Rio Grande.

Common name.—Western cottonmouth, western water moccasin.

Sistrurus Garman

Sistrurus Garman, 1883, Mem. Mus. Comp. Zool., **8,** no. 3, p. 110.—Type: *miliarius.*

Sistrurus catenatus Rafinesque

Crotalinus catenatus Rafinesque, 1818, Amer. Monthly Mag. Crit. Rev., **4:** 41.—Prairies of the upper Missouri; restr. to vicinity of Kansas City, Missouri.

Sistrurus catenatus Garman, 1883, Mem. Mus. Comp. Zool., **8,** no. 3, p. 176; Evans and Gloyd, 1948, Bull. Chicago Acad. Sci., **8:** 229, fig. 1 (map).

Range.—The Great Plains and prairie regions southward from Nebraska into northern Mexico; the Prairie Peninsula, eastward to Pennsylvania.

Common name.—Massasauga.

Sistrurus catenatus catenatus Rafinesque

Sistrurus catenatus catenatus Cope, 1900, Ann. Rep. U. S. Nat. Mus., **1898:** 1146, fig. 329.

Crotalus messaugus Kirtland, 1838, Mather's 2nd Rep. ·Geol. Surv. Ohio, p. 190.—Ohio.

Crotalophorus kirtlandi Holbrook, 1842, N. Amer. Herp., ed. 2, **3:** 31, pl. 6. —Ohio and Michigan; restr. to Trumbull County, Ohio.

Range.—Central New York and Pennsylvania through Ohio into Michigan, northern Indiana and Illinois, southern Wisconsin and Minnesota, and through Missouri.

Common name.—Eastern massasauga.

Sistrurus catenatus tergeminus Say

Crotalus tergeminus Say, 1823, *in* Long's Exped. Rocky Mts., **1:** 499.—Locality not stated; designated as headwaters of Arkansas River.

Sistrurus catenatus tergeminus Klauber, 1936, Occ. Papers San Diego Soc. Nat. Hist., **1:** 6.

Crotalophorus edwardsii Baird and Girard, 1853, Cat. N. Amer. Rept., pt. 1, p. 15.—Tamaulipas.

Range.—Great Plains, Nebraska, Kansas, and eastern Colorado through Oklahoma to western Texas, New Mexico, and southeastern Arizona; adjacent northeastern Mexico.

Common name.—Western massasauga.

Sistrurus miliarius Linnaeus

Crotalus miliarius Linnaeus, 1766, Syst. Nat., ed. 12, **1:** 372.—Carolina; restr. to Charleston, South Carolina.

Sistrurus miliarius Garman, 1883, Mem. Mus. Comp. Zool., **8,** no. 3, p. 177.

Range.—Southeastern United States.

Common name.—Pigmy rattlesnake.

Sistrurus miliarius miliarius Linnaeus

Sistrurus miliarius miliarius Gloyd, 1935, Occ. Papers Mus. Zool. Univ. Mich., **322**: 7.

Range.—Upper Atlantic and Gulf coastal plain, from North Carolina to Alabama, exclusive of Florida.

Common name.—Carolina pigmy rattlesnake.

Sistrurus miliarius barbouri Gloyd

Sistrurus miliarius barbouri Gloyd, 1935, Occ. Papers Mus. Zool. Univ. Mich., **322**: 2.—Royal Palm Hammock, Dade County, Florida.

Range.—Florida and lower Gulf coastal plain, westward to Mississippi, north to South Carolina.

Common name.—Southeastern pigmy rattlesnake.

Sistrurus miliarius streckeri Gloyd

Sistrurus miliarius streckeri Gloyd, 1935, Occ. Papers Mus. Zool. Univ. Mich., **322**: 4.—Imboden, Lawrence County, Arkansas.

Range.—Western Mississippi and southwestern Tennessee into southeastern Missouri, Arkansas, Oklahoma, and Louisiana; west to central Texas.

Common name.—Western pigmy rattlesnake.

Crotalus Linnaeus

Crotalus Linnaeus, 1758, Syst. Nat., ed. 10, **1**: 214.—Type: *horridus.*

Crotalus horridus Linnaeus

Crotalus horridus Linnaeus, 1758, Syst. Nat., ed. 10, **1**: 214.—America; restr. to vicinity of New York City.

Range.—Eastern North America.

Common name.—Timber rattlesnake.

Crotalus horridus horridus Linnaeus

Crotalus horridus horridus Gloyd, 1935, Copeia, **1935**: 176.

Crotalus boiquira Lacépède, 1789, Hist. Nat. Serp., **2**: 130, 390, pl. 18, fig. 1.—America; restr. to Lake Champlain.

Crotalinus cyanurus Rafinesque, 1818, Amer. Monthly Mag. Crit. Rev., **3**: 446; **4**: 41.—"The barrens of Kentucky."

Crotalus durissus var. *concolor* Jan, 1859, Rev. Mag. Zool., (2), **10**: 153.

Range.—Northeastern North America: New England[21] and the mid-Atlantic states (except Delaware), southward in the Appalachians through Virginia, the Carolinas, Georgia, and Alabama; westward in Ohio, southern Indiana, and Kentucky and Tennessee; western Arkansas and eastern Oklahoma; Missouri and eastern Kansas; southeastern Nebraska; in Illinois, Wisconsin, Iowa, and Minnesota in rock cliffs along rivers. Extreme southern Ontario.

Common name.—Timber rattlesnake.

Crotalus horridus atricaudatus Latreille

Crotalus atricaudatus Latreille, 1802, *in* Sonnini and Latreille, Hist. Nat. Rept., **3**: 209.—Carolina; restr. to Charleston, South Carolina.

Crotalus horridus atricaudatus Gloyd, 1935, Copeia, **1935**: 176.

Crotalus catesbaei Fitzinger, 1826, Neue Classif. Rept., p. 63.—North America; restr. to New Orleans.

Crotalus durissus var. *melanurus* Jan, 1859, Rev. Mag. Zool., (2), **10**: 153.

Range.—Coastal plains of South Atlantic and Gulf states, into northern Florida, west to central Texas and extreme southeastern Oklahoma; northward in the Mississippi Basin through Arkansas and Tennessee to southeastern Missouri, western Kentucky, and extreme southern Illinois.

Common name.—Canebrake rattlesnake.

Crotalus molossus Baird and Girard

Crotalus molossus Baird and Girard, 1853, Cat. N. Amer. Rept., pt. 1, p. 10.—Fort Webster, Santa Rita del Cobre, New Mexico.

Range.—Central Texas to Arizona; southward into Mexico.

Common name.—Black-tailed rattlesnake.

Crotalus molossus molossus Baird and Girard

Crotalus molossus molossus Gloyd, 1936, Occ. Papers Mus. Zool. Univ. Mich., **325**: 2.

Crotalus ornatus Hallowell, 1854, Proc. Acad. Nat. Sci. Phila., **7**: 192.—Pecos River between El Paso and San Antonio.

Range.—Arizona, New Mexico, and Trans-Pecos Texas; central Texas; adjacent states of Mexico.

Common name.—Northern black-tailed rattlesnake.

[21] Apparently extinct in Maine.

Crotalus pricei Van Denburgh

Crotalus pricei Van Denburgh, 1895, Proc. Calif. Acad. Sci., (2), **5**: 856.—
Huachuca Mountains, Cochise County, Arizona.

Range.—Southeastern Arizona; adjacent Sonora and Chihuahua,
and southward in Mexico.

Common name.—Twin-spotted rattlesnake.

Crotalus pricei pricei Van Denburgh

Crotalus pricei pricei Smith, 1946, Univ. Kansas Sci. Bull., **31**: 79.

Range.—Southeastern Arizona, southward to Durango in western
Mexico.

Common name.—Arizona twin-spotted rattlesnake.

Crotalus lepidus Kennicott

Caudisona lepida Kennicott, 1861, Proc. Acad. Nat. Sci. Phila., **13**: 206.—
Presidio del Norte and Eagle Pass, Texas; restr. to Presidio del Norte,
Texas.
Crotalus lepidus Cope, 1883, Proc. Acad. Nat. Sci. Phila., **35**: 13.

Range.—Western Texas to southern Arizona, southward on the
Mexican plateau.

Common name.—Rock rattlesnake.

Crotalus lepidus lepidus Kennicott

Crotalus lepidus lepidus Gloyd, 1936, Occ. Papers Mus. Zool. Univ. Mich.,
337: 4, pl. 1, fig. 2.
Crotalus palmeri Garman, 1887, Bull. Essex Inst., **19**: 124.—Monclova, Coahuila.

Range.—Trans-Pecos Texas, and southeastward to Real and Mav-
erick counties.

Common name.—Mottled rock rattlesnake.

Crotalus lepidus klauberi Gloyd

Crotalus lepidus klauberi Gloyd, 1936, Occ. Papers Mus. Zool. Univ. Mich.,
337: 2, pl. 1, fig. 1.—Carr Canyon, Huachuca Mountains, Arizona.

Range.—Southeastern Arizona, west central New Mexico, and extreme western Texas; adjacent states of Mexico.

Common name.—Banded rock rattlesnake.

Crotalus scutulatus Kennicott

Caudisona scutulata Kennicott, 1861, Proc. Acad. Nat. Sci. Phila., **13**: 207.—
Type locality not stated; designated as Mojave Desert, California.

Crotalus scutulatus Klauber, 1930, Trans. San Diego Soc. Nat. Hist., **6**: 117, 137, pl. 12, fig. 1.

Range.—Mexican plateau to the southwestern United States.

Common name.—Shield-headed rattlesnake.

Crotalus scutulatus scutulatus Kennicott

Crotalus scutulatus scutulatus Gloyd, 1940, Spec. Publ. Chicago Acad. Sci., **4**: 200, map 15.

Range.—Mojave Desert, into southern Nevada, the southwestern corner of Utah, western and southern Arizona, southwestern New Mexico, and Trans-Pecos Texas; adjacent states in Mexico, southward to central Mexico.

Common name.—Mojave rattlesnake.

Crotalus adamanteus Beauvois

Crotalus adamanteus Beauvois, 1799, Trans. Amer. Phil. Soc., **4**: 368.— United States; restr. to Charleston, South Carolina.

Crotalus rhombifer Latreille, 1802, *in* Sonnini and Latreille, Hist. Nat. Rept., **3**: 197.—America; restr. to Gainesville, Florida.

Range.—Coastal North Carolina, South Carolina, and Georgia, and Gulf coastal plain to eastern Louisiana; throughout Florida.

Common name.—Eastern diamond rattlesnake.

Crotalus atrox Baird and Girard

Crotalus atrox Baird and Girard, 1853, Cat. N. Amer. Rept., pt. 1, p. 5.— Indianola, Calhoun County, Texas.

Caudisona atrox var. *sonoraensis* Kennicott, 1861, Proc. Acad. Nat. Sci. Phila., **13**: 206.—Sonora and vicinity.

Range.—Central Arkansas, westward through southern and western Oklahoma, south through all of Texas except the extreme east; southern New Mexico and Arizona, into southeastern California; adjacent states of Mexico, with an isolated colony in Oaxaca.

Common name.—Western diamond rattlesnake.

Crotalus ruber Cope

Crotalus adamanteus ruber Cope, 1892, Proc. U. S. Nat. Mus., **14**: 690.— No type locality stated; designated as vicinity of San Diego, California.

Range.—Southwestern California, west of the Coast Range; southward into Lower California (with *C. r. lucasensis* at the south).

Common name.—Red diamond rattlesnake.

Crotalus ruber ruber Cope

Crotalus ruber ruber Klauber, 1949, Trans. San Diego Soc. Nat. Hist., **11**: 59.

Range.—Southwestern California, west of the Coast Range; southward in Lower California to the Sierra de la Giganta.

Common name.—Red diamond rattlesnake.

Crotalus viridis Rafinesque

Crotalinus viridis Rafinesque, 1818, Amer. Monthly Mag. Crit. Rev., **4**: 41.—The prairies of the upper Missouri; restr. to Pierre, South Dakota.
Crotalus viridis Klauber, 1936, Trans. San. Diego Soc. Nat. Hist., **8**: 240.

Range.—Western North America.

Common name.—Prairie rattlesnake.

Crotalus viridis viridis Rafinesque

Crotalus viridis viridis Klauber, 1936, Trans. San Diego Soc. Nat. Hist., **8**: 191.
Crotalus confluentus Say, 1823, *in* Long's Exped. Rocky Mts., **2**: 48.—"Valley of the Arkansa," near Bells Springs, Colorado.
Caudisona lecontei Hallowell, 1852, Proc. Acad. Nat. Sci. Phila., **6**: 180.—Cross Timbers, Oklahoma.
Crotalus confluentus pulverulentus Cope, 1883, Proc. Acad. Nat. Sci. Phila., **35**: 11.—Lake Valley, New Mexico.

Range.—Great Plains, from Alberta and Saskatchewan through Montana, southwestern North Dakota, eastern Wyoming, most of South Dakota (reaching the Iowa border), western Nebraska and Kansas, eastern Colorado, western Oklahoma and Texas, most of New Mexico, northeastern Arizona, northern Mexico.

Common name.—Prairie rattlesnake.

Crotalus viridis lutosus Klauber

Crotalus confluentus lutosus Klauber, 1930, Trans. San Diego Soc. Nat. Hist., **6**: 100.—10 miles northwest of Abraham, Millard County, Utah.
Crotalus viridis lutosus Klauber, 1936, Trans. San Diego Soc. Nat. Hist., **8**: 191.

Range.—The Great Basin, southeastern Oregon, southern Idaho, most of Utah and Nevada, northeastern California, and extreme northwestern Arizona.

Common name.—Great Basin rattlesnake.

Crotalus viridis oreganus Holbrook

 Crotalus oreganus Holbrook, 1840, N. Amer. Herp., ed. 1, **4:** 115, pl. 29
  [= 24].—Columbia River; restr. to confluence of Columbia and Snake
  rivers, Washington.
 Crotalus viridis oreganus Klauber, 1936, Trans. San Diego Soc. Nat. Hist.,
  8: 191.
 Crotalus lucifer Baird and Girard, 1852, Proc. Acad. Nat. Sci. Phila., **6:** 177.
  —California and Oregon; restr. to western Oregon.

Range.—Southern British Columbia, through central Washington, western Oregon except the coastal strip, and California southward to Monterey, and exclusive of the southeastern desert region.

Common name.—Northern Pacific rattlesnake.

Crotalus viridis helleri Meek

 Crotalus helleri Meek, 1905, Field Col. Mus., Zool. Ser., **7:** 17.—San José,
  Lower California.
 Crotalus viridis helleri Klauber, 1949, Trans. San Diego Soc. Nat. Hist.,
  11: 77, pl. 4, fig. 2.

Range.—Southwestern California; south into northwestern Lower California.

Common name.—Southern Pacific rattlesnake.

Crotalus viridis cerberus Coues

 Caudisona lucifer var. *cerberus* Coues, 1875, *in* Wheeler, Expl. Surv. W.
  100th Mer., Zool., **5:** 606.—San Francisco Mountains, Coconino County,
  Arizona.
 Crotalus viridis cerberus Klauber, 1949, Trans. San Diego Zool. Soc., **11:** 83,
  pl. 5, fig. 1.

Range.—Central eastern Arizona and extreme western New Mexico.

Common name.—Arizona black rattlesnake.

Crotalus viridis nuntius Klauber

 Crotalus confluentus nuntius Klauber, 1935, Trans. San Diego Zool. Soc.,
  8: 78, pl. 8, fig. 1, map 1.—Cañon Diablo, Coconino County, Arizona.
 Crotalus viridis nuntius Klauber, 1936, Trans. San Diego Zool. Soc., **8:** 242,
  figs. 68, 86.

Range.—Basin of the Little Colorado River, north central and northeastern Arizona.

Common name.—Arizona prairie rattlesnake.

Crotalus viridis abyssus Klauber

Crotalus confluentus abyssus Klauber, 1930, Trans. San Diego Soc. Nat. Hist., **6**: 114, pl. 11, fig. 1.—Tanner Trail, 300 feet below south rim of Grand Canyon, Coconino County, Arizona.

Crotalus viridis abyssus Klauber, 1936, Trans. San Diego Soc. Nat. Hist., **8**: 242, figs. 68, 87.

Range.—Grand Canyon of the Colorado, Coconino County, Arizona.

Common name.—Grand Canyon rattlesnake.

Crotalus viridis decolor Klauber

Crotalus concolor Woodbury, 1929, Bull. Univ. Utah, **20**: [3], figs. 1, 2.— King's Ranch, base of Henry Mountains, Garfield County, Utah (not of Jan).

Crotalus confluentus decolor Klauber, 1930, Trans. San Diego Soc. Nat. Hist., **6**: 111.—Grand Junction, Mesa County, Colorado.

Crotalus viridis decolor Gloyd, 1940, Spec. Publ. Chicago Acad. Sci., **4**: 216.

Range.—Basins of the Colorado and Green rivers in eastern Utah, southwestern Wyoming, and extreme western Colorado.

Common name.—Midget faded rattlesnake.

Crotalus mitchelli Cope

Caudisona mitchelli Cope, 1861, Proc. Acad. Nat. Sci. Phila., **13**: 293.— Cape San Lucas, Lower California.

Crotalus mitchellii Cope, 1875, *in* Yarrow, Surv. W. 100th Mer., **5**: 535.

Range.—Desert regions of southwestern United States, Lower California and Sonora.

Common name.—Speckled rattlesnake.

Crotalus mitchelli pyrrhus Cope

Caudisona pyrrha Cope, 1867, Proc. Acad. Nat. Sci. Phila., **18**: 308.—Cañon Prieto, Yavapai County, Arizona.

Crotalus mitchellii pyrrhus Stejneger, 1895, Ann. Rept. U. S. Nat. Mus., **1893**: 456.

Range.—Southern California, extreme southern Nevada, southwestern Arizona; northern Lower California.

Common name.—Southwestern speckled rattlesnake.

Crotalus mitchelli stephensi Klauber

Crotalus confluentus stephensi Klauber, 1930, Trans. San Diego Soc. Nat. Hist., **6**: 108.—2 miles west of Jackass Springs, 6,200 feet alt., Panamint Mountains, Inyo County, California.

Crotalus mitchellii stephensi Klauber, 1936, Trans. San Diego Soc. Nat. Hist., **8**: 162, pl. 20, fig. 2, text fig. 2.

Range.—Southeastern California and southwestern Nevada, north of the range of *pyrrhus*.

Common name.—Panamint rattlesnake.

Crotalus tigris Kennicott

Crotalus tigris Kennicott, 1859, *in* Baird, U. S. Mex. Bound. Surv., **2**, pt. 2, p. 14, pl. 4.—Sierra Verde and Pozo Verde, Arizona = Arizona boundary with Sonora near Sasabe, Arizona.

Range.—Southern and central Arizona; northeastern and central Sonora.

Common name.—Tiger rattlesnake.

Crotalus willardi Meek

Crotalus willardi Meek, 1905, Field Col. Mus., Zool. Ser., **7**: 18.—Tombstone, Cochise County, Arizona, *in errore* = above Hamburg, middle branch of Ramsey Canyon, Huachuca Mountains, southeastern Arizona.

Range.—Southeastern Arizona to the Mexican states of Durango and Zacatecas.

Common name.—Ridge-nosed rattlesnake.

Crotalus willardi willardi Meek

Crotalus willardi willardi Klauber, 1949, Trans. San Diego Soc. Nat. Hist., **11**: 125, pl. 8, fig. 1, map.

Range.—Southeastern Arizona grasslands in the Huachuca and Santa Rita mountains.

Common name.—Arizona ridge-nosed rattlesnake.

Crotalus cerastes Hallowell

Crotalus cerastes Hallowell, 1854, Proc. Acad. Nat. Sci. Phila., **7**: 95.—Mojave Desert.

Range.—Mojave and Colorado deserts.

Common name.—Sidewinder, horned rattlesnake.

Crotalus cerastes cerastes Hallowell

Crotalus cerastes cerastes Klauber, 1944, Trans. San Diego Soc. Nat. Hist., **10**, pl. 5, fig. 1.

Range.—Southeastern California and southern Nevada, extreme southwestern Utah, and western borders of Arizona, north of the range of *Crotalus cerastes laterorepens*.

Common name.—Mojave Desert sidewinder.

Crotalus cerastes laterorepens Klauber

Crotalus cerastes laterorepens Klauber, 1944, Trans. San Diego Soc. Nat. Hist., **10**, pl. 5, fig. 2, map.

Range.—Colorado Desert in southeastern California, southwestern Arizona, and adjacent Lower California and Sonora.

Common name.—Colorado Desert sidewinder.

INTRODUCED FORMS
AMPHIBIA: SALIENTIA

Hyla septentrionalis Boulenger

> *Hyla septentrionalis* Boulenger, 1882, Cat. Batr. Sal. Brit. Mus., p. 368.—Cuba and Santo Domingo; restr. to Cuba.

Range.—Cuba and Bahama Islands; introduced and established on Key West and Lower Matecumbe Key, Florida.

Common name.—Cuban tree frog.

Eleutherodactylus ricordi Duméril and Bibron

> *Hylodes ricordii* Duméril and Bibron, 1841, Erpét. Gén., **8**: 623.—Cuba; restr. to Oriente.
>
> *Eleutherodactylus ricordii* Stejneger, 1905, Shattuck's Bahama Islands, p. 331 [for form of name only].

Range.—Cuba and Bahama Islands; introduced in Florida.

Common name.—Ricord's frog.

Eleutherodactylus ricordi planirostris Cope

> *Hylodes planirostris* Cope, 1862, Proc. Acad. Nat. Sci. Phila., **14**: 153.—New Providence Island, Bahama Islands.
>
> *Eleutherodactylus ricordii planirostris* Shreve, 1945, Copeia, **1945**: 117.

Range.—Bahama Islands and western Cuba; introduced in Florida, where it ranges north to Alachua County.

Common name.—Greenhouse frog (for the Florida populations).

REPTILIA: SAURIA[22]

Gonatodes fuscus Hallowell

> *Stenodactylus fuscus* Hallowell, 1855, Jour. Acad. Nat. Sci. Phila., (2), **3**: 33.—Nicaragua.
>
> *Gonatodes fuscus* Carr, 1940, Copeia, **1939**: 232.

Range.—Caribbean coasts, West Indies generally; introduced in Key West and elsewhere in Florida.

Common name.—Yellow-headed gecko.

---

[22] *Lacerta melisellensis*, introduced in Philadelphia in 1927, persisted for a few years (Kauffeld, 1932, Copeia, **1931**: 163) but now seems to have disappeared (Conant, *in litt.*).

Hemidactylus turcicus Linnaeus

Lacerta turcica Linnaeus, 1758, Syst. Nat., ed. 10, **1**: 202.—In Oriente; restr. to Turkey in Asia.

Hemidactylus turcicus Boettger, 1876, Ber. Offenbacher Ver. Naturk., **1876**: 57.

Range.—Mediterranean coasts and islands southward on the coasts of the Red Sea; in eastern Africa to northern Kenya Colony, and eastward to northwestern India.

Common name.—Turkish gecko.

Hemidactylus turcicus turcicus Linnaeus

Hemidactylus turcicus turcicus Mertens, 1925, Abh. Senck. Naturf. Ges., **39**: 60.

Range.—Mediterranean coasts and islands; southward into Egypt and along the northern coasts of the Red Sea; introduced in the West Indies, and in Key West and the Miami area in Florida.

Common name.—Turkish gecko.

Sphaerodactylus cinereus Wagler

Sphaerodactylus cinereus Wagler, 1830, Syst. Amph., p. 143.—Haiti.

Range.—Haiti, Cuba, and adjacent islands; introduced on Key West and Key Largo, Florida.

Common name.—Ashy gecko.

Sphaerodactylus notatus Baird

Sphaerodactylus notatus Baird, 1858, Proc. Acad. Nat. Sci. Phila., **10**: 254. —Key West, Florida.

Range.—Bahama Islands and Cuba; apparently introduced in southern Florida.

Common name.—Reef gecko.

Anolis distichus Cope

Anolis distichus Cope, 1861, Proc. Acad. Nat. Sci. Phila., **13**: 208.—New Providence Island, Bahama Islands.

Anolis distichus floridanus Smith and McCauley, 1948, Proc. Biol. Soc. Wash., **61**: 160.—Brickell Park, Miami, Florida.

Range.—Hispaniola and Bahama Islands; introduced in the Miami area in Florida.

Common name.—Yellow-throated anolis.

Anolis sagrei Cocteau

Anolis sagrei Cocteau, 1837, *in* Duméril and Bibron, Erpét. Gén., **4**: 149.—Cuba.

Range.—Island of Cuba to Central American coasts, Bahamas, and Florida Keys.

Common name.—De la Sagra's anolis, brown anolis.

Anolis sagrei sagrei Cocteau

Anolis sagrei sagrei Oliver, 1948, Amer. Mus. Nov., **1383**: 25.

Range.—Cuba and the Isle of Pines; introduced in Florida in the Tampa area.

Common name.—Cuban brown anolis.

Anolis sagrei ordinatus Cope

Anolis ordinatus Cope, 1864, Proc. Acad. Nat. Sci. Phila., **16**: 175.—West Indies; restr. to New Providence, Bahama Islands.
Anolis sagrei ordinatus Oliver, 1948, Amer. Mus. Nov., **1383**: 25.

Range.—Bahama Islands; introduced in the Lake Worth area in Florida.

Common name.—Bahaman brown anolis.

Leiocephalus carinatus Gray

Leiocephalus carinatus Gray, 1827, Phil. Mag., (2), **2**: 208.—West Indies; restr. to Cuba.

Range.—Cuba and Bahama Islands.

Common name.—Bahaman crested lizard.

Leiocephalus carinatus virescens Stejneger

Leiocephalus virescens Stejneger, 1900, Proc. U. S. Nat. Mus., **23**: 471.—Green Cay, Bahama Islands.
Leiocephalus carinatus virescens Barbour, 1937, Bull. Mus. Comp. Zool., **82**: 135.

Range.—Green Cay, Bahama Islands; introduced in the Miami area, Florida.

Common name.—Green Cay crested lizard.

INDEX

PRINTED
IN U·S·A

RET'D JUL 29 1988
OCT 17 1994